600
PUZZLES
CROSS-
WORDS
hinkler

Published by Hinkler Pty Ltd
45–55 Fairchild Street
Heatherton Victoria 3202 Australia
www.hinkler.com


Cover design: Hinkler Studio



ISBN: 978 14889 3697 5

Printed and bound in China

# INSTRUCTIONS

# How to Solve a Crossword

If you're not familiar with crossword puzzles, here are some tips for how to solve them.

The goal is to solve the clues and write the answers, letter by letter, into the blank spaces in the grid. The numbered clues will direct you to fill in the answers both across and down the grid. Fill in the obvious answers first and then look again at the puzzle clues – there may be an easy answer you didn't notice or one that's easier now because some letters have been filled in.

Numbers in parentheses after each clue reveal the number of letters in each answer, matching the number of spaces in the grid. Multiple numbers separated with a comma indicate multiple words, while numbers separated with a hyphen indicate hyphenated words.

Clues ending in '(abbr.)' indicate that the solution is an abbreviation, while clues ending in '(init.)' indicate that the solution is a set of initials.

Don't forget little tricks like checking if an 's' in the last position works for plural clues and 'ed' works for past-tense clues. Keep working through the list of clues and, if you're stumped, try again later! Sometimes you just need a break for your brain to retrieve the answer.

# Solving Tips

These books are in British English, and use the Oxford Dictionary of English as a basis which can be found in stores or online at https://en.oxforddictionaries.com/.

If you are used to American English, look out for the following conversions to British English:

- "-or" usually becomes "-our"
  e.g. humour, neighbour and favourite

- "-er" often becomes "-re"
  e.g. theatre and fibre

- "-l" becomes "-ll"
  e.g. counsellor and fillet

- "-se" sometimes becomes "-ce"
  e.g. defence and licence (as a noun)

- "-g" becomes "-gue"
  e.g. dialogue and analogue

If you're unsure of a spelling, you can always refer to the Oxford Dictionary using the link above.

Happy solving!

# PUZZLES

# PUZZLE 1

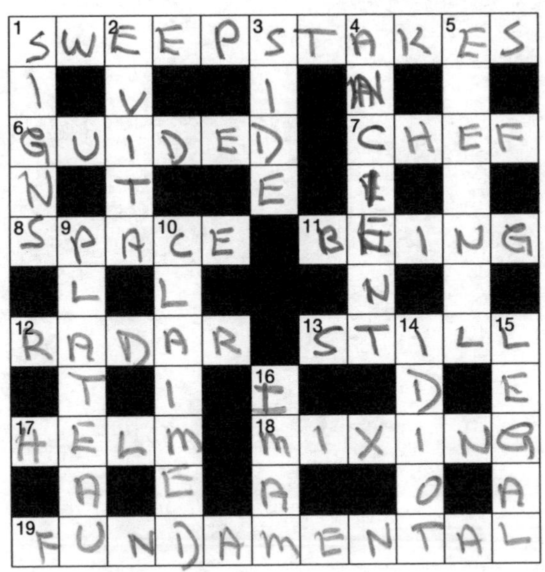

**Across**
1 Lotteries (11)
6 Steered (6)
7 Cook (4)
8 The universe beyond Earth (5)
11 Living creature (5)
12 Airport scanning system (5)
13 Motionless (5)
17 Tiller (4)
18 Blending music tracks (6)
19 Of central importance (11)

**Down**
1 Portents (5)
2 Lloyd Webber musical (5)
3 Edge (4)
4 Extremely old (7)
5 Everlasting (7)
9 Area of level high ground (7)
10 Requested (7)
14 Foolish person (5)
15 Juridical (5)
16 Muslim leader (4)

# PUZZLE 2

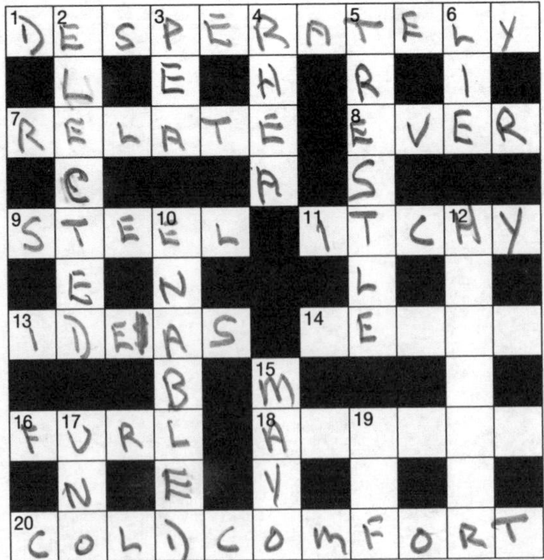

**Across**
1 Critically (11)
7 Show a connection between (6)
8 Always (4)
9 Girder material (5)
11 Restless (5)
13 Concepts (5)
14 Pace (5)
16 Roll up (4)
18 Very handsome young man (6)
20 Scarce consolation (4,7)

**Down**
2 Chosen (7)
3 Climbing plant, sweet ___ (3)
4 Flightless South American bird (4)
5 Table support (7)
6 Untruth (3)
10 Made possible (7)
12 More cheery (7)
15 Sandwich dressing (4)
17 Half of *dos* (3)
19 Amiss (3)

# PUZZLE 3

**Across**
**1** Beget (4,5,2)
**7** Female priest (11)
**8** Not even vaguely close (7,4)
**13** Advisers (11)
**18** Ice-cream dessert (6,5)
**20** Alas (11)

**Down**
**2** Dome-shaped Inuit house (5)
**3** Third planet (5)
**4** Wall-climbing plant (3)
**5** Plant barb (5)
**6** Ornamental headgear (5)
**9** Finish first (3)
**10** Large, flightless bird (3)
**11** *The Lord of the Rings* creature (3)
**12** A billion years (3)
**14** Elliptical (5)
**15** Used to connect floors (5)
**16** Dominant animal in a pack (5)
**17** Courtroom event (5)
**19** Works of creative imagination (3)

# PUZZLE 4

**Across**
**1** Rich chocolate cake (11)
**7** Tiny circus performer? (4)
**8** Conakry is its capital (6)
**9** Gawks at (5)
**10** Extremely corpulent (5)
**13** Din (5)
**15** Utters a short, sharp cry (5)
**17** US currency unit (6)
**18** Trickle (4)
**19** Sets up (11)

**Down**
**2** Briskly, tempo-wise (7)
**3** Skies (7)
**4** Heavy floor mats (4)
**5** Flush with water (5)
**6** Stay away from (5)
**11** Confers divine favour (7)
**12** Paramount (7)
**13** Gentle push (5)
**14** Small, water-surrounded area of land (5)
**16** Verbal (4)

# PUZZLE 5

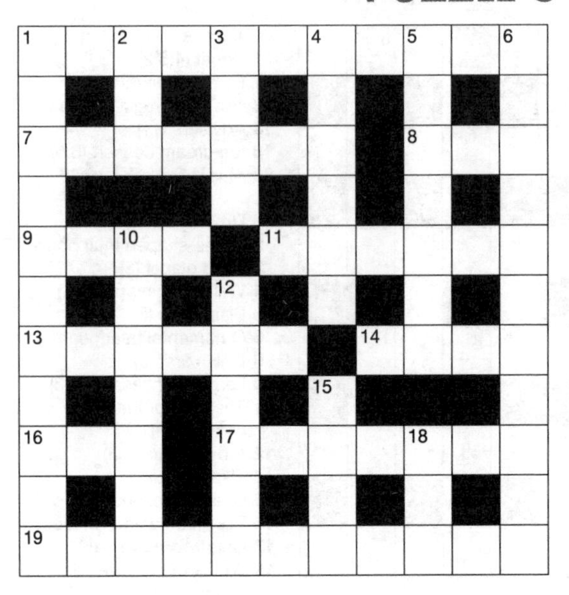

**Across**

**1** Instead of (2,7,2)
**7** Less transparent (7)
**8** Central email address symbols (3)
**9** Askew (4)
**11** Suds (6)
**13** Nuns' garments (6)
**14** Long story (4)
**16** Small part of something (3)
**17** Pakistani spoken language (7)
**19** Clear approval (11)

**Down**

**1** Fear of crowds (11)
**2** Female reproductive cells (3)
**3** Biblical apostle (4)
**4** Loud, shrill cry (6)
**5** Former Greek monetary unit (7)
**6** Remark (11)
**10** Like an automaton (7)
**12** Perfect place (6)
**15** Tennis player, Kournikova (4)
**18** 'Open Sesame' speaker, Baba (3)

# PUZZLE 6

**Across**

**1** Viewpoint (11)
**6** Tangle up (6)
**7** Govern (4)
**8** Bags (5)
**11** Breakfast tea component (5)
**12** Aquatic, fish-eating mammal (5)
**13** Colorado ski resort (5)
**17** Proton donor (4)
**18** Oat-based breakfast food (6)
**19** Principal actress (7,4)

**Down**

**1** Prayers (5)
**2** Object from an earlier time (5)
**3** Consumed frugally: ___ out (4)
**4** Pushes suddenly forward (7)
**5** Potential difference (7)
**9** Magazine feature (7)
**10** Worked dough (7)
**14** Linguine, eg (5)
**15** Unpleasant to listen to (5)
**16** 'I agree!' (4)

# PUZZLE 7

**Across**

**1** 'And' or 'but' (11)
**7** Supposes (7)
**8** Greek 'T' (3)
**9** Ahead (6)
**11** Martial art (4)
**13** Remedy (4)
**14** Electronic dance genre (6)
**16** Denoting a number in a list (3)
**17** Decorative paper-folding (7)
**19** Upgrade (11)

**Down**

**1** Knowledgeable people (11)
**2** Born (3)
**3** Hesitant (6)
**4** A legal action (4)
**5** Having contact with (2,5)
**6** Brain scientist (11)
**10** Combat vessel (7)
**12** Specify (6)
**15** Taboo act (2-2)
**18** Number of years old (3)

# PUZZLE 8

**Across**

**1** Spell-casting word (11)
**7** 44th US President (6,5)
**8** Distinguishing (11)
**13** Regrettable (11)
**18** Important (11)
**20** Assistants (11)

**Down**

**2** Type of facial hair (5)
**3** Another time (5)
**4** Short-winged, Arctic diver (3)
**5** Monks' building (5)
**6** Not italic (5)
**9** Legolas, in *The Lord of the Rings* (3)
**10** Hilltop (3)
**11** Winter ailment (3)
**12** Christina, to friends (3)
**14** Gullible (5)
**15** Shopkeeper, eg (5)
**16** More friendly (5)
**17** Slightly colour (5)
**19** Greasy food substance (3)

# PUZZLE 9

**Across**

**7** With awe (11)
**8** Short passage from a book (7)
**9** Lennon's wife (3)
**10** Quilt (5)
**12** Common birch-family tree (5)
**13** Id counterpart (3)
**14** Involves (7)
**16** Upkeep (11)

**Down**

**1** A wish for a good night's sleep (5,6)
**2** Single entity (4)
**3** Divisions (11)
**4** Drawing attention elsewhere (11)
**5** Having existed for a long while (3-3)
**6** Claims of virtuousness while doing otherwise (11)
**11** Fiddle (6)
**15** Charged molecules (4)

# PUZZLE 10

**Across**

**1** Teaching groups (7)
**5** Gullible fool (3)
**7** Not obtainable (11)
**8** Conceal (4)
**10** Try hard (6)
**12** They might be soap or comic (6)
**13** Hand over (4)
**15** Combined militaries (5,6)
**17** Archaic (3)
**18** Scary creature (7)

**Down**

**1** Idle TV watcher (5,6)
**2** She was once Mrs Sinatra (3)
**3** Burn the surface of (4)
**4** Breaks into parts (6)
**5** Abate (7)
**6** Ancestor (11)
**9** Imagined (7)
**11** Two-seater bicycle (6)
**14** Planted by scattering (4)
**16** Director's on-set call (3)

# PUZZLE 11

**Across**

**1** With a compelling charm (11)
**7** Hotel complexes (7)
**8** Ribcage muscles (3)
**9** Most extreme (6)
**11** Corrode with acid (4)
**13** Henry VIII's wife, Boleyn (4)
**14** Pumping organs (6)
**16** Toboggan runner (3)
**17** Hair detergent (7)
**19** Superbly (11)

**Down**

**1** Powered cutting blade (8,3)
**2** Promotional messages (3)
**3** Flood (6)
**4** Decorative face covering (4)
**5** Farm vehicle (7)
**6** Social worker's log (4,7)
**10** Bring up (7)
**12** Stead (6)
**15** Land surrounded by sea (4)
**18** Chum (3)

# PUZZLE 12

**Across**

**1** The Enlightenment (3,2,6)
**7** Found out for sure (11)
**8** Component (11)
**13** TV sports reviewer (11)
**18** Social scientist (11)
**20** Agreements (11)

**Down**

**2** Verve (5)
**3** Follows orders (5)
**4** Large, mouse-like rodent (3)
**5** Goodbye (5)
**6** Vast body of salt water (5)
**9** Classic object-taking game (3)
**10** Not indefinite (3)
**11** Tit for ___ (3)
**12** Chew and swallow (3)
**14** Endangered atmosphere layer (5)
**15** Damp (5)
**16** Quarrel (5)
**17** Start (5)
**19** Hammer horror actor, Christopher (3)

# PUZZLE 13

**Across**

**1** Noms de plume (7)
**5** New York museum, The ___ (3)
**7** In writing (2,5)
**8** *Glee* actress, Michele (3)
**9** Pod vegetable, sometimes deep-fried (4)
**10** Moorings (6)
**12** Back to back (2,1,3)
**13** ___ upon a time (4)
**15** Barman's query (3)
**16** Less reputable (7)
**17** Figure out (3)
**18** Sunshade (7)

**Down**

**1** Saying you are sorry (11)
**2** Not lasting (11)
**3** Tree juices (4)
**4** Maths progression (6)
**5** Aggressive tendencies as part of a cause (11)
**6** The action of moving something (11)
**11** Even chance (4-2)
**14** Wig material (4)

# PUZZLE 14

**Across**

**1** Reproduces (10)
**6** Various (6)
**7** Mosquito-like fly (4)
**10** Dismissal (5-2)
**12** Visual recording (3)
**13** Shred (3)
**14** Conflagration (7)
**15** Biblical Creation garden (4)
**18** Cranial contents (6)
**19** Excellently (10)

**Down**

**1** Acquittal (9)
**2** Spiky tropical fruit (9)
**3** A resident of Tel Aviv (7)
**4** Attach a label (3)
**5** Variation of reggae (3)
**8** 'Forget about it' (5,4)
**9** Laboriously (9)
**11** Proposed (7)
**16** Haircuts, informally (3)
**17** Non-existent (3)

# PUZZLE 15

**Across**

**1** Getting to know (11)
**7** Isolated, flat-topped hill (4)
**8** Practice (6)
**9** Leave the path (5)
**10** Search thoroughly (5)
**13** Attempted (5)
**15** Initial (5)
**17** Fall into the habit of (4,2)
**18** Of no value (4)
**19** Signs (11)

**Down**

**2** Inventor (7)
**3** Ignorant (7)
**4** Urge (4)
**5** Opening (5)
**6** *Halo* fan? (5)
**11** Dry red Italian wine (7)
**12** Twentieth Greek letter (7)
**13** In unison, musically (5)
**14** Irritated (5)
**16** Spiritual and physical relaxation technique (4)

# PUZZLE 16

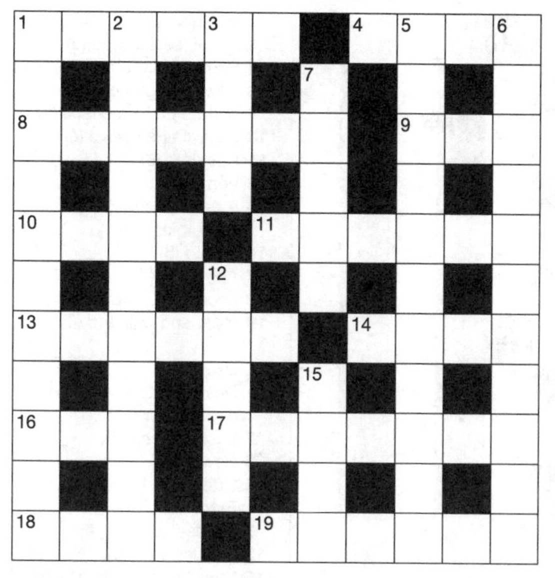

**Across**

**1** Summoning via a beeper (6)
**4** Digitally import a paper document (4)
**8** Clearly apparent (7)
**9** Fellow (3)
**10** Bait (4)
**11** Batter with wind or waves (6)
**13** Mutter (6)
**14** Maple or spruce (4)
**16** Lie in the sun, perhaps (3)
**17** Crepe (7)
**18** Cavity containing liquid secretion (4)
**19** Multitudes (6)

**Down**

**1** Dubious (11)
**2** National ruling bodies (11)
**3** Particular e-reader (4)
**5** Offer evidence about a crime (4,7)
**6** However (11)
**7** Edition of a magazine (5)
**12** Hebrew 'A' (5)
**15** Facts (4)

# PUZZLE 17

**Across**
1 Grumpy (3-8)
7 Music system (6)
8 On top of (4)
9 Restaurant choices (4)
10 Leaning typeface (6)
13 Electorate (6)
16 Has a meal (4)
17 Uncut bread (4)
18 Align in a particular direction (6)
19 Understood the full worth of (11)

**Down**
2 1920s architectural style (3,4)
3 Agonize (7)
4 New Zealand aboriginal (5)
5 Adversary (5)
6 Order of architecture (5)
11 Continent that straddles the Pacific and Atlantic oceans (7)
12 Profound (7)
13 Country house (5)
14 Walk heavily (5)
15 Betraying no emotion (5)

# PUZZLE 18

**Across**
1 Small, sealed bag (6)
4 Semicircular church recess (4)
8 Sewing together (7)
9 Middle Earth menace (3)
10 Martial arts sword (4)
11 Receipts (6)
13 Vertebral (6)
14 A person who is against something (4)
16 Forbid (3)
17 Apprizing (7)
18 Looks at with desire (4)
19 Hazy and polluted (6)

**Down**
1 Designed to operate underwater (11)
2 Ease of use (11)
3 Rewrite (4)
5 Uttering (11)
6 Extremely (11)
7 Intense suffering (5)
12 Reduce by 50% (5)
15 Stop talking, with 'up' (4)

# PUZZLE 19

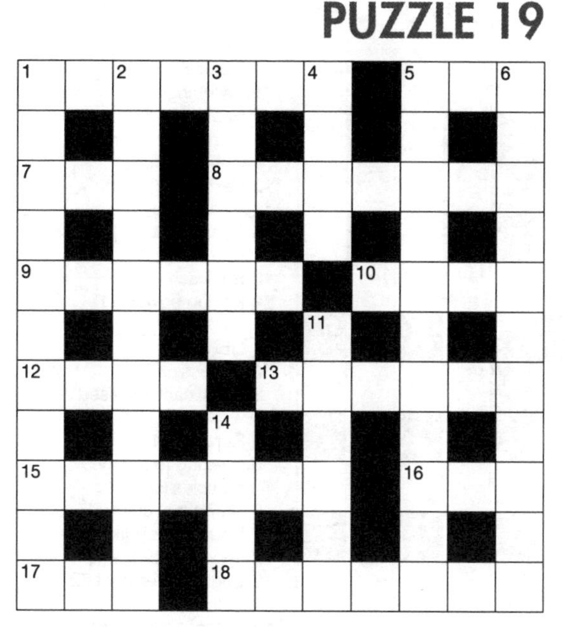

**Across**

**1** Mimic (7)
**5** Idle talk (3)
**7** Canadian baby, in *South Park* (3)
**8** Speaker's temporary platform (7)
**9** Work-experience trainee (6)
**10** Design (4)
**12** Diplomacy (4)
**13** Ascendant (6)
**15** Storybook baddy (7)
**16** Moreover (3)
**17** Japanese cooking sauce (3)
**18** Pedal vehicle (7)

**Down**

**1** Enterprises (11)
**2** Equivalently (11)
**3** Ridiculous (6)
**4** It may be multiple-choice? (4)
**5** Fly into a rage (2,9)
**6** Pugilist's equipment (6,5)
**11** Outdoor meal (6)
**14** Clothing (4)

# PUZZLE 20

**Across**

**1** Healing (6)
**4** Heavy book, perhaps (4)
**8** Most prying (7)
**9** Well-dressed chap (3)
**10** Common ornamental trees (4)
**11** Result of a negotiation (6)
**13** Earnings (6)
**14** Side (4)
**16** One of seven deadly things (3)
**17** Separated (7)
**18** Snow transport (4)
**19** Hoped (6)

**Down**

**1** General agreements (11)
**2** Similarity (11)
**3** Requirement (4)
**5** Without much thought (11)
**6** Foolish; unintelligent (5-6)
**7** Large shop (5)
**12** Groom's partner (5)
**15** Affirm (4)

# PUZZLE 21

**Across**
1 Ascribing (11)
7 Reply (6)
8 In the near future (4)
9 Cuban coin (4)
10 Vestiges (6)
13 All alone: by ___ (6)
16 Chess castle (4)
17 Domain (4)
18 Backlash (6)
19 Having power (11)

**Down**
2 Digression (7)
3 Significantly revised a work (7)
4 Rupture (5)
5 Relating to charged particles (5)
6 Hereditary units (5)
11 Small, peach-like fruit (7)
12 Imported curios (7)
13 Baghdad resident (5)
14 Ledge (5)
15 Improbable comedy (5)

# PUZZLE 22

**Across**
1 Soft colour shade (6)
4 Brief (4)
6 Possessing (6)
7 Very many (4)
8 Illegible handwriting (6)
11 Pale yellow Dutch cheese (4)
12 Key part of an argument (4)
13 Being (6)
16 Post-diving pressure reduction (abbr.) (4)
17 Gimmick (6)
18 Wife of Osiris (4)
19 Surrounded (6)

**Down**
1 Schemes (5)
2 More reasonable (5)
3 Valid coins and banknotes (5,6)
4 Assemble (7)
5 Withdraw (7)
9 Occupations (7)
10 Fretful (7)
14 Covering with frozen water (5)
15 Give up (5)

# PUZZLE 23

**Across**
**1** Inner-ear cavity (7)
**5** Hitchcock to his friends, maybe (3)
**7** Ornamental tree (3)
**8** Food packaging (7)
**9** Putrid (6)
**10** Craving (4)
**12** Detest (4)
**13** Repeating sound pattern (6)
**15** Sorcerer (7)
**16** Female chicken (3)
**17** *X-Factor* assent (3)
**18** Bed cover (7)

**Down**
**1** Remove an obstacle (5,3,3)
**2** Reconcile yourself (4,2,5)
**3** Attorney (6)
**4** Actor, Sandler (4)
**5** Completely on-message official? (11)
**6** Small, ornamental blue flower (6-2-3)
**11** Spiritual power centre, in yoga (6)
**14** Flop on the big-screen (4)

# PUZZLE 24

**Across**
**1** Morning meal (9)
**8** Venomous snake (5)
**9** Confess (5)
**10** Braking parachute (6)
**12** Indic language (4)
**14** Polish-German boundary river (4)
**15** Help (6)
**17** Digging tool (5)
**18** Conclude (5)
**20** Delayed (9)

**Down**
**2** Curved torso bone (3)
**3** Beaded counting tool (6)
**4** Open-topped tart (4)
**5** Japanese feudal warrior (7)
**6** Rave music, perhaps (4,5)
**7** Organizational system (9)
**11** Culinary herb related to mint (7)
**13** Inuit (6)
**16** Animal flesh eaten as food (4)
**19** Entry payment (3)

# PUZZLE 25

**Across**
**1** Throwing out (10)
**6** Losses of life (6)
**7** Unwanted email (4)
**10** Cleft (7)
**12** Not feel well (3)
**13** Intense temper (3)
**14** Distinguished orchestra leaders (7)
**15** Possible hair infection (4)
**18** Financial (6)
**19** Atomic scientists, eg (10)

**Down**
**1** Subtraction (9)
**2** Bank-account report (9)
**3** Lack of faith (7)
**4** Qualifiers (3)
**5** Formerly Portuguese part of India (3)
**8** Customs (9)
**9** Products (9)
**11** Melancholy (7)
**16** Cheeky devil (3)
**17** James Bond, eg (3)

# PUZZLE 26

**Across**
**1** Nana (11)
**7** Newspaper chief (6)
**8** Gazed at (4)
**9** Takes in, as a sail (5)
**11** Performed (5)
**13** Drug addicts (5)
**14** Muscular (5)
**16** Most active volcano in Europe (4)
**18** Cops (6)
**20** Most affable (11)

**Down**
**2** Blushes (7)
**3** Edible kernel (3)
**4** Grade schoolwork (4)
**5** Sugar syrup (7)
**6** Lady sheep (3)
**10** Stopped being angry towards (7)
**12** Results (7)
**15** Raced (4)
**17** Besmear (3)
**19** Floral chain (3)

# PUZZLE 27

**Across**
1 Very smart and tidy (4-7)
7 Whirled (4)
8 Figured out (6)
9 Honesty (5)
10 Fluster (5)
13 A consignment of goods (5)
15 Poppy-derived narcotic (5)
17 Elevates (6)
18 Carried out a hit on (slang) (4)
19 Appraisals (11)

**Down**
2 Stores with a wide range of goods (7)
3 Nutcase (7)
4 Peril (4)
5 Shifted (5)
6 Elude (5)
11 Impoverish (7)
12 At the greatest volume (7)
13 Islamic whole-body garment (5)
14 Same-aged siblings (5)
16 Queries (4)

# PUZZLE 28

**Across**
1 Duties (11)
7 Salve (4)
8 Defeated (6)
9 Ailments (5)
10 Divisions of a house (5)
13 Brew (5)
15 Inclined to verbosity (5)
17 Spectacle (6)
18 Camera opening (4)
19 Unstable and aggressive people (11)

**Down**
2 Obvious (7)
3 Enormous (7)
4 Swedish pop phenomenon (4)
5 Surpass (5)
6 Makes vocal music (5)
11 Egg-shaped wind instrument (7)
12 Saviour (7)
13 Swift curving movement (5)
14 Complete (5)
16 Former 'Tickle Me' toy (4)

# PUZZLE 29

**Across**

**1** Likely to be affected (11)
**6** Handing over money (6)
**7** Has (4)
**8** They neutralize alkalis (5)
**11** Avoids work (5)
**12** Interruption (5)
**13** Greek island (5)
**17** Goes out (4)
**18** Black magic (6)
**19** Highly advanced (7-4)

**Down**

**1** Monochrome photo shade (5)
**2** Engraving tools (5)
**3** Objects for hanging things on (4)
**4** Neat and tidy (2,5)
**5** Lax (7)
**9** Large North American deer (7)
**10** Strongly committed (4,3)
**14** Stopped (5)
**15** Wear down (5)
**16** Baking furnace (4)

# PUZZLE 30

**Across**

**1** Significantly (11)
**7** Increase in length (6)
**8** Departed (4)
**9** Orbit (5)
**11** Makes a reservation for (5)
**13** Association of workers (5)
**14** Charged atom or molecule (5)
**16** Not exceeding (2,2)
**18** Cliquey witticism (2-4)
**20** Stupefying munition (4,7)

**Down**

**2** Type of spicy cuisine (7)
**3** Be in the red (3)
**4** Task to be completed (2-2)
**5** Maternity-ward baby (7)
**6** Nickname for Evelyn (3)
**10** This, eg (7)
**12** Rapped on a door (7)
**15** Class (4)
**17** Fruit stone (3)
**19** Jennifer, familiarly (3)

# PUZZLE 31

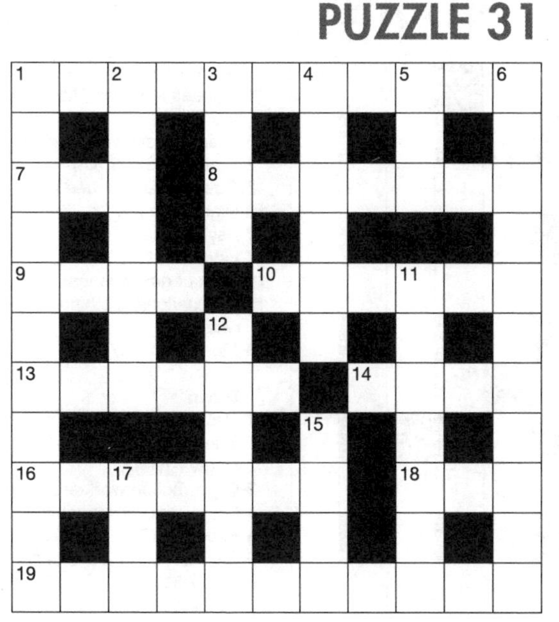

**Across**

**1** Added (11)
**7** Destiny (3)
**8** Heads (7)
**9** Straddling (4)
**10** Social class; set (6)
**13** Not present (6)
**14** Meat from a young sheep (4)
**16** Add in (7)
**18** Small hotel (3)
**19** Casual indifference (11)

**Down**

**1** Computation (11)
**2** Whimsies (7)
**3** Function (4)
**4** 'Leave!' (4,2)
**5** Golf-ball holder (3)
**6** Upset (11)
**11** Romance language (7)
**12** Adequate (6)
**15** Hades (4)
**17** Is able to (3)

# PUZZLE 32

**Across**

**1** Student grant (11)
**7** Least difficult (7)
**8** Object in space that's near to Earth (init.) (3)
**9** Skills (4)
**11** Assassin (6)
**13** Prepare, as in plans (4,2)
**14** Utilizes (4)
**16** 'Say that again?' (3)
**17** Trattoria dumplings (7)
**19** Capable of being convinced (11)

**Down**

**1** Management (11)
**2** That guy's (3)
**3** Onion relative (4)
**4** The sale of goods (6)
**5** Manages (7)
**6** Forward-looking (11)
**10** Educator (7)
**12** Karate-like martial art (4,2)
**15** Tended to the weeds, maybe (4)
**18** Driver's compartment (3)

# PUZZLE 33

**Across**

**1** It spans from the Atlantic to the Pacific (7)
**5** Great expanse of water (3)
**7** Deteriorate (2,2,3,4)
**8** Catches red-handed (4)
**10** Highfalutin (2-2-2)
**12** Asylum seeker (6)
**13** Feverish fit (4)
**15** Lack of graciousness (11)
**17** Multinational clothing retailer (3)
**18** Most difficult (7)

**Down**

**1** Design and building science (11)
**2** Hogwash (3)
**3** Construction work area (4)
**4** Large concert venues (6)
**5** Exposing (7)
**6** Satisfaction of a desire (11)
**9** Raise (5,2)
**11** Garland (6)
**14** Fibster (4)
**16** Four-stringed Hawaiian instrument (3)

# PUZZLE 34

**Across**

**1** Bank account deficit (9)
**8** Not abridged (5)
**9** Focused beam of light (5)
**10** Teaching unit (6)
**12** Small, thin piece of something (4)
**14** Group or society (4)
**15** Flat surfaces (6)
**17** Defamatory publication (5)
**18** Spiral-shelled mollusc (5)
**20** Subsidiary (9)

**Down**

**2** Australian state (3)
**3** Quantitative relations (6)
**4** Peeve (4)
**5** Style (7)
**6** Identical in size (4-5)
**7** Suggestions (9)
**11** Short facial growth (7)
**13** Not open (6)
**16** Plus (4)
**19** Broadcast (3)

# PUZZLE 35

**Across**
- **1** An expert in matter and energy (9)
- **8** Bury (5)
- **9** Visages (5)
- **10** Mexican national flower (6)
- **12** Escape from danger (4)
- **14** Mania (4)
- **15** Winged childlike being (6)
- **17** Fatty part of milk (5)
- **18** Divisible only by itself and 1 (5)
- **20** Astounding (9)

**Down**
- **2** Best-seller (3)
- **3** Seamy (6)
- **4** Chilly (4)
- **5** Plunderer (7)
- **6** Send to the wrong place (9)
- **7** Joined together (9)
- **11** Greatest (7)
- **13** A smaller part of a church (6)
- **16** Muslim ruler (4)
- **19** Charged atom (3)

# PUZZLE 36

**Across**
- **1** In effect (11)
- **7** ___ interface, computing term (4)
- **8** North American nation (6)
- **9** Heavily built (5)
- **10** Follow, as in advice (3,2)
- **13** Prices (5)
- **15** Tree supports (5)
- **17** Connected with vision (6)
- **18** Small lump of a substance (4)
- **19** Making someone more courageous (11)

**Down**
- **2** Italian rice dish (7)
- **3** Debased (7)
- **4** Twelfth of a foot (4)
- **5** Fewest (5)
- **6** Have an intense longing (5)
- **11** Note arrival at work (5,2)
- **12** Obsolete (7)
- **13** Elected (5)
- **14** Small firework (5)
- **16** Network of crossing lines (4)

# PUZZLE 37

**Across**

**1** Miscellanea (11)
**7** 'A long time ___' (3)
**8** Set of rearranged letters (7)
**9** Pinch, as of salt (4)
**10** Most broad (6)
**13** Contract (6)
**14** Prison sentence (4)
**16** Legally owned property (7)
**18** Fitting (3)
**19** Extremely colourful (11)

**Down**

**1** Command to forsake a vessel (7,4)
**2** Patron (7)
**3** Mixed-colour horse (4)
**4** Small-minded person, informally (6)
**5** 'Neither' correlative (3)
**6** Indicative (11)
**11** Examine up close (7)
**12** Burnish (6)
**15** Got older (4)
**17** Deposit (3)

# PUZZLE 38

**Across**

**1** Brightly coloured marker (11)
**7** Expected (3)
**8** Amends (7)
**9** Acquire (6)
**10** Earnest request (4)
**13** Not his... (4)
**14** Sardonic (6)
**16** Passionate (7)
**18** Barely make a living (3)
**19** Makes a formal judgement (11)

**Down**

**1** Irrational water fear (11)
**2** Better (7)
**3** Milk-related (6)
**4** Horned farmyard animal (4)
**5** Ship-dragging vessel (3)
**6** Scientific investigators (11)
**11** With greatest duration (7)
**12** Calamitous (6)
**15** Bound (4)
**17** British government in India (3)

# PUZZLE 39

**Across**
1 Variety (9)
7 Respect (5)
8 Loft (5)
10 Christmas carol (4)
11 Prepares for firing (6)
14 Warrant (6)
15 Busy doing nothing (4)
17 Likeness (5)
19 Not competent (5)
20 Or else (9)

**Down**
2 Ailment (7)
3 Barnyard bleaters (4)
4 Flight of steps (6)
5 Very young child (3)
6 Someone exerting mental control over another (8)
9 CD precursor (8)
12 Small people (7)
13 Air current (6)
16 Belief; opinion (4)
18 Aardvark's dinner (3)

# PUZZLE 40

**Across**
1 Promise on the Bible, eg (5,2,4)
7 'Three Stooges' member, Howard (3)
8 Ancient Greek battle formation (7)
9 'Pardon me...' (4)
10 Repaired (6)
13 Meaningless words (3,3)
14 *The Lord of the Rings*, eg (4)
16 Seven-piece shape puzzle (7)
18 Omega, to a scientist (3)
19 Large performance space (7,4)

**Down**
1 Good-hearted (11)
2 Component part (7)
3 Fibrous (4)
4 Less far away (6)
5 Blind __ _ bat (2,1)
6 Base 16 number system (11)
11 Educational award (7)
12 Savage (6)
15 Exclude (4)
17 Novice, perhaps (3)

# PUZZLE 41

**Across**

**1** Public transport marker (3,4)
**5** Average guy? (3)
**7** Item of clothing (3)
**8** Wear your best clothes (5,2)
**9** Carafe (4)
**10** Less attractive (6)
**12** Young cat (6)
**13** Very unpleasant (4)
**15** Set apart (7)
**16** Certain razor brand (3)
**17** Greek equivalent of Aurora (3)
**18** Luggage handlers (7)

**Down**

**1** Blunt cutlery, used for spreads (6,5)
**2** Proposals (11)
**3** Orderly (4)
**4** Solemn promise (6)
**5** Excusable (11)
**6** Events that have been undergone (11)
**11** Leave a place secretly (6)
**14** Sly look (4)

# PUZZLE 42

**Across**

**1** Island chain (11)
**7** Bird hunted to extinction by the Maori (3)
**8** Tropical or subarctic, eg (7)
**9** Drives (6)
**10** Imperfection (4)
**13** Drag (4)
**14** Revolve (6)
**16** Reproduction (7)
**18** Count up (3)
**19** Trained to expect (11)

**Down**

**1** Creating a distinctive mood (11)
**2** French castle (7)
**3** Becomes subject to (6)
**4** Dark forces, perhaps (4)
**5** Norwegian pop band (1-2)
**6** Deluged (11)
**11** Contact (7)
**12** Language spoken in Djibouti (6)
**15** Pint-sized (4)
**17** Writing instrument (3)

# PUZZLE 43

**Across**
**1** Curtails (9)
**8** Outer limits (5)
**9** Penalties (5)
**10** An hour before midnight (6)
**12** Celestial Christmas vision (4)
**14** Type of revolver (4)
**15** Take place (6)
**17** Vestibule (5)
**18** Eastern verse type (5)
**20** Driving backwards (9)

**Down**
**2** It can be poached (3)
**3** Tried out (6)
**4** Far from certain (4)
**5** Sleeveless pullover (4,3)
**6** Magnifying device (9)
**7** Space traveller (9)
**11** Make bigger (7)
**13** Cleans (6)
**16** 'You', once upon a time (4)
**19** Actor, McDiarmid (3)

# PUZZLE 44

**Across**
**1** Pictures (11)
**7** Toiletry powder (4)
**8** Injure (6)
**9** Radio tuners (5)
**10** Bird limbs (5)
**13** Vulgar (5)
**15** Walnut-like nut (5)
**17** Purify (6)
**18** Lean (4)
**19** Expected (11)

**Down**
**2** Weighing more (7)
**3** Made an attempt to deal with (7)
**4** Supreme beings (4)
**5** Evident (5)
**6** Dance moves (5)
**11** Initial movement resistance (7)
**12** Hard rock, sometimes used for work surfaces (7)
**13** Roughly (5)
**14** Not suitable (5)
**16** Mythical, hairy snow-monster (4)

# PUZZLE 45

**Across**
3 iPhone maker (5)
6 Cosmetic liquids (7)
7 Side-to-side dimension (5)
8 Fasten (5)
9 Diseased (3)
11 Grant (5)
13 Actors' words (5)
15 Pen tip (3)
18 Celtic priest (5)
19 Artificial waterway (5)
20 University awards (7)
21 Subway (5)

**Down**
1 Full of happiness (6)
2 Microchip element (7)
3 Also (2,4)
4 Protects with soft material (4)
5 Sound, on reflection? (4)
10 Book collection (7)
12 Statement agreeing to a request (4,2)
14 Amended (6)
16 Layer of dirt (4)
17 Tie together (4)

# PUZZLE 46

**Across**
1 Lowering in rank (11)
7 Facebook posting, perhaps (6)
8 Caresses (4)
9 Set (5)
11 Fangs, perhaps (5)
13 Observes (5)
14 Everyday (5)
16 Award (4)
18 Seize (6)
20 Qualification document (11)

**Down**
2 Surface rock formation (7)
3 Bad hair discovery (3)
4 Deception (4)
5 Push, as in a button (7)
6 'Right away!' (3)
10 Highly strung (7)
12 Ford van (7)
15 Homeless child (4)
17 Lyric poem (3)
19 *Arabian Nights* bird (3)

# PUZZLE 47

**Across**

**1** Tea sweetener (5,4)
**7** Dull work (5)
**8** Rant and rave (5)
**10** Senses of self-esteem (4)
**11** Unobserved (6)
**14** Resistant to infection (6)
**15** At some distance (4)
**17** Strike together, as teeth (5)
**19** Arrival of a newborn (5)
**20** Curtailed (9)

**Down**

**2** Required outfit (7)
**3** Helps (4)
**4** Cover (6)
**5** Prefix meaning 'relating to life' (3)
**6** Consenting (8)
**9** Government with a king or queen at the head (8)
**12** Compel compliance with (7)
**13** Central live TV presenter (6)
**16** Slender, tubular instrument (4)
**18** Bonfire leftovers (3)

# PUZZLE 48

**Across**

**1** Solicitation (10)
**7** Dusk (6)
**8** Involuntary mouth widening (4)
**9** Enquire (5)
**11** Moved by an air current (5)
**13** Monster slain by Hercules (5)
**14** Part of a play (5)
**16** The core, as in an idea (4)
**18** Bunny (6)
**20** Very fashionable (3,3,4)

**Down**

**2** Mischievous (7)
**3** Opposite of outs (3)
**4** Deeds (4)
**5** Extremely happy (7)
**6** In mint condition (3)
**10** Soft toffee (7)
**12** Lacking (7)
**15** Inner side of the foot (4)
**17** Peron's wife, popularly (3)
**19** Drinks counter (3)

# PUZZLE 49

**Across**

**1** In a prim and proper way (11)
**7** Appear (4)
**8** Nailed (6)
**9** Endured (5)
**10** Rhinal (5)
**13** Rely upon (5)
**15** Bullock (5)
**17** Consume (6)
**18** 'Excellent!' (4)
**19** Overstated (11)

**Down**

**2** Someone eligible to vote (7)
**3** Affectedly self-important (7)
**4** Camp beds (4)
**5** Cooks in the oven (5)
**6** Sing like a Tyrolean (5)
**11** Receiver (7)
**12** Typical (7)
**13** Clan (5)
**14** Shadow (5)
**16** Eugene, to his friends (4)

# PUZZLE 50

**Across**

**1** Decoration; honour (11)
**7** Sedative Polynesian drink (4)
**8** Jail (6)
**9** Thin fogs (5)
**10** Eight-person choir (5)
**13** Fatigued (5)
**15** The act of coming in (5)
**17** Distort (6)
**18** Give off (4)
**19** Periodicals (11)

**Down**

**2** Envisage (7)
**3** Device for grilling bread (7)
**4** 'Don't think so!' (4)
**5** A picture within a picture, eg (5)
**6** Nine-voice group (5)
**11** Harmony; agreement (7)
**12** In the past (7)
**13** Cart (5)
**14** Large dart (5)
**16** Used to exist (4)

# PUZZLE 51

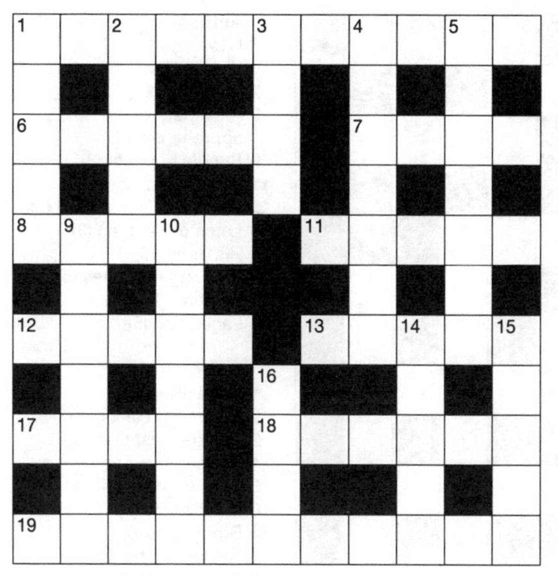

**Across**

**1** Cultural pigeonholes (11)
**6** Itemized (6)
**7** Loosen, as in a knot (4)
**8** Unwind (5)
**11** Shrek and friends? (5)
**12** Natural sweetener (5)
**13** Braid (5)
**17** Horse-breeding farm (4)
**18** Type of alcoholic cocktail (3,3)
**19** Old-fashioned (11)

**Down**

**1** Relating to the sun (5)
**2** Artist's stand (5)
**3** Chances (4)
**4** Junior (7)
**5** Unceasing (7)
**9** Earth's midriff? (7)
**10** Bestowed (7)
**14** Taken in (5)
**15** Expertise (5)
**16** Filth (4)

# PUZZLE 52

**Across**

**1** Infers (7)
**5** UK intelligence agency (init.) (3)
**7** Global heat source (3)
**8** Long, tapering, edible root (7)
**9** Levelled (6)
**10** Singer once married to Sonny Bono (4)
**12** Classic children's game (1,3)
**13** Sneaky, deceitful person (6)
**15** Roofed, external gallery (7)
**16** Wild-animal park (3)
**17** Dehydrate (3)
**18** Specialists (7)

**Down**

**1** Not trusted (11)
**2** Social dining occasion (6,5)
**3** Metal used in wires (6)
**4** Active (4)
**5** Electronic instrument (11)
**6** Unnecessary to requirements (11)
**11** Renovate (6)
**14** Thigh to lower leg joint (4)

# PUZZLE 53

**Across**

3 Lawn (5)
6 Vivid pictorial impression (7)
7 More glacial (5)
8 Anticipate with apprehension (5)
9 Bundle of paper (3)
11 Make a promise (5)
13 Not recently practised (5)
15 Lotus or Seat, eg (3)
18 His or her (5)
19 Weaving machines (5)
20 Deletion (7)
21 Laceration (5)

**Down**

1 Bone filling (6)
2 Reference calendar (7)
3 Stringed instrument (6)
4 Barren (4)
5 Bollywood dress (4)
10 Duke's wife (7)
12 Brought up (6)
14 Camera stand (6)
16 A whole bunch (4)
17 Vegetarian meat substitute (4)

# PUZZLE 54

**Across**

1 Operating costs (9)
8 In front (5)
9 Elected (5)
10 Reason out (6)
12 Go away quickly (4)
14 Hogwash (4)
15 Obscenity checker (6)
17 Coarse (5)
18 Spa facility (5)
20 Annulled (9)

**Down**

2 Strive; fight (3)
3 Deplete (6)
4 Extended underside of a roof (4)
5 Acts like Sherlock (7)
6 Complimentary (9)
7 Opinion piece (9)
11 Bother (7)
13 Key part of spectacles (6)
16 Singer, Collins (4)
19 Take advantage of (3)

# PUZZLE 55

**Across**
**1** Utensil (9)
**7** Pilot (5)
**8** Conjuring tricks (5)
**10** 'In memoriam' article (4)
**11** Parchment document (6)
**14** Consume (6)
**15** Phaser setting, in *Star Trek* (4)
**17** Italian seaport (5)
**19** Agave with sharp leaves (5)
**20** Brink (9)

**Down**
**2** Posting (7)
**3** Falsehoods (4)
**4** Copies (6)
**5** Repeatedly pester someone (3)
**6** Refusing to take notice of (8)
**9** Relating to former overseas rule (8)
**12** Visual (7)
**13** Large countryside land area (6)
**16** Widely held misconception (4)
**18** 'I'll pass' (3)

# PUZZLE 56

**Across**
**3** Sealing cement (5)
**6** City district (7)
**7** Powdered abrasive (5)
**8** Inclines (5)
**9** Had lunch (3)
**11** Beaver-like rodent (5)
**13** Jerks (5)
**15** One or more (3)
**18** Alternate (5)
**19** Hex (5)
**20** Sends in a form, perhaps (7)
**21** Risked (5)

**Down**
**1** Evening wear (6)
**2** Parent's father (7)
**3** Quite (6)
**4** Kicked, as in a ball (4)
**5** Round spinning toy (2-2)
**10** Emphasising adjective (7)
**12** Not dressed (6)
**14** Warden (6)
**16** Took advantage of (4)
**17** Emotion when in danger (4)

# PUZZLE 57

**Across**
**1** Ratios (11)
**6** Terminating (6)
**7** Public recreation area (4)
**8** Give medical attention to a sick person (5)
**11** Dissertation (5)
**12** Official order (5)
**13** Exactly right (5)
**17** Church ringer (4)
**18** Type of TV (6)
**19** Experts on celestial objects (11)

**Down**
**1** Song of triumph (5)
**2** More peculiar (5)
**3** Old pieces of cloth (4)
**4** Enforced (7)
**5** Paradise (7)
**9** Disrobe (7)
**10** Non-religious (7)
**14** Happen after (5)
**15** Soils of clay and sand (5)
**16** Allow access to (4)

# PUZZLE 58

**Across**
**1** Specifying (11)
**7** Remember (6)
**8** Sort (4)
**9** Harbour (4)
**10** Chilled (6)
**13** Grief (6)
**16** Make a copy of (4)
**17** Rings for mortal men, in *The Lord of the Rings* (4)
**18** Kind of (2,1,3)
**19** Sacrificing your own needs (4-7)

**Down**
**2** Diva's voice effect (7)
**3** Liturgical book (7)
**4** Small, fragrant shrub (5)
**5** Short, pastoral poem (5)
**6** Avarice (5)
**11** Wife (slang) (3,4)
**12** Justify (7)
**13** Vocal music (5)
**14** Relating to the kidneys (5)
**15** Bleached-flour bread (5)

# PUZZLE 59

**Across**

**1** Tool for gutting cod, eg (4,5)
**8** Enjoyed (5)
**9** Headache (5)
**10** Any country surrounded by water (6)
**12** Bet (4)
**14** Christmas delivery? (4)
**15** Cream-filled choux pastry (6)
**17** Truffles, eg (5)
**18** Hopping mad (5)
**20** Dishonest (9)

**Down**

**2** Bug (3)
**3** Concealing (6)
**4** TV reports (4)
**5** Chemical symbols equation (7)
**6** Someone who brings a legal action (9)
**7** Secrets (9)
**11** Berate (3,4)
**13** Be thrifty (6)
**16** Jetty (4)
**19** A pint, perhaps (3)

# PUZZLE 60

**Across**

**1** Period that followed baroque (9)
**8** Allow to escape (3,2)
**9** Long-legged wading bird (5)
**10** Theatrical dance (6)
**12** Froth (4)
**14** Sprint contest (4)
**15** Wild dog (6)
**17** Shortest digit (5)
**18** Incorrect (5)
**20** Cleaning agent (9)

**Down**

**2** Burning (3)
**3** Earlier (6)
**4** Agenda point (4)
**5** Space-station entry area (7)
**6** Ornate (9)
**7** Origin of a word (9)
**11** Educational talk (7)
**13** Small, elongated insect (6)
**16** Fit (4)
**19** Be the legal holder of (3)

# PUZZLE 61

**Across**

**1** By a very large amount (3,3,4)
**7** Relaxed (2,4)
**8** Type of salamander (4)
**9** Self-respect (5)
**11** Canvasses opinion (5)
**13** Popular heroes (5)
**14** Intimidate: ___ out (5)
**16** Unsightly (4)
**18** Providing (6)
**20** Tackles (10)

**Down**

**2** Dressed (7)
**3** Early computing pioneer, Lovelace (3)
**4** Stains (4)
**5** Wall openings (7)
**6** Rotate a helicopter (3)
**10** Late (7)
**12** Grant permission (7)
**15** Culture medium (4)
**17** Large, dark antelope (3)
**19** Going through (3)

# PUZZLE 62

**Across**

**1** Regarding feelings (11)
**7** Small amounts (11)
**8** Small fire-lighting stick (6,5)
**13** Obsessively self-centred (11)
**18** Personal items (11)
**20** Without awareness (11)

**Down**

**2** Italian mother (5)
**3** Appellation (5)
**4** Binary digit (3)
**5** Inner self (5)
**6** Reasoning (5)
**9** Bushy hairdo (abbr.) (3)
**10** Ceylon, eg (3)
**11** Cocktail, ___ tai (3)
**12** Facial spasm (3)
**14** Developed (5)
**15** A quark and an antiquark (5)
**16** Extraterrestrial (5)
**17** Declare invalid (5)
**19** Noticed something (3)

# PUZZLE 63

**Across**

**1** End in disaster (4,2,5)
**7** Be put through (7)
**8** Polite form of address (3)
**9** Carry (4)
**11** Layered, soft cake (6)
**13** Infested (6)
**14** Brainwave (4)
**16** One who goes to bed late (3)
**17** Cherish (7)
**19** Overly complex administration (11)

**Down**

**1** Multi-projectile munition (7,4)
**2** Median (3)
**3** Infringement, legally (4)
**4** Worldwide (6)
**5** Alternatively (7)
**6** Luckily (11)
**10** Young child (7)
**12** Protruding organ (6)
**15** Guitarist, Clapton (4)
**18** *Smash* actress, Thurman (3)

# PUZZLE 64

**Across**

**1** Efficient in terms of expense (10)
**7** Intensely (6)
**8** Scruff (4)
**9** Thin columns of smoke (5)
**11** Ignoramus (5)
**13** Greek Titan (5)
**14** Glued down (5)
**16** 'Immediately!' on a hospital ward (4)
**18** As tiny as can be (6)
**20** Modern devices (10)

**Down**

**2** Compounds and substances scientist (7)
**3** Sharp bite (3)
**4** Godly power to produce illusions (4)
**5** Deportment (7)
**6** Insolence (3)
**10** Artificial; unnatural (7)
**12** Travelling by pedal bike (7)
**15** Young deer (4)
**17** Express disapproval (3)
**19** Canola or olive, eg (3)

# PUZZLE 65

**Across**

**1** 18th-century furniture designer (11)
**7** Noon, in French (4)
**8** Dogmatic decree (6)
**9** 'The same thing again' (5)
**10** Provisional certificate of money (5)
**13** Battery terminal (5)
**15** Dog rope (5)
**17** Calm and dignified (6)
**18** Dozes (4)
**19** Very tall buildings (11)

**Down**

**2** Caribbean language (7)
**3** Decorated (7)
**4** Conclusions (4)
**5** Make a change (5)
**6** Finish a meal (3,2)
**11** Remove dirt and mess (5,2)
**12** Person privy to private information (7)
**13** Donkeys (5)
**14** Curiously (5)
**16** Inheritor (4)

# PUZZLE 66

**Across**

**1** Honours (10)
**7** Weighing device (6)
**8** Self-operating (4)
**9** Age (5)
**11** Strength (5)
**13** Seize by force (5)
**14** Negotiator (5)
**16** Opera lead's star moment (4)
**18** Risky (6)
**20** Be suitable (3,3,4)

**Down**

**2** Runs away (7)
**3** Sand or electric, eg (3)
**4** Take a break (4)
**5** Merchant activity (7)
**6** Convene (3)
**10** Small raisin (7)
**12** Smattering (7)
**15** Press forward (4)
**17** Sports arbiter (3)
**19** Underwater boat (3)

# PUZZLE 67

**Across**
1 What a leading initial stands for (5,4)
8 Make permanent (3,2)
9 Smell (5)
10 Tougher (6)
12 Bird often seen in hieroglyphics (4)
14 George W Bush's Deputy Chief of Staff, Karl (4)
15 Cure-all (6)
17 Penned (5)
18 Spicy cuisine (5)
20 Throwing away (9)

**Down**
2 Type (3)
3 Faculties (6)
4 Central facial feature (4)
5 Receptacle for letters (7)
6 Retracts (9)
7 Progeny (9)
11 Square pasta parcels (7)
13 Timepieces (6)
16 Cut and gather crops (4)
19 December follower (abbr.) (3)

# PUZZLE 68

**Across**
1 Respiring (9)
7 Really terrible (5)
8 October zodiac sign (5)
10 One of 52, perhaps (4)
11 Less well off (6)
14 Bureau (6)
15 Mix a liquid (4)
17 Petroleum company (5)
19 Strength of spirit? (5)
20 Least wide (9)

**Down**
2 Sports umpire (7)
3 Team up (4)
4 Empty (6)
5 Catch in wrongdoing (3)
6 Rectangle-based graph (3,5)
9 Flying machine (8)
12 Limited food supplies (7)
13 Having only magnitude (6)
16 Bring something up? (4)
18 Actress, Carrere (3)

# PUZZLE 69

**Across**
**1** Buyers (9)
**8** Not yet hardened (5)
**9** Tumbles (5)
**10** Area (6)
**12** Dry riverbed (4)
**14** Range; traverse (4)
**15** Very serious (6)
**17** Dizzy Gillespie's music (5)
**18** Loud, jarring sound (5)
**20** Clinton, eg (9)

**Down**
**2** Backup electricity source (init.) (3)
**3** Military bugle recall (6)
**4** Roman god of war (4)
**5** Free from prison (7)
**6** Sign up for regular copies of a publication (9)
**7** Spying (9)
**11** Room (7)
**13** Compulsory (6)
**16** Spring resorts (4)
**19** Beach Boys song, *Barbara* ___ (3)

# PUZZLE 70

**Across**
**1** Supporting (11)
**7** Obscured (6)
**8** Impression; aura (4)
**9** Cuts (5)
**11** Legal summary (5)
**13** Banded ornamental stone (5)
**14** Remains of a fire (5)
**16** Used to refer to waffle (4)
**18** Fertilized ovum (6)
**20** Rural scenery (11)

**Down**
**2** Apprehending; catching (7)
**3** Roulette bet, perhaps (3)
**4** Split (4)
**5** Rules (7)
**6** Crux (3)
**10** Meal-preparation room (7)
**12** Compelled to leave (7)
**15** Appointed government expert (4)
**17** Astrological sign (3)
**19** Talk endlessly (3)

# PUZZLE 71

**Across**
1 Homes (10)
7 Underlying motive (6)
8 Groups (4)
9 Buffalo (5)
11 Possible illness symptom (5)
13 Gawked at (5)
14 Camera aperture setting (1-4)
16 Former Spice Girl, Bunton (4)
18 Stay (6)
20 Concords (10)

**Down**
2 Continuing (7)
3 Parent's boy (3)
4 Warmth (4)
5 Eavesdrops (7)
6 Convened (3)
10 Outside; unenclosed (4,3)
12 Excessively conceited person (7)
15 Available (4)
17 'Give __ _ kiss' (2,1)
19 Iconic Hollywood actress, West (3)

# PUZZLE 72

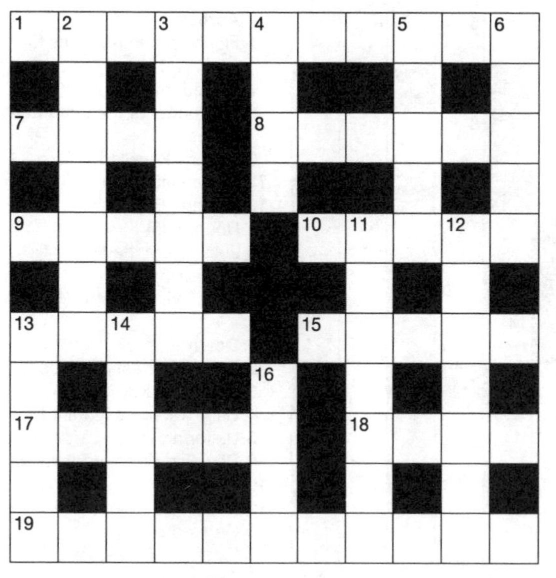

**Across**
1 Option (11)
7 Lump of clay or earth (4)
8 Be of the same opinion (6)
9 Old communications service (5)
10 Feathered animals (5)
13 Muscular tissue (5)
15 Grain husks (5)
17 Pillage (6)
18 Rear of the human body (4)
19 Creative thought (11)

**Down**
2 Drilled petroleum site (3,4)
3 Makes sorrowful (7)
4 Go against (4)
5 Become liable for (5)
6 Units of three feet (5)
11 Repress (7)
12 In reality, whether right or not (2,5)
13 Iranian language (5)
14 Projecting roof edges (5)
16 Psychic (4)

# PUZZLE 73

**Across**
1 Import duty (6)
4 Plants seeds (4)
6 Small firearm (6)
7 A bar in a fence (4)
8 Customer (6)
11 Tiny amount (4)
12 Cowardly person (4)
13 Chanced (6)
16 Uncouth (4)
17 Imperative (6)
18 Places to sleep (4)
19 Vitality (6)

**Down**
1 Theme (5)
2 Swiss grated potatoes dish (5)
3 Come to nothing (4,7)
4 Stretches with great effort (7)
5 Simple wind instrument (7)
9 Spare time (7)
10 Put into words (7)
14 Get ready to propose, maybe (5)
15 Trench (5)

# PUZZLE 74

**Across**
1 Financial contributions for profit (11)
7 Moved rhythmically (6)
8 The longer of the forearm bones (4)
9 Acquire knowledge (5)
11 Woven fabric (5)
13 Declare (5)
14 Doubter (5)
16 Just before the final? (4)
18 Amend (6)
20 Long, narrow paths (11)

**Down**
2 At the shortest distance (7)
3 Computer key (3)
4 Daily water movement (4)
5 Uniformly (7)
6 Downing Street address (3)
10 Keeps (7)
12 In need of water (7)
15 Cross-dressing (4)
17 Extended period (3)
19 Swear (3)

# PUZZLE 75

**Across**

**1** Formally hiring (11)
**6** Plan; mean (6)
**7** Curves (4)
**8** Official accounts check (5)
**11** Wrath (5)
**12** Sweeps along, like a cloud (5)
**13** Rainbow-forming glass (5)
**17** Cry feebly (4)
**18** Large, wild sheep (6)
**19** Large marine reptile with an olive-brown shell (5,6)

**Down**

**1** Porcelain (5)
**2** Well-known (5)
**3** Appends (4)
**4** Coach (7)
**5** Core (7)
**9** Hazy (7)
**10** Pander (7)
**14** Ill-suited (5)
**15** Interference pattern (5)
**16** Unit of power (4)

# PUZZLE 76

**Across**

**1** Renovation (11)
**7** Voucher (6)
**8** Pre-Euro Italian money (4)
**9** Ancient British neckband (4)
**10** Desires (6)
**13** Bikes (6)
**16** Alternative to Windows (4)
**17** Political assistant (4)
**18** Fire up (6)
**19** Founded (11)

**Down**

**2** A branch of biology (7)
**3** Average (7)
**4** Extend a subscription (5)
**5** Dublin residents (5)
**6** Draws nigh (5)
**11** Origins (7)
**12** Biblical letter (7)
**13** Thirst for (5)
**14** Trainee soldier (5)
**15** Odour (5)

# PUZZLE 77

**Across**
1 Completely developed (4-5)
8 Orders (5)
9 Hassle (5)
10 Part of a larger group (6)
12 Bawl (4)
14 Few and far between (4)
15 Debacle (6)
17 Clay building-block (5)
18 It's spoken in India (5)
20 Self-important display (9)

**Down**
2 Tea dispenser (3)
3 Endured (6)
4 Guide (4)
5 Victors (7)
6 Recommend as beneficial (9)
7 Harmonious (9)
11 Tortilla dish (7)
13 Angles (6)
16 Omit (4)
19 '... I don't think!' (3)

# PUZZLE 78

**Across**
1 Say sorry (9)
7 Amber, eg (5)
8 Poison (5)
10 Brio (4)
11 Small, cup-shaped cake (6)
14 Spain and Portugal (6)
15 Boast (4)
17 Andean transport animal (5)
19 'The Hunter' constellation (5)
20 Wins over (9)

**Down**
2 Mail fee (7)
3 Arrive, when on a plane (4)
4 Surrender (4,2)
5 Meditative Buddhism (3)
6 The ability to make choices (4,4)
9 Overseeing (8)
12 Pardon (7)
13 Tournament-concluding matches (6)
16 Luke Skywalker's mentor (4)
18 Affirmative answer (3)

# PUZZLE 79

**Across**
1 Merge together (9)
7 Portents (5)
8 Beneath (5)
10 Trip over (4)
11 Miniature tree (6)
14 Hasty (6)
15 Pimply skin condition (4)
17 Modern ballroom routine (5)
19 Nephew's sister (5)
20 Lawyers (9)

**Down**
2 Provokes (7)
3 Direction to look to see the sun rise (4)
4 Decoration for a present (6)
5 Phone number (abbr.) (3)
6 Says yes (8)
9 Bleach (8)
12 Guild (7)
13 Creamy ice cream (6)
16 Aware of (2,2)
18 Bathroom floor covering (3)

# PUZZLE 80

**Across**
1 Breaded snacks (10)
7 Group of competing teams (6)
8 Large stone (4)
9 Erodes (5)
11 Measures (5)
13 Academy award (5)
14 Bodily sacs (5)
16 Weapon supplies (4)
18 Medieval shooter (6)
20 Causes suffering (10)

**Down**
2 Never dating (7)
3 Made a hole (3)
4 Alpine goat (4)
5 Greatly distress (7)
6 'Precisely as written' (3)
10 Deduces (7)
12 Outer limit (7)
15 Duo (4)
17 Damaging allegations (3)
19 Trig function (abbr.) (3)

# PUZZLE 81

**Across**

**1** Oversee (9)
**8** Part (5)
**9** Multiplied by (5)
**10** Competitors (6)
**12** Opposite of female (4)
**14** Country pubs (4)
**15** Followed orders (6)
**17** Bad treatment (5)
**18** Sap (5)
**20** Asked for (9)

**Down**

**2** Native American tribe (3)
**3** Fairly (6)
**4** Ballot selection (4)
**5** Overview (7)
**6** Valuation (9)
**7** Rising (9)
**11** Daring journey (7)
**13** Dwells (6)
**16** Sweetheart (4)
**19** Do an impression of (3)

# PUZZLE 82

**Across**

**1** Shortened (11)
**7** Bloke (3)
**8** Long-distance clubs (7)
**9** Metallic element that rusts (4)
**10** Acid counterpart (6)
**13** Be at (6)
**14** Postal delivery (4)
**16** Asked over (7)
**18** Kyoto cash (3)
**19** Influences unfairly (11)

**Down**

**1** The Church of England religion (11)
**2** Refuse to take part in (7)
**3** Whirling mist (4)
**4** Winter stalactite (6)
**5** Something to wear with a suit? (3)
**6** Punishes (11)
**11** Financial researcher (7)
**12** Together (2,4)
**15** Graven image (4)
**17** Vehicle for transporting goods (3)

# PUZZLE 83

**Across**

**1** Fail, as in a business (2,2,3,4)
**7** Apportion, with 'out' (4)
**8** Average (6)
**9** Hose a garden (5)
**10** Jumps a rope (5)
**13** Economical with words (5)
**15** Without doubt (2,3)
**17** Pea or lentil, eg (6)
**18** Small children (4)
**19** Preparatory (11)

**Down**

**2** Function (7)
**3** Unified state (7)
**4** Sewn clothing borders (4)
**5** Corroboration (5)
**6** Arms and legs (5)
**11** Noble gas used in lasers (7)
**12** Strip for covering a cut (7)
**13** Dutch bulb (5)
**14** Scoundrel (5)
**16** Smile (4)

# PUZZLE 84

**Across**

**1** Dispersing (10)
**7** Small pieces of rock (6)
**8** Food given to poor people (4)
**9** Tropical trees (5)
**11** Male monarchs (5)
**13** Poetry (5)
**14** Parent's brother (5)
**16** Genuine (4)
**18** Computer-based video recorder (6)
**20** Writing sections (10)

**Down**

**2** Small country house (7)
**3** A large amount (3)
**4** Allay (4)
**5** Tehran resident (7)
**6** Fitness club (3)
**10** Get the wrong idea, perhaps (7)
**12** David's biblical conquest (7)
**15** Burglar's booty (4)
**17** Sales agent (3)
**19** Fur scarf (3)

# PUZZLE 85

**Across**

**1** Reckoning (10)
**7** Silent-film successor (6)
**8** Little spirits (4)
**9** Key for upper case (5)
**11** Contraption (5)
**13** Customary practice (5)
**14** Alarm call (5)
**16** Self-governing Palestinian territory (4)
**18** Red gems (6)
**20** Supporter of a trade-based system (10)

**Down**

**2** Overhead shots (7)
**3** Write in (3)
**4** Parodied (4)
**5** First name abbreviation (7)
**6** Quick rest (3)
**10** Vehicle light used in misty conditions (3,4)
**12** Indicating objects (7)
**15** Agonize (4)
**17** Curved line (3)
**19** Audio intensity unit (3)

# PUZZLE 86

**Across**

**1** Gathers (11)
**6** Late baroque style of decoration (6)
**7** Short note of debt (4)
**8** Fish eggs (5)
**11** Allium (5)
**12** Boring tool (5)
**13** Looking pale with fear (5)
**17** Haughty, spoiled woman (4)
**18** Confer (6)
**19** In theory (11)

**Down**

**1** Soft glows (5)
**2** Hot, brown drink (5)
**3** Japanese pasta strips (4)
**4** Scales (7)
**5** One part of a TV series (7)
**9** Porch (7)
**10** Well-being (7)
**14** Place to stay overnight (5)
**15** Recently (5)
**16** Share a boundary with (4)

# PUZZLE 87

**Across**
**1** Limited to local concerns (9)
**7** Begin to wilt (5)
**8** Fantasy (5)
**10** Knowledge test (4)
**11** Bleak and lifeless (6)
**14** Coalition forces (6)
**15** Early Michael Jackson hairstyle (4)
**17** Choose (5)
**19** Halt; ___ and desist (5)
**20** Female dancer (9)

**Down**
**2** Not good at mixing (7)
**3** 'My bad!' (4)
**4** Relating to the underworld (6)
**5** Prayer, '___ Maria' (3)
**6** Sufficient (8)
**9** Workforce (8)
**12** Chorus (7)
**13** Intellectual (6)
**16** *The Lion King* villain (4)
**18** Letter before theta (3)

# PUZZLE 88

**Across**
**1** Duplicate piece of paper (9)
**8** Threads (5)
**9** Baked dough (5)
**10** Contrition (6)
**12** Profound (4)
**14** Cart for delivering heavy loads (4)
**15** Loathing or disgust (6)
**17** Humped mammal (5)
**18** Sung part (5)
**20** Food blender (9)

**Down**
**2** That woman (3)
**3** Samples (6)
**4** Young foxes (4)
**5** Vegetable skin removers (7)
**6** Spin-off (2-7)
**7** Able to adjust to new conditions (9)
**11** The structure of a language (7)
**13** One-way flow devices (6)
**16** Group of countries (4)
**19** Talk fondly (3)

# PUZZLE 89

**Across**

1 Summarize (11)
7 Vocalist (6)
8 Great delight (4)
9 Appendage (4)
10 Bear-like, burrowing marsupial (6)
13 Not in the correct position (6)
16 Expert in a technical field? (4)
17 Journeyed by horse (4)
18 Manually (2,4)
19 Formulaic (11)

**Down**

2 More clamorous (7)
3 Branch of mathematics (7)
4 Sprinkle untidily (5)
5 Speak without a script (2-3)
6 Build, as in a structure (5)
11 Like many magazines (7)
12 Organize (7)
13 Merits (5)
14 Roof apex line (5)
15 Sacrosanct (5)

# PUZZLE 90

**Across**

1 Amusement ground (5,4)
7 Kick out (5)
8 Fight (3-2)
10 Equal, as in odds (4)
11 Make possible (6)
14 Sampled (6)
15 Predatory reptile (abbr.) (4)
17 Church tenets (5)
19 Strong dislike (5)
20 Published writing collection (9)

**Down**

2 Takes place (7)
3 Temperate (4)
4 Working as a model, perhaps (6)
5 Dull habit that's hard to change (3)
6 Crazy, colloquially (8)
9 Vanquish (8)
12 Excluding (7)
13 Separate (6)
16 Ballot (4)
18 Race starter (3)

# PUZZLE 91

**Across**
**1** Extortion (9)
**7** Cleric (5)
**8** Forest nymph (5)
**10** Takes a seat (4)
**11** Slippery playground chutes (6)
**14** Consecrate a priest (6)
**15** Bucket (4)
**17** Absolute (5)
**19** Matrix (5)
**20** Living things (9)

**Down**
**2** Placed (7)
**3** Form into a spiral shape (4)
**4** Halfway point (6)
**5** Unfriendly (3)
**6** Dodges (8)
**9** Exhibits (8)
**12** Schematic (7)
**13** Code word for 'S' (6)
**16** Twelfth Night visitors (4)
**18** A talent for music or language (3)

# PUZZLE 92

**Across**
**1** Derived from observation (9)
**8** Viking (5)
**9** Circular paths (5)
**10** Unduly; unreasonably (6)
**12** Funeral fire heap (4)
**14** Sudden attack (4)
**15** Least seen (6)
**17** Large, white waterbird (5)
**18** 100 aurar, in Iceland (5)
**20** Clothing creators (9)

**Down**
**2** Detract from (3)
**3** Paragons (6)
**4** Without much thought (4)
**5** Painkiller (7)
**6** Promote (9)
**7** Required (9)
**11** Perfect example (7)
**13** Table handkerchief (6)
**16** Fresh-food products counter (4)
**19** Rower (3)

# PUZZLE 93

**Across**

**1** Made to order (6-5)
**7** Better weather (6)
**8** Bell sound (4)
**9** Andean capital (4)
**10** Nailing tool (6)
**13** Legato, musically (6)
**16** The London Underground (4)
**17** Hot on (4)
**18** Ball (6)
**19** Prevention (11)

**Down**

**2** Nuclear-reactor fuel (7)
**3** Violent windstorm (7)
**4** Transform (5)
**5** Upper part of the pelvis (5)
**6** It may be Bengal or Siberian (5)
**11** Equals (7)
**12** Commerce restriction (7)
**13** Narrow openings (5)
**14** Ready to be poured (2,3)
**15** Speed (5)

# PUZZLE 94

**Across**

**1** Flawed (9)
**7** Unclear (5)
**8** Confusion (3-2)
**10** Crazy (slang) (4)
**11** Warmest part of the year (6)
**14** Not awake (6)
**15** Soft, French cheese (4)
**17** Minor actor (5)
**19** Surprise attacks (5)
**20** Opening (9)

**Down**

**2** Enchanting (7)
**3** Periods of time before events (4)
**4** Well-known (6)
**5** *Friends* actress, Courteney (3)
**6** Appraise (8)
**9** Contrary (8)
**12** From the red planet (7)
**13** Smoothly, in music (6)
**16** Sci-fi franchise, *Star* ___ (4)
**18** Silvery-white metal (3)

# PUZZLE 95

**Across**

**1** Relating to a particular language form (9)
**7** Social trip, perhaps (5)
**8** Nerve type (5)
**10** Bank; trust (4)
**11** Picked (6)
**14** Flowed out (6)
**15** Double rainbow, eg (4)
**17** Pass, as a law (5)
**19** Aspirations (5)
**20** Mixtures (9)

**Down**

**2** Calls names (7)
**3** Long-necked string instrument (4)
**4** Put garments on (6)
**5** Keyboard modifier (3)
**6** Extended work period (8)
**9** Abridge (8)
**12** Strode (7)
**13** In a state of disrepair (4-2)
**16** Old 'you' (4)
**18** *Much ___ About Nothing* (3)

# PUZZLE 96

**Across**

**1** Gather together (11)
**6** Functioning (6)
**7** Bite repeatedly before swallowing (4)
**8** Miley Cyrus move (5)
**11** Watery mist (5)
**12** Crop-growing establishments (5)
**13** Michaelmas daisy (5)
**17** 'Gosh!' (4)
**18** A macaw, eg (6)
**19** Pompous (11)

**Down**

**1** Grown-up (5)
**2** Be crazy (2,3)
**3** Come together (4)
**4** Food preparation instructions (7)
**5** Adolescent (7)
**9** Meteorological report (7)
**10** Uncontrolled (7)
**14** Trunk of a statue (5)
**15** Charges per periods (5)
**16** Hand width (4)

# PUZZLE 97

**Across**

**1** Forced to undergo, with 'to' (9)
**7** Accessory device (3-2)
**8** More certain (5)
**10** Stumble (4)
**11** Obstructs (6)
**14** Get back (6)
**15** Founder of the Holy Roman Empire (4)
**17** Deduction of money (5)
**19** Harbour towns (5)
**20** Citrus fruit preserve (9)

**Down**

**2** Reversing (7)
**3** Novelist, Austen (4)
**4** Expensive (6)
**5** Get this clue wrong, eg (3)
**6** Taken (8)
**9** Reply (8)
**12** Provided food for (7)
**13** One who has suffered harm (6)
**16** Milky-white gem (4)
**18** Ewe's call (3)

# PUZZLE 98

**Across**

**1** Trendy (11)
**7** Go, when playing a game (4)
**8** Jumped suddenly (6)
**9** Steps in and out of a field, perhaps (5)
**10** Shoplifted (5)
**13** Nut from an oak tree (5)
**15** Investigate (5)
**17** Break the surface (6)
**18** Tribulations (4)
**19** Based on counts (11)

**Down**

**2** Relating to water (7)
**3** Animal trainer (7)
**4** Depose (4)
**5** 'Well done!' (5)
**6** Large bird of prey (5)
**11** End points (7)
**12** Flowering bedding plant (7)
**13** Asserts to be the case (5)
**14** *The Magic Flute*, eg (5)
**16** Disorder (4)

# PUZZLE 99

**Across**
**1** Mechanical failure (9)
**7** Come to maturity (5)
**8** Turkish title (5)
**10** Central part (4)
**11** Summer trousers (6)
**14** Take a weapon away from (6)
**15** Egg cell (4)
**17** Mannequin (5)
**19** Relating to hearing (5)
**20** Saw (9)

**Down**
**2** Accounts (7)
**3** Uncle's wife (4)
**4** Extents (6)
**5** Used to exist (3)
**6** Came before (8)
**9** Gather (8)
**12** Change direction (7)
**13** Wax drawing stick (6)
**16** Major conflicts (4)
**18** Facetiously affected claim of innocence (3)

# PUZZLE 100

**Across**
**1** Road surface (6)
**4** Chew like a beaver (4)
**6** Daily routine (6)
**7** Close, as an envelope (4)
**8** Style of blues piano (6)
**11** Hot drink dispensers (4)
**12** Cope (4)
**13** Goodies (6)
**16** Shoe fastener (4)
**17** The distance something is out of line (6)
**18** Also (4)
**19** Uses money (6)

**Down**
**1** Pulsate (5)
**2** Four to one, eg (5)
**3** Compendiums (11)
**4** Hand signal (7)
**5** Opposed (7)
**9** In general (7)
**10** Female deity (7)
**14** Pyromaniac's crime (5)
**15** Locations (5)

# PUZZLE 101

**Across**
1 Inflatable hose inside a tyre (5,4)
8 Discourage (5)
9 Said in a grating voice (5)
10 Goes in (6)
12 Leaning Tower city (4)
14 Knocks lightly (4)
15 Couldn't remember (6)
17 Piece of cake? (5)
18 Evil spirit (5)
20 Contingent (9)

**Down**
2 Ball's target? (3)
3 Software bugs (6)
4 Become weary (4)
5 Berating (7)
6 Publicize (9)
7 Excessively complicated (9)
11 Popular beef cut for roasting (7)
13 Phrased (6)
16 Festival; celebration (4)
19 The opposite of women (3)

# PUZZLE 102

**Across**
1 Doorman (10)
7 Small river (6)
8 Sea greeting (4)
9 Grumpy expression (5)
11 Lowest-value British coin (5)
13 Religious verse (5)
14 Balance sheet resource (5)
16 Bangkok citizen (4)
18 North Pole area (6)
20 Origins (10)

**Down**
2 Onslaughts (7)
3 Day before a wedding? (3)
4 *Beautiful Creatures* actress, Rossum (4)
5 Heavenly requests (7)
6 Greek letter following pi (3)
10 Ambulatory (7)
12 Requiring (7)
15 Small mountain lake (4)
17 Fireplace shelf (3)
19 Chinese life force (3)

# PUZZLE 103

**Across**

**1** Thoughtful (11)
**7** Metal with atomic number 30 (4)
**8** For all of a given time interval (6)
**9** Lazy start to the day (3-2)
**10** The clear sky (5)
**13** Upright (2,3)
**15** Tracks (5)
**17** Large tropical lizard (6)
**18** Small lies (4)
**19** Kill by electricity (11)

**Down**

**2** Perspective (7)
**3** Segment (7)
**4** Previous Mauritius inhabitant (4)
**5** Plain-living US sect (5)
**6** Enthusiastic; keen (5)
**11** Congestion (7)
**12** Display (7)
**13** Small, green, oval fruit (5)
**14** Radiate, as an emotion (5)
**16** Wild animal's home (4)

# PUZZLE 104

**Across**

**1** Walkers (11)
**6** Subtlety (6)
**7** Title given to female knight (4)
**8** Trainer (5)
**11** Rush (5)
**12** Starts to move (5)
**13** Pile (5)
**17** Carved (4)
**18** Son of Zeus (6)
**19** Troop assembly point (5,2,4)

**Down**

**1** Relating to ancient Carthage (5)
**2** Former Princess of Wales (5)
**3** At that time (4)
**4** Open to question (2,5)
**5** Consisting of numbers (7)
**9** Porridge ingredient (7)
**10** Deep-seated (7)
**14** More adept (5)
**15** Is aware of (5)
**16** Popular Xbox game series (4)

# PUZZLE 105

**Across**

**3** Healed (5)
**6** Etch (7)
**7** Ancient Egyptian symbols of life (5)
**8** Financial resources (5)
**9** Plus (3)
**11** Competing (5)
**13** Makes watertight (5)
**15** Like a fox? (3)
**18** Wandering person (5)
**19** Camera image (5)
**20** Carping (7)
**21** Put off to a later time (5)

**Down**

**1** Live in (6)
**2** Toughens (7)
**3** Shackles (6)
**4** Playboy (4)
**5** School table (4)
**10** Repudiating (7)
**12** Depressing (6)
**14** Coming last, perhaps (6)
**16** Tater (4)
**17** Wind in loops (4)

# PUZZLE 106

**Across**

**1** Obnoxiously (11)
**7** Obtains (4)
**8** Universal Buddhist truth (6)
**9** Very dark wood (5)
**10** Objects (5)
**13** Send to a medical specialist (5)
**15** Surrounded by (5)
**17** Portable climbing frame (6)
**18** Weaponry (4)
**19** Accountable (11)

**Down**

**2** Giveaway (7)
**3** Extract (7)
**4** Froth (4)
**5** Spooky (5)
**6** Groups of twelve months (5)
**11** Orchestral drum set (7)
**12** Negligible (7)
**13** Measuring strip (5)
**14** Gradually disappears (5)
**16** Press clothes (4)

# PUZZLE 107

**Across**
1 Expressing in fewer words (10)
7 Brass, plate-like instrument (6)
8 Male offspring (4)
9 Lopsided (5)
11 Spry (5)
13 Common false beliefs (5)
14 Exaggerated (5)
16 *Star Wars* character, Darth ___ (4)
18 Flat-bladed oar (6)
20 Longitudinally (10)

**Down**
2 Lengthy undertaking (7)
3 Voice over a soundtrack (3)
4 World's longest river (4)
5 Visible (2,5)
6 Clear alcoholic spirit (3)
10 Organizational level (7)
12 According to law (7)
15 Distinctive Dalmatian feature (4)
17 The whole lot (3)
19 Dawn grass deposit (3)

# PUZZLE 108

**Across**
1 Diplomatic official (10)
7 Those older than children (6)
8 Pull with a jerk (4)
9 Notable descendant (5)
11 Spiky-leaved plant (5)
13 Casino machines (5)
14 Large, flat, diamond-shaped fish (5)
16 Squalid residential area (4)
18 Common type of dove (6)
20 Gain consciousness (4,2,4)

**Down**
2 Health check (7)
3 Leather-piercing tool (3)
4 Just about acceptable (2-2)
5 Boat-repair site (3,4)
6 Oversaw (3)
10 Most favourable (7)
12 Release (3,2,2)
15 Rotisserie rod (4)
17 *The Fifth Element* director, Besson (3)
19 Lass (3)

# PUZZLE 109

**Across**

**1** Cleans (6)
**4** Plunge (4)
**6** Eloquent speaker (6)
**7** Know about (2,2)
**8** Spanish dish cooked in a shallow pan (6)
**11** Against a background of (4)
**12** Round, griddled bread (4)
**13** Having lots of money (6)
**16** Horse's hoof protector (4)
**17** Make tidy (6)
**18** Blunders (4)
**19** Made haste (6)

**Down**

**1** Group of soldiers (5)
**2** Cover with cloth (5)
**3** Aerodynamic (11)
**4** Model landscape scene (7)
**5** Exterior (7)
**9** Further (7)
**10** Lingers (7)
**14** Relating to the Netherlands (5)
**15** Ate (5)

# PUZZLE 110

**Across**

**1** Spades and hoes, eg (6,5)
**6** Moves slowly (6)
**7** Roman drape (4)
**8** Small aquarium fish (5)
**11** Critical (5)
**12** News exclusive (5)
**13** Bed covering (5)
**17** Hired transport vehicle (4)
**18** Excessively (6)
**19** Job position (11)

**Down**

**1** Leaving (5)
**2** Go over (5)
**3** Headland (4)
**4** Swift-running African bird (7)
**5** Travel bags (7)
**9** Unfasten (7)
**10** Stipulation (7)
**14** Escape (5)
**15** Lovers' meet-up (5)
**16** Unstable subatomic particle (4)

# PUZZLE 111

**Across**

**1** Deceived (11)
**7** Manure (4)
**8** Deciduous flowering shrub (6)
**9** Shrub of genus *Erica*; open country (5)
**10** Gulf (5)
**13** Past tense of will (5)
**15** Take pleasure in (5)
**17** Sultana (6)
**18** Insect colony dwellers (4)
**19** Discourses (11)

**Down**

**2** Within the womb (2,5)
**3** Made up of 0s and 1s (7)
**4** True life (4)
**5** Current score (5)
**6** Hauls (5)
**11** Bangladeshi language (7)
**12** Reduce in length (7)
**13** Earth (5)
**14** Ikea purchase, perhaps (5)
**16** Duty (4)

# PUZZLE 112

**Across**

**1** Place of learning (9)
**7** Coils of hair (5)
**8** Glorify (5)
**10** First son of Adam and Eve (4)
**11** More concise (6)
**14** Key gas required for life (6)
**15** Free from bias (4)
**17** Post-shower essential (5)
**19** Changes a document (5)
**20** Historical peak (6,3)

**Down**

**2** Fortunately (7)
**3** Over-the-shoulder scarf (4)
**4** Thief (6)
**5** It's mined for minerals (3)
**6** Obscure with dark ink (5,3)
**9** Amaze (8)
**12** Positioning apart (7)
**13** Stuck closed (6)
**16** Blood vessel (4)
**18** Try to win (3)

# PUZZLE 113

**Across**

**3** Ward off (5)
**6** Combat period (7)
**7** Utilize again (5)
**8** Mind (5)
**9** Is endowed with (3)
**11** Leftover piece of food (5)
**13** Gives for a while (5)
**15** Youngster (3)
**18** Make use of (5)
**19** Touch-based healing technique (5)
**20** Storm noise (7)
**21** Flaming (5)

**Down**

**1** Cloth (6)
**2** Moral (7)
**3** In the air (6)
**4** Largest Australian birds (4)
**5** Fastens a knot (4)
**10** Personal attendant (7)
**12** Equality (6)
**14** Motivated (6)
**16** Senior lecturer (4)
**17** Happening right now (4)

# PUZZLE 114

**Across**

**1** European nobleman (5,4)
**7** Airs (5)
**8** Lavishly honoured (5)
**10** Wheel shaft (4)
**11** Film-set electrician (6)
**14** Topics for debate (6)
**15** Beam (4)
**17** Entire spectrum (5)
**19** Assists with a crime (5)
**20** Physicist or chemist (9)

**Down**

**2** Exam marks (7)
**3** Egg-laying location (4)
**4** Vanquish (6)
**5** Set of pieces to assemble (3)
**6** Talking (8)
**9** Absence of light (8)
**12** Surgery pincers (7)
**13** Colonize (6)
**16** Float through the air (4)
**18** Apple computer (3)

# PUZZLE 115

**Across**

**3** Typically colourful, seed-eating bird (5)
**6** Short spiral pasta (7)
**7** Dirty looks (5)
**8** To any degree (2,3)
**9** *Scream* director, Craven (3)
**11** Arrive at (5)
**13** Basic principle (5)
**15** Comforting toy (abbr.) (3)
**18** Abstain from (5)
**19** Multitude (5)
**20** Mysteries (7)
**21** Sugary sweet (5)

**Down**

**1** Not obvious (6)
**2** Regional language variation (7)
**3** Boneless meat (6)
**4** Repeated refusals (4)
**5** Pipe for watering (4)
**10** internet hosts (7)
**12** Unorthodoxy (6)
**14** Has being (6)
**16** In fashion (4)
**17** Husk remains (4)

# PUZZLE 116

**Across**

**1** Panorama (9)
**8** One having lunch, perhaps (5)
**9** Exhausts through lack of interest (5)
**10** Church keyboards (6)
**12** A barren plateau in Asia (4)
**14** Causes an artificial advantage in a system (4)
**15** Frequent (6)
**17** Transport (5)
**18** Waiflike (5)
**20** Forefathers (9)

**Down**

**2** Tread the boards (3)
**3** Audacity (6)
**4** Round loaves of bread (4)
**5** Execute (7)
**6** A form of government (9)
**7** Apportioning (9)
**11** Famous Russian cosmonaut (7)
**13** Large wood (6)
**16** Over-the-top publicity (4)
**19** Conifer (3)

# PUZZLE 117

**Across**
1 Make instant coffee, eg (6-3)
7 Small savoury dishes (5)
8 Overwhelming fear (5)
10 Churn (4)
11 Recent (6)
14 Reduce (6)
15 Lightweight boxing move (4)
17 Narrow material piece (5)
19 Misplaces (5)
20 Each person (9)

**Down**
2 Mends (7)
3 In the past (archaic) (4)
4 Hire (6)
5 *Hellboy* actor, Perlman (3)
6 Causes sudden alarm to (8)
9 Clear difference (8)
12 Laid bare (7)
13 Angry mood (6)
16 Viscous drop (4)
18 Priest (abbr.) (3)

# PUZZLE 118

**Across**
3 Histories (5)
6 Gun-firing lever (7)
7 Unaffiliated record label (5)
8 Squander (5)
9 Final letter, in the US (3)
11 Smallest EU member (5)
13 Church assembly (5)
15 Large-horned deer (3)
18 Hints (5)
19 Concert venue (5)
20 Very near (5,2)
21 Jason's jilted wife, in myth (5)

**Down**
1 Historical Spanish fleet (6)
2 Foment (7)
3 Costs (6)
4 *Candy Crush* sequel suffix (4)
5 Formally appeals (4)
10 Mascara target (7)
12 South American wool-provider (6)
14 Unlock a shop (4,2)
16 Seriously harm (4)
17 Loan (4)

# PUZZLE 119

**Across**

**1** Important events (9)
**8** Curie's gas (5)
**9** Solo (5)
**10** Pointing (6)
**12** Extent (4)
**14** Musical ending (4)
**15** Bigger (6)
**17** Saddle fall (5)
**18** Lure (5)
**20** Brief section of text (9)

**Down**

**2** Medical help, 'first ___' (3)
**3** Eating (6)
**4** Not fully closed (4)
**5** Cognizant (7)
**6** Transmit (9)
**7** Commemorate (9)
**11** Type of fortified wine (7)
**13** Crucifixion memorial (6)
**16** Simple aquatic plant (4)
**19** Thick mass of hair (3)

# PUZZLE 120

**Across**

**1** Absolutely nothing (6-5)
**7** Sketch (4)
**8** Hoped (6)
**9** Foot-operated lever (5)
**10** Join in matrimony (5)
**13** Vigorous attack (5)
**15** Attest (5)
**17** Modernize (6)
**18** Motion supporters (4)
**19** Type of male underwear (5,6)

**Down**

**2** Dipping pot for a quill pen (7)
**3** Diminish the value of, with 'from' (7)
**4** Contagious tropical disease (4)
**5** Court official (5)
**6** Toy named after Roosevelt (5)
**11** Pear-shaped salad fruit (7)
**12** Most affluent (7)
**13** Advertising text (5)
**14** Item-to-location reference (5)
**16** Strokes (4)

# PUZZLE 121

**Across**

**1** Italian sausage variety (6)
**4** Material made of interlaced threads (4)
**6** Get back (6)
**7** Denim (4)
**8** Related to cats (6)
**11** Stench (4)
**12** Opposite of push (4)
**13** Overwhelms (6)
**16** Henry VIII's final wife, Katherine (4)
**17** A mix of red and yellow (6)
**18** Cranium (4)
**19** Remained (6)

**Down**

**1** Letter-finishing stroke (5)
**2** Nearby (5)
**3** Opinions (11)
**4** Palma's island (7)
**5** Develop in a promising way (5,2)
**9** Edify (7)
**10** Badly brought up (3-4)
**14** Coins and notes, eg (5)
**15** Tachometer reading (5)

# PUZZLE 122

**Across**

**1** Deliberate (11)
**7** Marketing speeches (6)
**8** Nitwit (4)
**9** Duck sound (5)
**11** Bump (5)
**13** Photocopier brand (5)
**14** Transparent (5)
**16** Asana teacher (4)
**18** Blue shade (6)
**20** Fortified places (11)

**Down**

**2** Roman water god (7)
**3** Poetic 'before' (3)
**4** Trial (4)
**5** First or second, eg (7)
**6** High, snow-capped peak (3)
**10** Spicy pork sausage (7)
**12** Accused (7)
**15** Chinese dynasty (4)
**17** Repeatedly (3)
**19** A pair of people (3)

# PUZZLE 123

**Across**
**1** Gauging (9)
**8** Common European viper (5)
**9** Experience (5)
**10** Portable phone (6)
**12** Black-and-white, toothed whale (4)
**14** One of a matching pair (4)
**15** Large, wooden hammer (6)
**17** Proverb (5)
**18** Passage between seats (5)
**20** Millions of digital storage units (9)

**Down**
**2** Purpose (3)
**3** In a lively way (6)
**4** Wheel furrows (4)
**5** Nasal opening (7)
**6** Large, spotted dog (9)
**7** Deductions (9)
**11** Body of troops (7)
**13** Bright-yellow finch (6)
**16** Ewe's-milk cheese (4)
**19** Bring action against (3)

# PUZZLE 124

**Across**
**1** Nervous (3,2,4)
**8** Specks (5)
**9** Following on behind (2,3)
**10** Prehistoric animal remains (6)
**12** Melancholy (4)
**14** Thug (4)
**15** Pursues (6)
**17** Repulse (5)
**18** Japanese cuisine (5)
**20** Made up of various parts (9)

**Down**
**2** Lease (3)
**3** Rappel (6)
**4** Way out (4)
**5** Stops fidgeting (7)
**6** Deface (9)
**7** Possession (9)
**11** Late October star sign (7)
**13** Essay (6)
**16** Bird's wing movement (4)
**19** Regular drunkard (3)

# PUZZLE 125

**Across**

**1** Things you are aware of through your senses (11)
**7** Short branch road (4)
**8** Smallest values (6)
**9** Circle around (5)
**10** Stalks (5)
**13** Vulgar (5)
**15** A destroyed ship (5)
**17** Run out (6)
**18** Reclined (4)
**19** Inked on top (11)

**Down**

**2** Penguin, perhaps (7)
**3** Bears (7)
**4** Mountain lion (4)
**5** Chilled (2,3)
**6** Moves like a tree (5)
**11** Small pastry (7)
**12** Automaton (7)
**13** Statement of beliefs (5)
**14** Bounteous (5)
**16** Apple relative (4)

# PUZZLE 126

**Across**

**1** Sanctioning (9)
**8** Put a ship out of use (3,2)
**9** Engine (5)
**10** Illicit relationship (6)
**12** Type of freshwater fish (4)
**14** Ethereal (4)
**15** One-dimensional (6)
**17** Polite (5)
**18** Parable (5)
**20** Interpret (9)

**Down**

**2** Stick your nose in (3)
**3** Fix (6)
**4** Repeated jazz intro (4)
**5** Eccentric person (7)
**6** Headroom (9)
**7** Kept (9)
**11** Eternally (7)
**13** Wicked (6)
**16** Mountain valley (4)
**19** Android, perhaps (3)

# PUZZLE 127

**Across**

**1** Temporary discount, perhaps (9)
**8** Necessities (5)
**9** Talents (5)
**10** Not so strict (6)
**12** Poker stake (4)
**14** Successful Broadway musical (4)
**15** The start of something (6)
**17** Mend (5)
**18** Lucky numbers game (5)
**20** Cause to fall (5,4)

**Down**

**2** Bewail (3)
**3** Expert (6)
**4** Yanks (4)
**5** Scandalizes (7)
**6** Barge in (9)
**7** Allegation (9)
**11** Member of US upper house (7)
**13** Spiralled (6)
**16** Between knee and ankle (4)
**19** Pull (3)

# PUZZLE 128

**Across**

**7** Substitute (11)
**8** Believe to be guilty (7)
**9** Clumsy and unintelligent person (3)
**10** Severe (5)
**12** Cook's protective garment (5)
**13** Ribcage muscle (3)
**14** Energetic (7)
**16** Able to be comprehended (11)

**Down**

**1** Chirping insect (11)
**2** Picks, with 'for' (4)
**3** Make a lot of noise (4,3,4)
**4** Confining (11)
**5** Diversion (6)
**6** Haughty (5-6)
**11** Cooking instructions (6)
**15** Disorderly crowds (4)

# PUZZLE 129

**Across**

**1** Finding of the area under a curve (11)
**7** Fumes (6)
**8** Make money (4)
**9** Bluff (5)
**11** Ballroom dance (5)
**13** Boat or ship (5)
**14** Extremely energetic (5)
**16** Middle Eastern hors d'oeuvre dishes (4)
**18** Long-tailed crow (6)
**20** Insignificant (11)

**Down**

**2** More agile (7)
**3** Cartoon cry (3)
**4** Skin eruption (4)
**5** Healing treatment (7)
**6** Prayer, ___ Father (3)
**10** Mid-teens year (7)
**12** Smallest taxonomic group (7)
**15** Warning sign (4)
**17** Ogle (3)
**19** Work well together (3)

# PUZZLE 130

**Across**

**1** All-embracing (9)
**7** Madcap act (5)
**8** Fourth Greek letter (5)
**10** Opposite of gave (4)
**11** Radio code word for 'Q' (6)
**14** Dashes (6)
**15** Offers a price at an auction (4)
**17** In accordance with (2,3)
**19** Mexican friend (5)
**20** Outstanding part of an event (9)

**Down**

**2** Countries (7)
**3** Deficiency (4)
**4** Element with atomic number 11 (6)
**5** *Batman* actor, Kilmer (3)
**6** Unicellular organisms (8)
**9** Forebear (8)
**12** From London, eg (7)
**13** Quest (6)
**16** West African republic (4)
**18** Letter following chi (3)

# PUZZLE 131

**Across**

1 Artificial (9)
7 Fresher (5)
8 Selfish person (5)
10 Is behind on payment (4)
11 Arcs (6)
14 Watched (6)
15 Sticking substance (4)
17 Warehouse (5)
19 Anticipate (5)
20 Aspect of a situation (9)

**Down**

2 Not any location (7)
3 4,840 square yards (4)
4 False (6)
5 Put a question to (3)
6 Complicated (8)
9 Highly regards (8)
12 Erupting mountain (7)
13 To settle comfortably (6)
16 Young women, informally (4)
18 'Golden ratio' letter (3)

# PUZZLE 132

**Across**

1 Accepting (11)
7 Website checkout container (4)
8 String-shaped piece of pasta (6)
9 Companies (5)
10 Light bite (5)
13 Lunch and dinner, eg (5)
15 Taking advantage of (5)
17 Trope (6)
18 Ancient god of love (4)
19 Simplifying metaphor (11)

**Down**

2 Scrutinize (7)
3 Best possible (7)
4 Not any (4)
5 Large South-Asian country (5)
6 One from Athens, eg (5)
11 Just beginning to exist (7)
12 Briskly, in music (3,4)
13 Soft leather made from sheepskin (5)
14 Farewell (5)
16 Sonic the Hedgehog company (4)

# PUZZLE 133

**Across**

**1** Broadcast aerial (11)
**7** Jar (4)
**8** In person (6)
**9** Words that say what is happening (5)
**10** Fish covering (5)
**13** Dated expression of surprise (2,3)
**15** Buenos Aires dance (5)
**17** Stay attached (6)
**18** Satisfy (4)
**19** Giving up for the greater good (11)

**Down**

**2** Type of bird colony (7)
**3** In particular (7)
**4** Silent actor (4)
**5** Letter after eta (5)
**6** Hurriedly search (5)
**11** Enduring artistic work (7)
**12** Become less dark (7)
**13** Complains about things (5)
**14** Guiding philosophy (5)
**16** Complaint (4)

# PUZZLE 134

**Across**

**1** Print again (9)
**8** Jewish scholar (5)
**9** Hazardous (5)
**10** Dining furniture (6)
**12** Adroit (4)
**14** Foot digits (4)
**15** Walk like a duck (6)
**17** Tea, orange ___ (5)
**18** *Monster* actress, Christina (5)
**20** Persecuted (9)

**Down**

**2** Flow back (3)
**3** Combines (6)
**4** Cooking fat (4)
**5** Adjourn (7)
**6** Preliminary version (9)
**7** Making a whole out of parts (9)
**11** Split with a partner (5,2)
**13** Large, tusked marine mammal (6)
**16** Twelve months (4)
**19** Forgetful actor's need? (3)

# PUZZLE 135

**Across**

**1** Occurring in several forms (11)
**7** He pulls Santa's sleigh (7)
**8** Smuggle (3)
**9** Network intersection (4)
**11** Aged metal coating (6)
**13** Bushy, aromatic plant of the mint family (6)
**14** Eye up (4)
**16** Series of tennis games (3)
**17** Difficult decision (7)
**19** Overlay (11)

**Down**

**1** Phrase used as a written aside (11)
**2** Removable container top (3)
**3** Dairy product (4)
**4** Microwave, perhaps (6)
**5** In pain (7)
**6** Join together in series (11)
**10** Non-portable computer (7)
**12** Pulverize (6)
**15** Purple, fleshy fruit (4)
**18** Cultural Revolution leader (3)

# PUZZLE 136

**Across**

**1** Generous (9)
**7** Impulses (5)
**8** Easily scared (5)
**10** Abound (4)
**11** Buffoons (6)
**14** Baby's toy (6)
**15** In this location (4)
**17** English white cliffs locale (5)
**19** Not the odds? (5)
**20** Make self-conscious (9)

**Down**

**2** Disregard (7)
**3** On the other hand (4)
**4** Useless (6)
**5** Phone ID card (init.) (3)
**6** Spoke barely audibly (8)
**9** Scatter (8)
**12** Although (7)
**13** Christian service prayer (6)
**16** Doe and roe, eg (4)
**18** Vitality (3)

# PUZZLE 137

**Across**

**1** Most important things (10)
**7** Grim Reaper's tool? (6)
**8** Pleasing (4)
**9** Stretch (5)
**11** Developed (5)
**13** Heats up (5)
**14** Off the cuff (2,3)
**16** Scored 100% on (4)
**18** Muscle spasms (6)
**20** Advocates for (10)

**Down**

**2** Cannoli filling (7)
**3** Cereal plant (3)
**4** Mid-month day (4)
**5** Disregarded (7)
**6** Sixtieth of a minute (abbr.) (3)
**10** Wandering (7)
**12** Ended (7)
**15** Swindle (4)
**17** Despicable person (3)
**19** Japanese PM (3)

# PUZZLE 138

**Across**

**1** Egyptian language (6)
**4** Destiny (4)
**6** Roasting bird (6)
**7** Music boosters (4)
**8** Hair-splitting person (6)
**11** Sail diagonally with the wind (4)
**12** Part of an underwater forest? (4)
**13** Nearby residents (6)
**16** Spanish painter, Joan (4)
**17** Type of edible nut (6)
**18** Man-eating giant (4)
**19** Desolate (6)

**Down**

**1** Make mischief (3,2)
**2** Ventilated (5)
**3** Fortune-telling globe (7,4)
**4** Frenzied (7)
**5** Of current relevance (7)
**9** Time when the sun sets (7)
**10** Sanction (7)
**14** At a higher level than (5)
**15** Unhappily (5)

# PUZZLE 139

**Across**

**1** Wrong (9)
**8** Tribal leader (5)
**9** Distrust (5)
**10** Most pleasant (6)
**12** Dull throbbing (4)
**14** Comparison connector (4)
**15** Domains (6)
**17** Captured (5)
**18** Scowl (5)
**20** Common type of pasta (9)

**Down**

**2** Get the ___, to be selected (3)
**3** Surge (6)
**4** Clarets, eg (4)
**5** Assembly (7)
**6** Restore to a former position (9)
**7** Emphasizing (9)
**11** Burst into laughter (5,2)
**13** Hot caffeine-rich drink (6)
**16** Tight; close-fitting (4)
**19** Go for (3)

# PUZZLE 140

**Across**

**1** Electronic investigator (6)
**4** School sleeping area (4)
**6** Champagne and juice drink (6)
**7** Becomes ill (4)
**8** Core parts (6)
**11** Animal-catching device (4)
**12** Dancer's dress (4)
**13** Secret (6)
**16** Famous baseball player, Babe (4)
**17** Damage (6)
**18** Walk with heavy steps (4)
**19** That is to say (6)

**Down**

**1** You, eg (5)
**2** Wit (5)
**3** The act of becoming aware of something (11)
**4** Severe (7)
**5** Get educated again (7)
**9** Contrary to the norm (7)
**10** Expressed mirth (7)
**14** Open-jawed (5)
**15** Dawn, to most people (5)

# PUZZLE 141

**Across**
**1** Red citrus fruit variety (5,6)
**7** Assist in wrongdoing (4)
**8** Trapped (6)
**9** Wheat, eg (5)
**10** Member of a company (5)
**13** Educational group (5)
**15** Atolls (5)
**17** Elastic material (6)
**18** Units of electrical resistance (4)
**19** Likely to happen soon (2,3,6)

**Down**
**2** Left-leaning (7)
**3** Acquires (7)
**4** Toe-stubbing word (4)
**5** Time without sun (5)
**6** Go-ahead key (5)
**11** Unfasten a boat (4,3)
**12** Supply too many staff (7)
**13** Short-legged breed of dog (5)
**14** Superior of a monastery (5)
**16** Spiritedness (4)

# PUZZLE 142

**Across**
**1** In respect of (2,7)
**8** Yellow light (5)
**9** Make extremely happy (5)
**10** Tried to catch cod, eg (6)
**12** Glimpse (4)
**14** Step (4)
**15** Delay (4-2)
**17** Verb form (5)
**18** Root (5)
**20** Staff (9)

**Down**
**2** Cry noisily (3)
**3** Won (6)
**4** Greek equivalent of Mars (4)
**5** Blind alley (4,3)
**6** Misleading statement (4-5)
**7** The distant universe (4,5)
**11** Equivalent word (7)
**13** Cattle herder (6)
**16** Ridge along a bird's breastbone (4)
**19** Any ship (3)

# PUZZLE 143

**Across**

**1** Apple web browser (6)
**4** Former Peruvian citizen (4)
**6** Free from an obligation (6)
**7** Competes (4)
**8** Placard (6)
**11** Do injury to, as in pride (4)
**12** Bigger than kilo but smaller than giga (4)
**13** Take in and understand (6)
**16** Mathematical positions (4)
**17** Take a firm stand (6)
**18** Hart (4)
**19** Hotel patrons (6)

**Down**

**1** Slumber (5)
**2** Nourishes (5)
**3** Connecting (11)
**4** Infiltrates (7)
**5** Less dirty (7)
**9** Unfold (4,3)
**10** Splitting apart (7)
**14** Excludes (5)
**15** Large washing tubs (5)

# PUZZLE 144

**Across**

**1** Attractively (11)
**7** Swami (4)
**8** Go aboard (6)
**9** Large rooms (5)
**10** Detective's workload (5)
**13** Emerald or aquamarine, eg (5)
**15** Slaver (5)
**17** Uncover (6)
**18** Spiked metal fastener (4)
**19** Placement (11)

**Down**

**2** Imitate (7)
**3** Normally (7)
**4** Covers with sugary coating (4)
**5** Guides (5)
**6** Wooden frames for oxen (5)
**11** Initial-based abbreviation (7)
**12** Sentiment (7)
**13** Country whose capital is Naypyidaw (5)
**14** Large stream (5)
**16** Slimy garden pest (4)

# PUZZLE 145

**Across**

**1** Most intelligent (9)
**8** Goes on and on (5)
**9** Trinity (5)
**10** Take small bites (6)
**12** Nothing more (4)
**14** Shaving injury (4)
**15** Lactase or pepsin, eg (6)
**17** Small, furry rodent (5)
**18** Poisonous (5)
**20** Doctrines of the Methodists (9)

**Down**

**2** Leonard, familiarly (3)
**3** Immensely (6)
**4** Mechanical and repetitive (4)
**5** GP practice (7)
**6** Trademark (5,4)
**7** Allusion (9)
**11** Since (7)
**13** Conjoined (6)
**16** Casual word of agreement (4)
**19** Some fourteenth letters (3)

# PUZZLE 146

**Across**

**1** Say bad things about (5,4,2)
**7** Walking limbs (4)
**8** Small, useful tool (6)
**9** Priest (5)
**10** Many times (5)
**13** Shut (5)
**15** Lit-up (5)
**17** Completely erase (6)
**18** Reduce, as in number (4)
**19** Organizing (11)

**Down**

**2** Win (7)
**3** Guarantees (7)
**4** For this reason (4)
**5** Lamp (5)
**6** Conform (3,2)
**11** Pugilist (7)
**12** Natural wearing-away (7)
**13** Classic board game (5)
**14** Tender (5)
**16** Purple vegetable plant (4)

# PUZZLE 147

**Across**
1 Neckband (6)
4 Weighted weapon (4)
6 Subject to death (6)
7 Nigh (4)
8 Without being asked (2,4)
11 Makes public (4)
12 Large edible fish (4)
13 Towards the back of a ship (6)
16 Community website (4)
17 Short-sleeved informal top (1-5)
18 Muffled engine sound (4)
19 Restless and turbulent (6)

**Down**
1 Carved gemstone (5)
2 Men of noble rank (5)
3 Sullenly (11)
4 Fabricate (7)
5 Appetizer (7)
9 Provide with healthy food (7)
10 Locating (7)
14 Bad deeds (5)
15 Smart (5)

# PUZZLE 148

**Across**
1 Type of toiletry item (7,4)
7 Troika (4)
8 100 centimos (6)
9 Concluding competition (5)
10 Detached (5)
13 Farmyard mammary gland (5)
15 Plummets (5)
17 'Again!' (6)
18 Thousands of millions of years (4)
19 Goal (11)

**Down**
2 Hasty (7)
3 Infract (7)
4 Pinches; squeezes (4)
5 Alpha's counterpart (5)
6 Intended (5)
11 Flawless (7)
12 Verbally attack (3,4)
13 Throw into confusion (5)
14 Quickly lowers the head (5)
16 Legume (4)

# PUZZLE 149

**Across**

1 Set of musical movements (6)
4 Flower jar (4)
6 Continue (6)
7 Identifying word (4)
8 Pay the balance (3,3)
11 Overdue (4)
12 Grasping hand pose (4)
13 Supplication (6)
16 One thousand grams (4)
17 Soothing, as of sound (6)
18 Not a natural colour (4)
19 Sitting down (6)

**Down**

1 Heathland with stunted vegetation (5)
2 Not very nice at all (5)
3 Highest-ranking card (3,2,6)
4 Unexciting; flavourless (7)
5 Retired spacecraft (7)
9 Tool app (7)
10 Audibly (3,4)
14 Marina vessel (5)
15 Gave five stars, perhaps (5)

# PUZZLE 150

**Across**

1 Weak; feeble (9)
7 Provide food (5)
8 Baby's potential affliction (5)
10 Raised platform (4)
11 Individual (6)
14 Long-haired breed of cat (6)
15 Rounded and slightly elongated (4)
17 Black-and-white horse? (5)
19 Employed (5)
20 Patently (9)

**Down**

2 Naught (7)
3 Actor, James ___ Jones (4)
4 Secured with a key (6)
5 *2001: A Space Odyssey* computer (3)
6 Fusion dance music (4,4)
9 Terminate (8)
12 A few more than a few (7)
13 Small job (6)
16 How soon? (4)
18 Soul singer Knight, familiarly (3)

# PUZZLE 151

**Across**
1 Half of February (9)
8 Later (5)
9 Varieties (5)
10 Place of education (6)
12 Frost (4)
14 Rows a boat (4)
15 Stature (6)
17 Italian cathedral (5)
18 Initiate (5)
20 Occurrences (9)

**Down**
2 Away from home (3)
3 Panic (6)
4 Marks (4)
5 Searching (7)
6 Secret sequences (9)
7 Agreeing (9)
11 Whaling spear (7)
13 Lacking strength (6)
16 Central points (4)
19 Understood (3)

# PUZZLE 152

**Across**
3 Police con (5)
6 Distribute (4,3)
7 Declares (5)
8 Rot (5)
9 Sharp turn (3)
11 Widespread destruction (5)
13 Pressed drink (5)
15 Headless Stark, in *Game of Thrones* (3)
18 Advance spotter (5)
19 Hangout (5)
20 Dwell in (7)
21 Rock or country (5)

**Down**
1 Big-screen venue (6)
2 Six-sided shape (7)
3 Inert (6)
4 Visual app identifier (4)
5 Substance of a speech (4)
10 Hellenic (7)
12 Cornish, Irish or Scottish Gaelic, eg (6)
14 Inane (6)
16 Those people (4)
17 Large liquid containers (4)

# PUZZLE 153

**Across**

**1** Pay attention (11)
**7** Greek letter 'z' (4)
**8** Type of Indian dish (6)
**9** Canteen (5)
**10** Spirit of a culture (5)
**13** Sudden convulsion (5)
**15** Digitally captures a document (5)
**17** Safe to be eaten (6)
**18** At the summit of (4)
**19** Basically (11)

**Down**

**2** Common area of interest (7)
**3** Particular stipulations (7)
**4** Christen (4)
**5** Disconcert (5)
**6** Formal quizzes (5)
**11** Fugue companion, often (7)
**12** Possible result of a defensive error in soccer (3,4)
**13** Stockholm resident (5)
**14** Awry (5)
**16** Where the sun sets (4)

# PUZZLE 154

**Across**

**1** Experiments (6)
**4** Prickly seed case (4)
**6** Per head (6)
**7** Fervour (4)
**8** Twins zodiac sign (6)
**11** Solemn promise (4)
**12** Exercise locations (4)
**13** Not in good health (6)
**16** Over-the-air internet (2-2)
**17** Bring in from abroad (6)
**18** Captain Hook's right-hand man (4)
**19** Old Faithful, eg (6)

**Down**

**1** Pluck a guitar string (5)
**2** Turn of phrase (5)
**3** Removing bacteria (11)
**4** 'Go away!' (4,3)
**5** Someone who responds to a stimulus (7)
**9** Heaven, to ancient Greeks (7)
**10** Fill with spirit (7)
**14** Computer app identifiers (5)
**15** Measuring device (5)

# PUZZLE 155

**Across**

**1** Most intelligent (9)
**8** Inspire (5)
**9** Car routes (5)
**10** Nominating (6)
**12** Indian butter (4)
**14** Baronets (4)
**15** Surrounded by (6)
**17** Spreadsheet software (5)
**18** Ink mark (5)
**20** Proscribed (9)

**Down**

**2** Polish (3)
**3** Infers from various sources (6)
**4** Besmirches (4)
**5** Violently broken (7)
**6** Sees happen (9)
**7** Avowing (9)
**11** North-west African country (7)
**13** Entertained (6)
**16** Dollop (4)
**19** Astonish (3)

# PUZZLE 156

**Across**

**1** Relating to the making of laws (11)
**6** Hidden hacking software (6)
**7** Mound (4)
**8** Steal (5)
**11** Chinese or Thai, eg (5)
**12** Nozzle (5)
**13** Total (5)
**17** Abundant supply (4)
**18** Deceived (6)
**19** Diminuendo (11)

**Down**

**1** Lull (3-2)
**2** Complain (5)
**3** Website connection (4)
**4** Laid out, as a book (7)
**5** Large hamlet (7)
**9** Sudden whim (7)
**10** Knot (7)
**14** Claw (5)
**15** TV without pictures? (5)
**16** Yule, informally (4)

# PUZZLE 157

**Across**
**1** Story (9)
**8** Happening (5)
**9** Confine (5)
**10** Chucked (6)
**12** Saved computer document (4)
**14** Time periods (4)
**15** Text that has not been looked at (6)
**17** Same (5)
**18** A show being broadcast again (5)
**20** Drug bust, perhaps (9)

**Down**
**2** Expert (3)
**3** Kind of (6)
**4** Cash register (4)
**5** Dracula, eg (7)
**6** Chivalrous guy (9)
**7** Servant (9)
**11** Mexican language (7)
**13** Hereditary (6)
**16** Bird's bill (4)
**19** In its natural state (3)

# PUZZLE 158

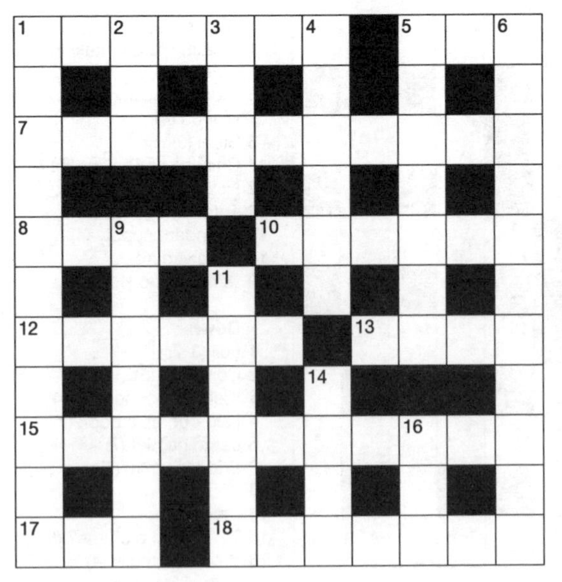

**Across**
**1** Aerodrome (7)
**5** Smidgen (3)
**7** Makes more difficult (11)
**8** Tears (4)
**10** Scoop (6)
**12** Stupidity (6)
**13** Group of binary digits (4)
**15** Parent's paternal parent (11)
**17** Celebratory cheer (3)
**18** Chewed the fat (7)

**Down**
**1** As a result (11)
**2** Drink distilled from molasses (3)
**3** Slippery; slick (4)
**4** Magnate (6)
**5** Entirely (7)
**6** Vanished (11)
**9** First in rank (7)
**11** Opposite of alkaline (6)
**14** Pops (4)
**16** Cabin (3)

# PUZZLE 159

**Across**

**1** Those that comply with social norms (11)
**7** Stable (6)
**8** Chemical element with atomic number 10 (4)
**9** Proceeds, financially speaking (4)
**10** Becomes aware of (6)
**13** Combat tool (6)
**16** Very similar (4)
**17** Fishing poles (4)
**18** Prize cup (6)
**19** Seers (11)

**Down**

**2** Appalling act (7)
**3** Sudden outburst (5-2)
**4** Relating to a sovereign (5)
**5** Besmirch (5)
**6** Nasal cavity (5)
**11** Bodily structure science (7)
**12** Not this one nor that one (7)
**13** Electrical conductors (5)
**14** Music and sound in general (5)
**15** Brief written records (5)

# PUZZLE 160

**Across**

**1** Ascertaining (11)
**6** One or the other (6)
**7** Evil; wickedness (4)
**8** Type of frozen dessert (5)
**11** Melancholy feelings (5)
**12** Casual comment (5)
**13** The Magi's incense (5)
**17** Traditional Japanese sport (4)
**18** Sycophant (3-3)
**19** Vocabulary (11)

**Down**

**1** Nerd (5)
**2** Spiritual emblem (5)
**3** Mother of Jesus (4)
**4** Originality (7)
**5** Fusion power type (7)
**9** Barely known (7)
**10** Sleeping chamber (7)
**14** Juliet's lover (5)
**15** Useful (5)
**16** Blue-green colour (4)

# PUZZLE 161

**Across**
- **1** Button press (9)
- **7** Put on (5)
- **8** Shin up (5)
- **10** Frozen rain (4)
- **11** Misgivings (6)
- **14** Minor (6)
- **15** Plant fungal disease (4)
- **17** Large violin (5)
- **19** Medicine bottle (5)
- **20** Game point, in tennis (9)

**Down**
- **2** Drains (7)
- **3** Hellish river (4)
- **4** Suppose (6)
- **5** Japanese carp (3)
- **6** Of the Pope's faith (8)
- **9** Rounders-like game (8)
- **12** Support (7)
- **13** Spanish racket game (6)
- **16** Expectorated (4)
- **18** Fronted (3)

# PUZZLE 162

**Across**
- **1** Putting off to a future time (10)
- **7** Target (6)
- **8** Close at hand (4)
- **9** Employees (5)
- **11** Courageous (5)
- **13** Not static (5)
- **14** Quizzed (5)
- **16** Tip (4)
- **18** Abreast (2,4)
- **20** Energy (3-2-3-2)

**Down**
- **2** Relating to a circular path (7)
- **3** Bodily extremity (3)
- **4** Type of grain (4)
- **5** Pays no attention to (7)
- **6** Wisecrack (3)
- **10** Most beautiful (7)
- **12** Seeing (7)
- **15** Compact by pounding (4)
- **17** Limb for walking on (3)
- **19** It's used by a fish to steer (3)

# PUZZLE 163

**Across**

**1** Outstanding (11)
**7** Ancient Chinese dynasty (4)
**8** Model used for testing (4-2)
**9** Attach with glue (5)
**10** Chemical analysis (5)
**13** Put clothes on (5)
**15** Roman garments (5)
**17** Savage (6)
**18** Money to avoid jail (4)
**19** Permitting (11)

**Down**

**2** Publishing essential (7)
**3** Preferences (7)
**4** Points at a target (4)
**5** Enjoys (5)
**6** Response (5)
**11** Celebrity life (7)
**12** Middle-Eastern horse (7)
**13** Sensation; unexpected event (5)
**14** Remove from a house (5)
**16** Make fuzzy (4)

# PUZZLE 164

**Across**

**1** Ken (9)
**8** Small fairy (5)
**9** Central African river (5)
**10** Huggable (6)
**12** Come to an end (4)
**14** Former Yahoo CEO, Jerry (4)
**15** 'Understood' (6)
**17** Small, edible-nut-producing tree (5)
**18** Go to the gym, perhaps (5)
**20** Large northern constellation (9)

**Down**

**2** Veto (3)
**3** Rotating load bearers (6)
**4** Apiece (4)
**5** Hereditary (7)
**6** Non-canonical scripture (9)
**7** Ailment (9)
**11** Inhabitant (7)
**13** Underside (6)
**16** Defamatory remark (4)
**19** Find the sum of (3)

# PUZZLE 165

**Across**

- **1** Short-haired, mid-sized dog (4,7)
- **7** Side (4)
- **8** Visual plots (6)
- **9** Business clothes (5)
- **10** Rend (5)
- **13** Oar (5)
- **15** Hand-to-forearm joint (5)
- **17** Coated shrimp or lobster dish (6)
- **18** Middle of the day (4)
- **19** Deputies (11)

**Down**

- **2** Not of the same value (7)
- **3** Restricted (7)
- **4** Roe (4)
- **5** Incite; goad (5)
- **6** Return to zero (5)
- **11** Predatory South American fish (7)
- **12** Concisely (2,5)
- **13** Culinary herb (5)
- **14** Stop sleeping (5)
- **16** Place where bees live (4)

# PUZZLE 166

**Across**

- **1** Flags (9)
- **7** Sugary (5)
- **8** Rabbit pen (5)
- **10** Seed-bearing cereal heads (4)
- **11** South American wildcat (6)
- **14** Emblem (6)
- **15** Slipped (4)
- **17** Liabilities (5)
- **19** Back of the feet (5)
- **20** Relating to a mild climate (9)

**Down**

- **2** Proposition (7)
- **3** Brief letter (4)
- **4** Hindu retreat (6)
- **5** Half a colon? (3)
- **6** Gauged (8)
- **9** Computer storage unit (4,4)
- **12** Least beautiful (7)
- **13** Tittle-tattle (6)
- **16** Burn some meat, perhaps (4)
- **18** Casual word of parting (3)

# PUZZLE 167

**Across**

1 Rebuke (5,4)
8 More mature (5)
9 Dried grain stalks (5)
10 University qualification (6)
12 Change direction suddenly (4)
14 Horse's restraint (4)
15 Toxin (6)
17 Free from knots (5)
18 Flaws, as in arguments (5)
20 Original example (9)

**Down**

2 Rock singer, Stewart (3)
3 Worked for (6)
4 Fading evening light (4)
5 Employees, eg (7)
6 Terrific (9)
7 Consciousness (9)
11 Sparkle (7)
13 Tall, cylindrical headwear (3,3)
16 Electronic equipment (4)
19 Remove branches from (3)

# PUZZLE 168

**Across**

1 Free (2,7)
7 Swallow liquid (5)
8 Fish-catching devices (5)
10 Large town (4)
11 Do not deviate from (4,2)
14 Back-of-mouth passage (6)
15 'Curses!' (4)
17 Handled; ___ with (5)
19 Ascends (5)
20 Volume (9)

**Down**

2 Tremulous bird chirp (7)
3 Nastily sticky (4)
4 Sound repetitions (6)
5 Eastern philosophical principle (3)
6 Learned (8)
9 Glaswegian, eg (8)
12 Expressed (7)
13 Fireplace shelf (6)
16 Courage; resolve (4)
18 Intel rival (3)

# PUZZLE 169

**Across**

**1** Intake (11)
**6** Tab in (6)
**7** Final (4)
**8** Might (5)
**11** Events calendar (5)
**12** Philatelist's love (5)
**13** Tally (5)
**17** Test version, in software (4)
**18** Ceremonial fur (6)
**19** Heavily; very slowly (11)

**Down**

**1** Ruler (5)
**2** Lowest point (5)
**3** A speck (4)
**4** Speaking (7)
**5** Notice (7)
**9** Active (2,3,2)
**10** Direct instruction (7)
**14** Precipitates (5)
**15** Funeral poem (5)
**16** Clothing (4)

# PUZZLE 170

**Across**

**1** Dried petal mix (9)
**7** Instructor (5)
**8** Doglike African mammal (5)
**10** Water (4)
**11** Linked to the universe (6)
**14** Touched with the lips (6)
**15** Opposite of cons (4)
**17** Male duck (5)
**19** Someone receiving money (5)
**20** Post-child home (5,4)

**Down**

**2** Yields (7)
**3** Unalloyed (4)
**4** Release from a catch (6)
**5** Small Eurasian deer (3)
**6** Raided (8)
**9** Gains entry to (8)
**12** Those killed for religious beliefs (7)
**13** Abhor (6)
**16** Public relations work? (4)
**18** Target (3)

# PUZZLE 171

**Across**

**1** Round brackets (11)
**7** Light volcanic rock (6)
**8** South African native (4)
**9** Fluff (4)
**10** Burrow (6)
**13** Not very often (6)
**16** Branch of a tribe (4)
**17** Possessive pronoun (4)
**18** Maker of suits (6)
**19** Moved from one place to another (11)

**Down**

**2** Personally offensive (7)
**3** Lived (7)
**4** Special reward (5)
**5** Reject with contempt (5)
**6** Cranium (5)
**11** Viler (7)
**12** Investigate (7)
**13** Animal's nose (5)
**14** Grub (5)
**15** Recurring theme (5)

# PUZZLE 172

**Across**

**1** Street intersection (9)
**8** Adversary (5)
**9** Trap (5)
**10** Degree (6)
**12** Consider (4)
**14** Given birth to (4)
**15** Gorges (6)
**17** Horned African animal (5)
**18** Prophet (5)
**20** Compact writing method (9)

**Down**

**2** Type of cereal plant (3)
**3** Saw (6)
**4** Affluent (4)
**5** Woman in a play (7)
**6** Recollects (9)
**7** Elemental science (9)
**11** From Ankara, perhaps (7)
**13** Beat decisively (6)
**16** Two squared (4)
**19** Low-down (3)

# PUZZLE 173

**Across**

**1** Peak viewing period (5,4)
**8** A word encoded as pictures (5)
**9** Carelessly (5)
**10** Happens (6)
**12** Falsetto male voice (4)
**14** Broadcasts (4)
**15** Annoyance (6)
**17** Move on hands and knees (5)
**18** Rogue (5)
**20** Pledge (9)

**Down**

**2** Ransack (3)
**3** Despair (6)
**4** Column spacings (4)
**5** Component units (7)
**6** Haughtiness (9)
**7** Revelation (3-6)
**11** Window covering (7)
**13** Trading place (6)
**16** Floating Arctic sheet (4)
**19** Animal-preserving boat (3)

# PUZZLE 174

**Across**

**1** Meaty; vigorous (4-7)
**6** Release a pair of oxen, perhaps (6)
**7** Not pass (4)
**8** Chickpea or lentil (5)
**11** Chat-show group (5)
**12** Fatty compound (5)
**13** Avoided work (5)
**17** Select (4)
**18** Immediately (2,4)
**19** Know-nothings (11)

**Down**

**1** Dowdy woman (5)
**2** Steadfast (5)
**3** Popular jeans (4)
**4** Casual (7)
**5** Malevolent gaze (4,3)
**9** Joining (7)
**10** Continue doing (5,2)
**14** Respiratory organs (5)
**15** Those who get things done (5
**16** Computer records (4)

# PUZZLE 175

**Across**
- **3** Customer (5)
- **6** Mandarin (7)
- **7** Make a comeback (5)
- **8** Surface for walking on (5)
- **9** Drinker's accidental sound (3)
- **11** Subsidiary theorem in a proof (5)
- **13** Standards (5)
- **15** Pig's house (3)
- **18** Use up (5)
- **19** Not these (5)
- **20** Platinum anniversary (7)
- **21** Brag (5)

**Down**
- **1** Put a book away (6)
- **2** Tells (7)
- **3** German capital (6)
- **4** December holiday season (4)
- **5** Shafts of light (4)
- **10** Paired up (7)
- **12** Not moving (2,4)
- **14** Sixty seconds (6)
- **16** Wild guess (4)
- **17** Capital of Italy, to an Italian (4)

# PUZZLE 176

**Across**
- **3** Start a tennis point (5)
- **6** Accumulated (5-2)
- **7** Coastal sea danger (5)
- **8** Not previously (5)
- **9** Mandible (3)
- **11** Despised (5)
- **13** Goes out with (5)
- **15** Hideout (3)
- **18** Investigate closely (5)
- **19** Put down (5)
- **20** Meat-and-vegetable pasty type (7)
- **21** Slumbered (5)

**Down**
- **1** 'I've worked it out!' (6)
- **2** Purported (7)
- **3** Move apart (6)
- **4** Common Indian food side (4)
- **5** Simple difficulty level (4)
- **10** Drifting (7)
- **12** Discover (6)
- **14** Least young (6)
- **16** Large, tailless primates (4)
- **17** Be wide open (4)

# PUZZLE 177

**Across**
**1** Set up (9)
**7** Juicy, tropical fruit (5)
**8** Walked through water (5)
**10** Impressed (4)
**11** Savage (6)
**14** Health spa (6)
**15** Small, pointed missile (4)
**17** 'Eat up!' (3,2)
**19** Excited exclamation (5)
**20** The state of being prepared (9)

**Down**
**2** Vocalists (7)
**3** Eagerly excited (4)
**4** Decreases (6)
**5** Former Pink Floyd member, Barrett (3)
**6** Rendered less effective (8)
**9** Removed passage of text (8)
**12** Instructs (7)
**13** Smoothed some shirts, perhaps (6)
**16** Anthem (4)
**18** Expression of mild sympathy (3)

# PUZZLE 178

**Across**
**1** Resembling verse (6)
**4** Ancient symbol of life (4)
**6** Brain cell (6)
**7** Penalty (4)
**8** 'Finally!' (2,4)
**11** A refined woman (4)
**12** Musical scales (4)
**13** Wound (6)
**16** Remove fat from milk (4)
**17** Walk like a baby (6)
**18** Exasperates (4)
**19** Sunglasses (6)

**Down**
**1** Bamboo-eating animal (5)
**2** Of the same value (5)
**3** Comprises (11)
**4** Flowering plant grown as fodder (7)
**5** Realm (7)
**9** Hiker (7)
**10** Takes for granted (7)
**14** Reversed (5)
**15** Zones (5)

# PUZZLE 179

**Across**

**1** Creativity (11)
**6** Inclined (6)
**7** Breaks down naturally (4)
**8** Drug recovery course (5)
**11** Written reminder notes (5)
**12** Sixth zodiac sign (5)
**13** Elector (5)
**17** New Zealander (4)
**18** Baloney (6)
**19** Sorceress (11)

**Down**

**1** Slacker (5)
**2** Inundated (5)
**3** In the altogether (4)
**4** Underwater missile (7)
**5** Consequence (7)
**9** Version (7)
**10** Heartache (7)
**14** Furniture suitable for eating at (5)
**15** Tempers (5)
**16** Lower jaw (4)

# PUZZLE 180

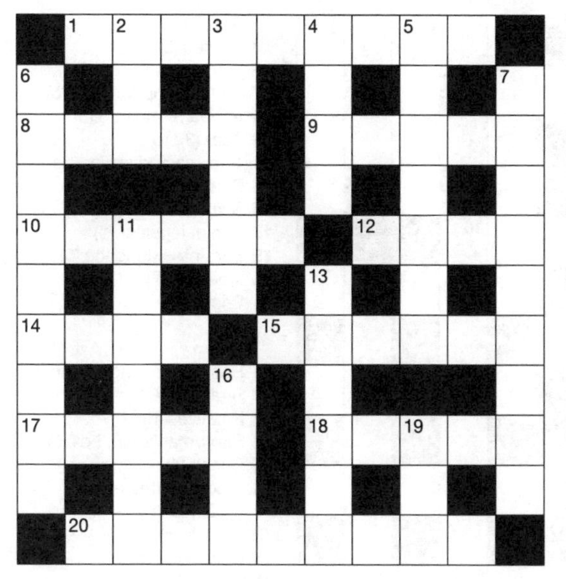

**Across**

**1** Serious disagreements (9)
**8** Dark-brown pigment (5)
**9** Thrills (5)
**10** Pay attention to (6)
**12** Bargain (4)
**14** Used to catch animals or fish (4)
**15** Small room (6)
**17** Horizontal (5)
**18** Glossy fabric (5)
**20** Senior academic (9)

**Down**

**2** Eye, in a literary sense (3)
**3** Wild enthusiasm (6)
**4** Very black (4)
**5** Entry documents (7)
**6** Presently (9)
**7** Separating (9)
**11** Recover from (3,4)
**13** Explosions (6)
**16** Stave identifier (4)
**19** Low dice roll (3)

# PUZZLE 181

**Across**
**1** Exit (9)
**7** Wall-climbing lizard (5)
**8** Ape (5)
**10** Herds of whales (4)
**11** Boat (6)
**14** Mild antiseptic (6)
**15** Cross-border document (4)
**17** Chutzpah (5)
**19** Pains (5)
**20** Globally (9)

**Down**
**2** Encrypted (7)
**3** Sunburn relief (4)
**4** Carpentry wood (6)
**5** Hydraulic lifting machine (3)
**6** Cairo resident (8)
**9** Give way (8)
**12** Disturbed (7)
**13** Take from a spindle (6)
**16** Demonstrate (4)
**18** Brazil's second-largest city (3)

# PUZZLE 182

**Across**
**3** Movies (5)
**6** Kingston's island (7)
**7** Software option lists (5)
**8** Adhesive mixture (5)
**9** Soar (3)
**11** Two-masted sailing boat (5)
**13** Delectable (5)
**15** Scatter seeds (3)
**18** Denim legwear (5)
**19** Sort into sequence (5)
**20** Indecent (7)
**21** Pried (5)

**Down**
**1** Home for a king or queen (6)
**2** Strategy (7)
**3** Relatives (6)
**4** Superman's girl, Lois (4)
**5** Cheek (4)
**10** Wood burned at Christmas (4,3)
**12** Beastly (6)
**14** Handbook (6)
**16** Lend (4)
**17** Dedicated poems (4)

# PUZZLE 183

**Across**
3 Shaving blade (5)
6 Extreme tiredness (7)
7 Strike repeatedly (5)
8 Largest moon of Saturn (5)
9 Employed sportsman (3)
11 Cry of excitement (5)
13 Sticky ribbons (5)
15 Pallid (3)
18 Inventory (5)
19 Greeting word (5)
20 Death, in a legal statement (7)
21 Cunningly (5)

**Down**
1 Boorish (6)
2 Repudiate (7)
3 Written account (6)
4 Supreme Greek god (4)
5 Start again (4)
10 Durable timber source (3,4)
12 Ridiculous imitation (6)
14 Allow to leave (6)
16 Ergo (4)
17 Ruse (4)

# PUZZLE 184

**Across**
3 Alleviated (5)
6 Transitions into (7)
7 Serious wrongdoing (5)
8 Matter (5)
9 Heated bath (3)
11 Profits (5)
13 Devoid of content (5)
15 Christian creator of all (3)
18 Information submitted to a computer (5)
19 Unpaid (5)
20 Extremely ugly (7)
21 Hover (5)

**Down**
1 Gangsters' hat? (6)
2 Linking (7)
3 Getaway (6)
4 Snick (4)
5 Stopped living (4)
10 Fixed (7)
12 Looked for (6)
14 Astrological bull (6)
16 Horse's foot (4)
17 Queen of Carthage (4)

## PUZZLE 185

**Across**

**1** Change directly from solid to vapour (9)
**7** Inched (5)
**8** Aristocrat (5)
**10** Kill (4)
**11** Scribble (6)
**14** At some point (3,3)
**15** Pasty-faced (4)
**17** Bedouin, eg (5)
**19** String quartet member (5)
**20** Economic good (9)

**Down**

**2** Improve (7)
**3** Covers (4)
**4** Small fish (6)
**5** Bath vessel (3)
**6** Cooking measurement (8)
**9** Quotidian (8)
**12** Twist out of shape (7)
**13** Indiscriminate (6)
**16** Having a keen desire (4)
**18** Cow sound (3)

## PUZZLE 186

**Across**

**3** Group of singers (5)
**6** Post sent to celebrities (3,4)
**7** Make a speech (5)
**8** Correspond (5)
**9** Treasure (3)
**11** Discussion place (5)
**13** The opposite of left (5)
**15** Fictional Hollywood fixer, Donovan (3)
**18** Tale (5)
**19** Even in score (5)
**20** Converts to a cipher (7)
**21** Type of waterbird (5)

**Down**

**1** Bob, bun or beehive (6)
**2** Non-professional (7)
**3** Less far away (6)
**4** Adequate (4)
**5** Tall water grass (4)
**10** Was wrong about (7)
**12** Cattle trough (6)
**14** Toughen (6)
**16** Cook slowly in water (4)
**17** Made things up (4)

# PUZZLE 187

**Across**

1 With genuine intent (9)
7 Cherishes (5)
8 Involving a third dimension (5)
10 Dashed (4)
11 Ambush (6)
14 Chooses (6)
15 King who didn't turn the tide back (4)
17 Lodge (5)
19 Steering device (5)
20 Endorsing (9)

**Down**

2 Reciprocal (7)
3 Price paid (4)
4 Ethnological (6)
5 Hit a ball over an opponent (3)
6 Compos mentis (3,5)
9 Clear mineral pieces (8)
12 Portable lamp (7)
13 Type of apartment (6)
16 Got into debt (4)
18 Nectar gatherer (3)

# PUZZLE 188

**Across**

1 Love of the mysterious and exotic (11)
7 Irrational fear (6)
8 Agricultural holding (4)
9 Brisk walk, for a horse (4)
10 Only (6)
13 Socialize with those of higher status (6)
16 Birds hunted for food (4)
17 Tide-causing satellite (4)
18 Country (6)
19 Making less complex (11)

**Down**

2 Playful musical movement (7)
3 A Sherpa, perhaps (7)
4 Peruses (5)
5 Absurd (5)
6 Preserved dead body (5)
11 Gently (7)
12 Satirize (7)
13 Residences (5)
14 Come into full beauty (5)
15 Hindu forehead decoration (5)

# PUZZLE 189

**Across**

**1** Supposedly (9)
**8** Silver bar (5)
**9** Distinct period (5)
**10** Diplomatic agreement (6)
**12** Walk with difficulty (4)
**14** Lift with a grabbing utensil (4)
**15** Alarm (6)
**17** Bucolic (5)
**18** First-class, informally (5)
**20** Step mark (9)

**Down**

**2** Delay (3)
**3** With no part left out (6)
**4** Trade show (4)
**5** At the front (7)
**6** Calamities (9)
**7** Everlasting (9)
**11** Spirited, as a musical direction (3,4)
**13** Suitable; appropriate (6)
**16** Make a long cut in (4)
**19** Flesh and blood (3)

# PUZZLE 190

**Across**

**1** Dead ringer (9)
**7** Raises (5)
**8** Frenzy (5)
**10** Top of a bottle (4)
**11** Panda food (6)
**14** Text insertion marker (6)
**15** Elitist (4)
**17** Hungarian composer (5)
**19** Collection of songs (5)
**20** Computer input devices (9)

**Down**

**2** Policeman or policewoman (7)
**3** Slight touch of a ball, in pool (4)
**4** Relating to the lower spine (6)
**5** Mattel doll (3)
**6** Strictly objective (8)
**9** Nuclear weapon (4,4)
**12** Two-storey sleep furniture (4,3)
**13** Social bath, perhaps (3,3)
**16** Mother (4)
**18** Visit for a consultation (3)

# PUZZLE 191

**Across**
**1** Works out (10)
**7** Region (6)
**8** Wait for an appropriate time (4)
**9** Secret supply (5)
**11** Fright (5)
**13** Skilled (5)
**14** Sharpen (5)
**16** Type of 1960s lamp (4)
**18** Foreign childcarer (2,4)
**20** Buildings (10)

**Down**
**2** Fostered (7)
**3** Jailbird (3)
**4** Produces an egg (4)
**5** Smoker's vice (7)
**6** Actor Poitier, familiarly (3)
**10** Choir voice above alto (7)
**12** Mundane (7)
**15** A grown-up leveret (4)
**17** Sound-level booster (3)
**19** Set; locate (3)

# PUZZLE 192

**Across**
**1** Fight (4-2)
**4** Set forth in a ship (4)
**6** Someone who carries luggage (6)
**7** Sleeps during the day (4)
**8** Its capital is Honolulu (6)
**11** Protective covering (4)
**12** Pop musician, Lady ___ (4)
**13** Gaps (6)
**16** Missile chamber (4)
**17** Tropical fruit (6)
**18** Dipped in yolk (4)
**19** Rubbed out (6)

**Down**
**1** Swimming pool statistic (5)
**2** Twist (5)
**3** Allowable (11)
**4** Red wine mixed with fruit (7)
**5** Make better (7)
**9** Fantastic (7)
**10** Comparison (7)
**14** Has an informal conversation (5)
**15** Grassy land surface (5)

# PUZZLE 193

**Across**
**1** Lettuce and anchovies dish (6,5)
**7** Speckled (6)
**8** Collateral property (4)
**9** Deluxe (4)
**10** Solitary (6)
**13** Biked (6)
**16** Simpsons creator, Groening (4)
**17** Competed (4)
**18** Homily (6)
**19** Moderating (11)

**Down**
**2** Regretful admission (7)
**3** Type of shoulder bag (7)
**4** Travels on (5)
**5** Saying something false (5)
**6** Jive (5)
**11** Digit (7)
**12** Disappoint (3,4)
**13** Municipal (5)
**14** Unsoiled (5)
**15** Musical party (5)

# PUZZLE 194

**Across**
**1** Getting the better of (10)
**7** Happily (6)
**8** Experimentally trendy (4)
**9** Profane expression (5)
**11** Enquiry (5)
**13** Yields (5)
**14** Housing contract (5)
**16** Dram (4)
**18** Strata (6)
**20** Oppressed (10)

**Down**
**2** Someone who preys on others (7)
**3** Opposite of green? (3)
**4** Gemstone (4)
**5** Block of frozen water (3,4)
**6** Band's live event (3)
**10** Refuge (7)
**12** Modesty (7)
**15** Air duct (4)
**17** Short journey (3)
**19** Thee, less archaically (3)

# PUZZLE 195

**Across**
1 Plaza (6)
4 Floor of a ship (4)
6 Portable computer (6)
7 Spun knitting thread (4)
8 Layers of rock (6)
11 Talk incoherently (4)
12 In the company of (4)
13 Be about to happen (6)
16 Aching (4)
17 Unbroken (6)
18 Small, U-shaped harp (4)
19 Softly (6)

**Down**
1 Foot undersurfaces (5)
2 Situated above something else (5)
3 Stressing (11)
4 Non-overnight excursion (3,4)
5 Movable residence (7)
9 Three-part work (7)
10 Sprinter, eg (7)
14 Strict; meticulous (5)
15 Little song (5)

# PUZZLE 196

**Across**
1 Sleuth (9)
7 Trainee (5)
8 Fiction book (5)
10 Expand (4)
11 Outdoor jacket (6)
14 National song (6)
15 Long-necked waterbird (4)
17 Not drunk (5)
19 Lies in wait (5)
20 Depth (9)

**Down**
2 Take advantage of (7)
3 Fish, electric ___ (4)
4 Calibrating an instrument (6)
5 Vivian, to her friends (3)
6 Small telescope (8)
9 Similarity (8)
12 Prizes (7)
13 Imperial counterpart (6)
16 Family (4)
18 'Harrumph!' (3)

# PUZZLE 197

**Across**

**1** Poker hand (4,5)
**7** Low-cost (5)
**8** Sprints (5)
**10** Conscious action (4)
**11** Pencil remover (6)
**14** Compact mountain group (6)
**15** Piece of blind (4)
**17** Satellite alternative (5)
**19** Get-up-and-go (5)
**20** Ingredient (9)

**Down**

**2** Futile (7)
**3** Circuits of a track (4)
**4** Planetarium (6)
**5** Baglike cavity in an organism (3)
**6** Only of theoretical interest (8)
**9** Elastic (8)
**12** Biblical king of Israel (7)
**13** Fill with enthusiasm (4,2)
**16** Attach (4)
**18** Ghostly cry (3)

# PUZZLE 198

**Across**

**1** Without remorse (11)
**7** Hurriedly dispose of (4)
**8** Distant (6)
**9** Previous (5)
**10** Black playing card (5)
**13** Cymbal-hitting sound (5)
**15** Turning point (5)
**17** *Den* denizen? (6)
**18** Item in a garden shed? (4)
**19** Extravagant purchaser (11)

**Down**

**2** Impartial (7)
**3** Hires for work (7)
**4** It replaced the franc and mark (4)
**5** Wafting scent (5)
**6** When repeated, a comforting phrase (5)
**11** On-screen cursor (7)
**12** Deliver (4,3)
**13** Encryptions (5)
**14** Conscious (5)
**16** Nautical speed unit (4)

# PUZZLE 199

**Across**
- **3** Insolent (5)
- **6** Keepsake (7)
- **7** Most remote from the outside (5)
- **8** Aids (5)
- **9** Ash day (abbr.) (3)
- **11** Troop (5)
- **13** Settle a debt (5)
- **15** The highest part of something (3)
- **18** Terrible fates (5)
- **19** Functions as expected (5)
- **20** Sanguine (7)
- **21** Marshy lake or river outlet (5)

**Down**
- **1** Swiss city (6)
- **2** Regard; esteem (7)
- **3** Hang around (6)
- **4** Roundly criticizes (4)
- **5** Former times (4)
- **10** Indicates (7)
- **12** Island containing Tokyo (6)
- **14** As much as can be held (6)
- **16** Medical lab specimen (4)
- **17** Interested in painting (4)

# PUZZLE 200

**Across**
- **1** Tell the difference (11)
- **6** Staring lecherously (6)
- **7** Be extremely fond of (4)
- **8** Run away (5)
- **11** Thieve (5)
- **12** Trouser measurement (5)
- **13** Summed (5)
- **17** Strike forcefully (4)
- **18** Achieve (6)
- **19** Head of an order of chivalry (5,6)

**Down**
- **1** One-way electronic component (5)
- **2** Artillery burst (5)
- **3** Annoys with persistent fault-finding (4)
- **4** Revised (7)
- **5** Build in a certain place (7)
- **9** Cured animal skin (7)
- **10** Mail deliverer (7)
- **14** Outline drawing (5)
- **15** Buffet car (5)
- **16** Fairly hot (4)

# PUZZLE 201

**Across**
1 Shrewd (11)
7 Compel (4)
8 Insurrection (6)
9 Goes against (5)
10 Fine and feathery (5)
13 Legumes (5)
15 Heroic tales (5)
17 Tidily (6)
18 Laugh loudly (4)
19 Playground game (4-3-4)

**Down**
2 Generally speaking (2,1,4)
3 Register at a hotel (5,2)
4 Skulk (4)
5 Fetters (5)
6 Bold (5)
11 Brings into a country (7)
12 Bundle (7)
13 Group of similar objects (5)
14 Mark of recognition for an achievement (5)
16 Printer-ink colour (4)

# PUZZLE 202

**Across**
1 Without intending to do so (2,7)
8 Selected (5)
9 Clothes can go out of this (5)
10 Anticipate (6)
12 Poultry pen (4)
14 Hooligan (4)
15 Stiff and awkward (6)
17 Existing (5)
18 Correspond in sound endings (5)
20 Tornado (9)

**Down**
2 Up until now (3)
3 Give rise to (6)
4 Chore (4)
5 Summary term (7)
6 Prospective (9)
7 Replies (9)
11 Prissy (7)
13 Take from a library (6)
16 Get wind of (4)
19 Opposite of yang (3)

# PUZZLE 203

**Across**

**1** Test the circuit breaker, perhaps (4,1,4)
**8** Is required (5)
**9** Cartoon sheep (5)
**10** Safe (6)
**12** Block up (4)
**14** Moves like a frog? (4)
**15** Combated (6)
**17** Really bad (5)
**18** *Pac-Man*, perhaps (5)
**20** Exaggerated theatrics (9)

**Down**

**2** Heave (3)
**3** Irrigates (6)
**4** Speedy (4)
**5** Removing outer fish parts (7)
**6** Domiciliary (9)
**7** Rising prices (9)
**11** Apprehend (7)
**13** Strong aversion (6)
**16** Printing error? (4)
**19** Actor, Cruise (3)

# PUZZLE 204

**Across**

**3** Kinds (5)
**6** Disturb (7)
**7** Rule as monarch (5)
**8** Bird's resting place (5)
**9** Relax and do nothing (slang) (3)
**11** Dirigible (5)
**13** Cook in an oven (5)
**15** Buddy (3)
**18** Socket counterparts (5)
**19** Siren (5)
**20** Causing distress (7)
**21** First square on a board game (5)

**Down**

**1** Extreme experience (6)
**2** Give in (7)
**3** Waiter or waitress (6)
**4** Spoil (4)
**5** Perform karaoke, eg (4)
**10** Young goose (7)
**12** Punctual (6)
**14** Enrol (4,2)
**16** Sacks or suitcases (4)
**17** Kanji counterpart (4)

# PUZZLE 205

**Across**

**1** Not real (9)
**8** Private room on a ship (5)
**9** Smelling organs (5)
**10** Neatened (6)
**12** Division of the brain (4)
**14** Ordered to (archaic) (4)
**15** Device for taking pictures (6)
**17** 'There you go!' (5)
**18** Bay or cove (5)
**20** Stress (9)

**Down**

**2** Unruly crowd (3)
**3** Fragrant spice root (6)
**4** Women living in convents (4)
**5** Return to original condition (7)
**6** Better than (1,3,5)
**7** Artificial European language (9)
**11** Early 20th-century art movement (7)
**13** Wirelesses (6)
**16** Walking track (4)
**19** Actress, Hurley (3)

# PUZZLE 206

**Across**

**1** Third-place award (6,5)
**7** Silly person (4)
**8** Damaging animals (6)
**9** Bereaved woman (5)
**10** Belonging to which person? (5)
**13** Calendar periods (5)
**15** Feeling of dread (5)
**17** Heir to a throne (6)
**18** Declares off-limits (4)
**19** Visual audio plot (11)

**Down**

**2** Compose again (7)
**3** Set of connected computers (7)
**4** Deadly sin (4)
**5** Disney's flying elephant (5)
**6** Fencing move (5)
**11** Large, woman's clutch (7)
**12** Woman in the Book of Daniel (7)
**13** Cleans with a cloth (5)
**14** Upper classes (5)
**16** Tail end (4)

# PUZZLE 207

**Across**
**3** Sudden impact (5)
**6** Separation (7)
**7** Arctic native (5)
**8** Allege (5)
**9** Apiece (3)
**11** Chuck (5)
**13** Crack (5)
**15** Duster, eg (3)
**18** Lethal (5)
**19** Words from a song (5)
**20** Discloses (7)
**21** Remembrance flower (5)

**Down**
**1** Affluence (6)
**2** Observe over time (7)
**3** Pizza pieces (6)
**4** Set of musical works (4)
**5** Majestic bird of prey (4)
**10** Goes around (7)
**12** Soldier's rallying call (3,3)
**14** Practicable (6)
**16** Spill (4)
**17** Clench (4)

# PUZZLE 208

**Across**
**1** Introverted (9)
**7** Tilts to one side (5)
**8** Wide (5)
**10** Small bouquet (4)
**11** Mentally prepares for a task, with 'up' (6)
**14** Valuable possessions (6)
**15** Glitch (4)
**17** High building (5)
**19** Slack (5)
**20** Translate (9)

**Down**
**2** Takes a firm stand (7)
**3** Master of ceremonies (4)
**4** Vigorous (6)
**5** TV show, *Doctor* ___ (3)
**6** Large, trunked animal (8)
**9** Argue (8)
**12** Accept (7)
**13** Be very hungry (6)
**16** Hit to the cheek (4)
**18** Earned (3)

# PUZZLE 209

**Across**
- **1** Emergency transport vehicle (9)
- **8** Seashore (5)
- **9** Takes a break (5)
- **10** Rosary division (6)
- **12** Contact by telephone (4)
- **14** Note (4)
- **15** Assets (6)
- **17** Cultivated plants (5)
- **18** Record a TV show (5)
- **20** Converting waste into reusable material (9)

**Down**
- **2** Unaccounted for after combat (init.) (3)
- **3** Messy (6)
- **4** Ambience; mood (4)
- **5** Comedic type of pie? (7)
- **6** Professors (9)
- **7** Separation (9)
- **11** Write music (7)
- **13** Gibberish (6)
- **16** Notice (4)
- **19** Karate level (3)

# PUZZLE 210

**Across**
- **1** Midday meal interval (9)
- **7** Geological depression (5)
- **8** Sped (5)
- **10** Tense, as in muscles (4)
- **11** Fume (6)
- **14** A chocoholic, eg (6)
- **15** Pointer on a clock (4)
- **17** Cooker alarm, eg (5)
- **19** Straighten up (5)
- **20** A set of foundation stories (9)

**Down**
- **2** Faulty (7)
- **3** Persuades using deception (4)
- **4** Aim (6)
- **5** Karaoke requirement (3)
- **6** Non-concrete (8)
- **9** Frightened of (8)
- **12** Drawing over (7)
- **13** Sear (6)
- **16** Shadow, as a detective (4)
- **18** Could (3)

# PUZZLE 211

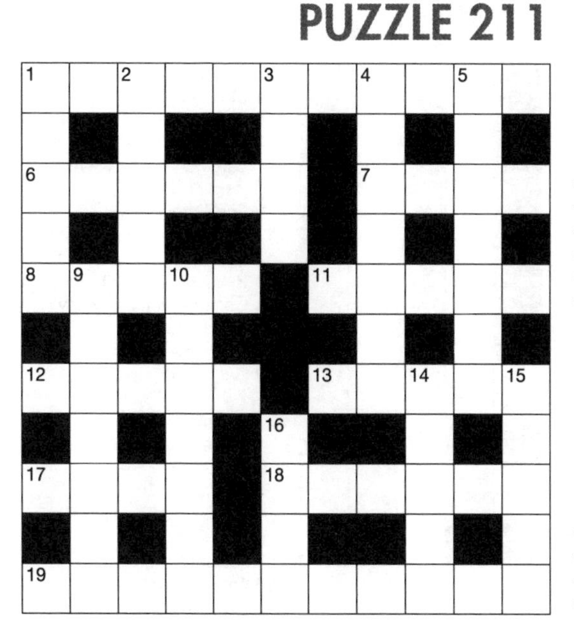

**Across**

**1** Changes (11)
**6** Exaggerate (6)
**7** Solid oils (4)
**8** Long-necked waterbird (5)
**11** Closes teeth on (5)
**12** Unite (5)
**13** Persists (5)
**17** Exploding star (4)
**18** Vine fruit (6)
**19** Inept (11)

**Down**

**1** In the same direction as (5)
**2** Topic (5)
**3** Extremely small amount (4)
**4** Impose, as in a punishment (7)
**5** To a low degree (3,4)
**9** Dilapidated (3-4)
**10** Large wild ox (7)
**14** Really surprise (5)
**15** Fire a gun (5)
**16** Action in a series (4)

# PUZZLE 212

**Across**

**1** Plant-killing substance (9)
**7** Inflexible (5)
**8** Small, poisonous snake (5)
**10** Lost blood (4)
**11** Border (6)
**14** Imply (6)
**15** Store (4)
**17** Drunken woodland god (5)
**19** Make more beautiful (5)
**20** Conjecture (9)

**Down**

**2** Most nervous and irritable (7)
**3** Portend (4)
**4** Warning (6)
**5** Decline (3)
**6** Difficulties (8)
**9** Making fresh again (8)
**12** 'Scram!' (3,4)
**13** Common type of acid (6)
**16** Shopping centre (4)
**18** Hit gently (3)

# PUZZLE 213

**Across**
**1** Most ignoble (6)
**4** Musician's performances (4)
**6** Feeling of resentment (6)
**7** Large and impressive display (4)
**8** Food preview (6)
**11** Throws through the air (4)
**12** Small piece of wood (4)
**13** Buys and sells (6)
**16** Construction block toy (4)
**17** Cheddar, eg (6)
**18** Young person (4)
**19** Deficits (6)

**Down**
**1** Intolerant person (5)
**2** Dazes (5)
**3** Abstract (11)
**4** *Donkey Kong* villain (7)
**5** Farewell (7)
**9** Attain (7)
**10** Tropical cyclone (7)
**14** Judges (5)
**15** Looks for (5)

# PUZZLE 214

**Across**
**1** Member of a learned society (6)
**4** Ken's doll mate, in brief? (4)
**6** Broke up with (6)
**7** Sadly (4)
**8** Toasted Italian sandwiches (6)
**11** Key graph line (4)
**12** High-value playing cards (4)
**13** Shone (6)
**16** Italian hi and bye (4)
**17** Imbeciles (6)
**18** Mountaintop (4)
**19** Protects (6)

**Down**
**1** Annoyed; tired (3,2)
**2** Fruit-machine symbol (5)
**3** Matrimonial band (7,4)
**4** Bluster (7)
**5** Come to understand (7)
**9** Document repository (7)
**10** Available for immediate purchase (2,5)
**14** Active admirer? (5)
**15** Drug quantities (5)

# PUZZLE 215

**Across**
**1** Realm (6)
**4** Ogres (4)
**6** Film classification (6)
**7** That group (4)
**8** Speechless (6)
**11** Equine female (4)
**12** Opposite of ons? (4)
**13** Vexes (6)
**16** Couch (4)
**17** In truth; absolutely (6)
**18** 'Stop, Rover!' (4)
**19** Equines (6)

**Down**
**1** Is brave enough (5)
**2** Iron, eg (5)
**3** Dystopian (11)
**4** Seat with storage within (7)
**5** Without a doubt (7)
**9** Leading (2,5)
**10** Great joy (7)
**14** Unseals an envelope (5)
**15** Shape edges (5)

# PUZZLE 216

**Across**
**1** The upper portion of the back (9)
**8** Spread of values (5)
**9** Viral disease that can cause paralysis (5)
**10** Drew a top-down plan (6)
**12** Flower's support (4)
**14** Edible root (4)
**15** Probable (4-2)
**17** Cowboy display (5)
**18** Italian baked dough dish (5)
**20** Extremely tired (9)

**Down**
**2** Main Chinese ethnic group (3)
**3** Not uniform (6)
**4** Immerses (4)
**5** Pertains (7)
**6** Early (9)
**7** Long-established legal rights (6,3)
**11** Impossible situation (7)
**13** Makes suitable for a new use (6)
**16** Sweet, brown, fizzy drink (4)
**19** *Avatar* actress, Saldana (3)

# PUZZLE 217

**Across**
**3** Supports (5)
**6** In any case (7)
**7** Solidarity (5)
**8** Brusque (5)
**9** Dog cub (3)
**11** Bend in the arm (5)
**13** Wobbly (5)
**15** Be into, colloquially (3)
**18** Sleeping sound (5)
**19** Residence (5)
**20** Moped (7)
**21** Vision (5)

**Down**
**1** US livestock pen (6)
**2** Edible fish or shellfish (7)
**3** Julius Caesar's nemesis (6)
**4** Paper fastening (4)
**5** Puts into words (4)
**10** Ghost (7)
**12** Most omniscient (6)
**14** Core (6)
**16** A particular one of these (4)
**17** Suspended (4)

# PUZZLE 218

**Across**
**1** Anticipation (11)
**6** Not clever (6)
**7** Egyptian, eg (4)
**8** Analyse, as in a sentence (5)
**11** Speedy (5)
**12** Butcher's leftovers (5)
**13** Mix together (5)
**17** Dawn to lunch, poetically (4)
**18** Double-reed player (6)
**19** Ill-fated (4-7)

**Down**
**1** Fit out (5)
**2** Strength (5)
**3** Golf-ball rests (4)
**4** Painful effort (7)
**5** Sustained show of appreciation (7)
**9** Outrage (7)
**10** Barcode reader (7)
**14** Ways out (5)
**15** Out of fashion (5)
**16** Heath (4)

# PUZZLE 219

**Across**

**3** Hint at (5)
**6** Small toothed whale (7)
**7** More despicable (5)
**8** Avowed (5)
**9** Atmosphere (3)
**11** Parody (5)
**13** Two cubed (5)
**15** Bowl-shaped frying pan (3)
**18** Make one's own (5)
**19** Give new weapons to (5)
**20** What a funny joke is (7)
**21** Raise a glass to (5)

**Down**

**1** Close-harmony rock and roll style (3-3)
**2** Type of songbird (7)
**3** Call upon (6)
**4** Game played on horseback (4)
**5** Three feet (4)
**10** European Jewish language (7)
**12** Visual appearance (6)
**14** Yearning (6)
**16** Young troublemaker (4)
**17** Large Indonesian island (4)

# PUZZLE 220

**Across**

**1** The study of space (9)
**8** Computers on a network (5)
**9** Outfits (5)
**10** Animosity (6)
**12** Low ground between hills (4)
**14** Prompts (4)
**15** Marks (6)
**17** Maxim (5)
**18** Egret (5)
**20** Arrive and depart as you please (4,3,2)

**Down**

**2** Glum (3)
**3** Reverts to factory state (6)
**4** In vain (2,2)
**5** Part person, part fish (7)
**6** Not wanted (9)
**7** Appraising (9)
**11** Conductor (7)
**13** Oliver Twist, eg (6)
**16** Correct amount of medicine (4)
**19** Small carpet (3)

# PUZZLE 221

**Across**
**1** Histrionics (11)
**7** Tore (6)
**8** Glasses; drinking vessels (4)
**9** Like a reptile's skin (5)
**11** Beer units (5)
**13** Maintain an upright position (5)
**14** Water vapour (5)
**16** Hit sharply, as an insect (4)
**18** Motor (6)
**20** Have a heated argument (5,6)

**Down**
**2** Coiffure (7)
**3** Type of viper (3)
**4** *This Is 40* actor, Paul (4)
**5** Two-wheeled road user (7)
**6** Kiddy seat? (3)
**10** Extents (7)
**12** Taught (7)
**15** Gambles (4)
**17** Combat (3)
**19** Gunk (3)

# PUZZLE 222

**Across**
**1** Patience (9)
**8** Dessert items (5)
**9** Flared skirt type (1-4)
**10** Authorized document certifier (6)
**12** All over again (4)
**14** Foremost (4)
**15** Male child sponsored at a baptism (6)
**17** Punctuation mark (5)
**18** Small donkey (5)
**20** Confront (9)

**Down**
**2** Tree of the genus *Quercus* (3)
**3** Guarantee (6)
**4** Apart (4)
**5** Customers of lawyers, eg (7)
**6** Academic finance subject (9)
**7** Learn about (3,4,2)
**11** Victory (7)
**13** Horror movie staple (6)
**16** Extended cry of pain (4)
**19** Offshore oil platform (3)

# PUZZLE 223

**Across**
- **3** Manages (5)
- **6** Vehicle-cleaning facility (3,4)
- **7** Cast out (5)
- **8** Type of keyboard instrument (5)
- **9** Have a go (3)
- **11** Censor's sound (5)
- **13** Mails (5)
- **15** Lose a life (3)
- **18** Sorrow (5)
- **19** Formal ballroom dance (5)
- **20** Liabilities (7)
- **21** Stares stupidly (5)

**Down**
- **1** Part of a gun (6)
- **2** Perspired (7)
- **3** Applauds (6)
- **4** Ache (4)
- **5** Warp (4)
- **10** Longed for (7)
- **12** Oven-baked Italian 'pies' (6)
- **14** Depressing (6)
- **16** Snowman decoration? (4)
- **17** Shine (4)

# PUZZLE 224

**Across**
- **1** Next to (9)
- **7** Less common (5)
- **8** Ties together (5)
- **10** Tap dancer, Astaire (4)
- **11** Extremely inebriated (slang) (6)
- **14** Plan; map (6)
- **15** Taj Mahal, eg (4)
- **17** Separates, as in flour (5)
- **19** Beer (5)
- **20** Point in a particular direction (9)

**Down**
- **2** In the main (7)
- **3** Ordinary value (4)
- **4** Discreetly (6)
- **5** Continued jarring noise (3)
- **6** Side views (8)
- **9** High-handedness (8)
- **12** Notion (7)
- **13** Chase (6)
- **16** Narrow opening (4)
- **18** Distant (3)

# PUZZLE 225

**Across**
**1** The Goat (9)
**7** Writings (5)
**8** PC–phone interface (5)
**10** Regretted (4)
**11** Shows scorn (6)
**14** Weeping (6)
**15** Cupola (4)
**17** Greek letter before tau (5)
**19** Kid (5)
**20** Foolishness (9)

**Down**
**2** Mental uneasiness (7)
**3** A coarse metal file (4)
**4** Funny people (6)
**5** Radiation exposure unit (3)
**6** Draws in (8)
**9** Misdirects (8)
**12** Bouquet provider (7)
**13** Build a temporary shelter (6)
**16** Surface-to-surface missile (4)
**18** Stomach (3)

# PUZZLE 226

**Across**
**1** Ledger-copying sheet (6,5)
**7** Trap (6)
**8** Paint without care (4)
**9** One of two equal parts (4)
**10** Large wasp (6)
**13** Set of things working together (6)
**16** Blend into one (4)
**17** Lacking in sensation (4)
**18** Fashion chain (6)
**19** Coming (11)

**Down**
**2** Irregularity (7)
**3** Advantage (7)
**4** The top of a map, usually (5)
**5** Edible shrimp-like crustacean (5)
**6** Automaton (5)
**11** Energize (7)
**12** Asian (7)
**13** Reindeer driver? (5)
**14** Conclude a speech (3,2)
**15** Newspapers and television in general (5)

# PUZZLE 227

**Across**
**1** Usual (9)
**7** Rouses (5)
**8** Awesome (5)
**10** Assert (4)
**11** Doctors' assistants (6)
**14** Overlook (6)
**15** Loud, unrestrained call (4)
**17** Hospital garments (5)
**19** Intense (5)
**20** Daily printed publication (9)

**Down**
**2** Not identified (7)
**3** Coin throw (4)
**4** Building with historical exhibits (6)
**5** Knock on a door (3)
**6** Cursing (8)
**9** Decides (8)
**12** A written law (7)
**13** Believes in (6)
**16** Park boundary ditch (2-2)
**18** Anguish (3)

# PUZZLE 228

**Across**
**3** Replace the internals of (5)
**6** Pendulous ornamental shrub (7)
**7** Metal spikes (5)
**8** Simple ear adornments (5)
**9** Garden plot (3)
**11** Sear in a pan (5)
**13** Illustrated (5)
**15** Easy concession (3)
**18** Building schematics (5)
**19** Kingdom (5)
**20** Forsake (7)
**21** Olympic decoration (5)

**Down**
**1** Dairy spread (6)
**2** Trails (7)
**3** Extended (6)
**4** Move swiftly and quickly (4)
**5** Long, pointed tooth (4)
**10** Solid ground (3,4)
**12** Routine (6)
**14** Wall opening (6)
**16** *Dracula* creator, Stoker (4)
**17** Female domestic servant (4)

# PUZZLE 229

**Across**

**1** Physical treatment expert (9)
**8** Exterior (5)
**9** Cares (5)
**10** Crazy; eccentric (6)
**12** Nil (4)
**14** Frilled (4)
**15** Big brother? (6)
**17** Fit a pane (5)
**18** Built-up (5)
**20** Stand for (9)

**Down**

**2** Snowman decoration? (3)
**3** Take in an article a second time, eg (6)
**4** Push and pull up and down (4)
**5** Earnest (7)
**6** Study of the universe (9)
**7** Classifying (9)
**11** Give orders (7)
**13** Photo collections (6)
**16** Rush (4)
**19** Tallest UK mountain, ___ Nevis (3)

# PUZZLE 230

**Across**

**1** Say again (9)
**7** Twosomes (5)
**8** Jettisons (5)
**10** Those who staff a ship (4)
**11** Type of neutron star (6)
**14** Hold (6)
**15** Covered with gold leaf (4)
**17** Elle Macpherson, eg (5)
**19** Midday meal (5)
**20** Edited (9)

**Down**

**2** Famous and admired (7)
**3** Former Soviet news service (4)
**4** Half the diameter (6)
**5** *Batman* director, Burton (3)
**6** Range of colours (8)
**9** Itchy (8)
**12** Biology, eg (7)
**13** Flour producer (6)
**16** Arterial blockage (4)
**18** Stain (3)

# PUZZLE 231

**Across**

**1** Mercy (11)
**7** Type of edible nut (6)
**8** Festivity (4)
**9** Motorcycle (4)
**10** Mollusc casings (6)
**13** Moved back and forth (6)
**16** Pulls along (4)
**17** Absorb text (4)
**18** Tension (6)
**19** Be killed (4,3,4)

**Down**

**2** Full of euphoria (2,1,4)
**3** Weapons location on a ship (3,4)
**4** Elects (5)
**5** Inbox content (5)
**6** Exchanges (5)
**11** Went in (7)
**12** Attorneys (7)
**13** Bush (5)
**14** Adjust (5)
**15** Beethoven's last symphony (5)

# PUZZLE 232

**Across**

**1** Tens of hundreds (9)
**8** Swellings (5)
**9** Cowboy's rope (5)
**10** Increase (6)
**12** 'Forever!' (4)
**14** Graffiti identifiers (4)
**15** Carnival (6)
**17** Nice weather, perhaps (5)
**18** Tag (5)
**20** Go along with (9)

**Down**

**2** Pointing word (3)
**3** Angers (6)
**4** Expertly (4)
**5** Blueprints (7)
**6** Tiniest (9)
**7** Royal castle governor (9)
**11** Entirely natural (7)
**13** Put in petrol (4-2)
**16** True-north compass (4)
**19** Tightly coiled hairstyle (3)

# PUZZLE 233

**Across**

**1** Series of ranks (9)
**7** What leavened bread is, after baking (5)
**8** Inscribed column (5)
**10** Golden-yellow sea fish (4)
**11** Not sporting (6)
**14** Offhand (6)
**15** Bumps (4)
**17** *Mr Bean* star, Atkinson (5)
**19** Come together (5)
**20** Change the time of (9)

**Down**

**2** Puts in (7)
**3** Circular band (4)
**4** Dislike (6)
**5** Character; aspect (3)
**6** Commodity creator (8)
**9** Took to the police station, perhaps (8)
**12** Subsiding (7)
**13** Attitude (6)
**16** Post-larval insect (4)
**18** Y-shaped structure (3)

# PUZZLE 234

**Across**

**1** Riding a horse (2,3,6)
**7** Remains of a ticket (4)
**8** Bathing top and bottoms (6)
**9** Ire (5)
**10** Shabby (5)
**13** Cartoon canine (5)
**15** Slender woman (5)
**17** A bond held pending a condition (6)
**18** Charts (4)
**19** Continue to fool (6,5)

**Down**

**2** Without a sharp or a flat (7)
**3** Home environs (7)
**4** Cries uncontrollably (4)
**5** Float (5)
**6** Enlighten (5)
**11** Awful (7)
**12** Type of ball rotation (7)
**13** Verse writers (5)
**14** Open sore (5)
**16** Drink in large gulps (4)

# PUZZLE 235

**Across**

1 Priam's prophet daughter (9)
8 'I might do' (5)
9 Recorded (5)
10 Although (6)
12 Skin-loving insects (4)
14 Summit (4)
15 Aircraft journey (6)
17 Attractive young woman (5)
18 Alcoholic fermented-juice drink (5)
20 Reinvigorated (9)

**Down**

2 Deceased singer, Winehouse (3)
3 Picturesque (6)
4 Hard-shelled fruits (4)
5 Crudely splitting paper (7)
6 Instability (9)
7 Escapade (9)
11 Respire (7)
13 Locations (6)
16 Much loved (4)
19 Ex-Korean president, Kim ___-jung (3)

# PUZZLE 236

**Across**

1 Puts too much into (9)
8 Up to (5)
9 The body's largest glandular organ (5)
10 Intense beams of light (6)
12 Alcoholic drink (4)
14 Street (4)
15 Gnawing mammal (6)
17 Broader (5)
18 Element with atomic number 5 (5)
20 Cease business (5,4)

**Down**

2 Large tank (3)
3 Measuring sticks (6)
4 Exclusively (4)
5 Varied (7)
6 Adult (4-5)
7 Scares (9)
11 Public disgrace (7)
13 Flunked (6)
16 Mine extracts (4)
19 Straight line of items (3)

# PUZZLE 237

**Across**

**1** Practicality (11)
**6** Chemical twin (6)
**7** Duration (4)
**8** Visitor (5)
**11** Liberates (5)
**12** Feather (5)
**13** Flat food dish (5)
**17** Peasant or commoner (archaic) (4)
**18** Writer (6)
**19** Investor (11)

**Down**

**1** Throw forcefully (5)
**2** Love (5)
**3** Flying animal (4)
**4** To the side (7)
**5** Violent storm (7)
**9** Let loose (7)
**10** Digital music recorder (7)
**14** Yearned (5)
**15** Fault (5)
**16** Large basin (4)

# PUZZLE 238

**Across**

**1** Encouraging (9)
**8** Henry VIII, eg (5)
**9** Stood up to (5)
**10** Peculiarity (6)
**12** Thick (4)
**14** Departs (4)
**15** Sits on the throne (6)
**17** Plant pore (5)
**18** Related to sea-based military (5)
**20** Strength (9)

**Down**

**2** Cleanse (3)
**3** Earns (6)
**4** Remove large particles (4)
**5** Cutting slightly (7)
**6** Most powerful (9)
**7** Detrimentally (9)
**11** Subside (3,4)
**13** Type of racket sport (6)
**16** Decrease in size (4)
**19** Dog medic (3)

# PUZZLE 239

**Across**
**1** Spoken dialects (11)
**7** Apartment (4)
**8** See (6)
**9** Reel (5)
**10** Reside (5)
**13** Sells (5)
**15** Flower segment (5)
**17** Throw into the air (6)
**18** Scrabble piece (4)
**19** Unplugs (11)

**Down**
**2** Cast a shadow over (7)
**3** A serve must clear it in tennis (3,4)
**4** Metal containers (4)
**5** Spring up (5)
**6** Protective covering (5)
**11** Grapple in a fight (7)
**12** Pamphlet (7)
**13** Legitimate (5)
**14** Name words (5)
**16** Avoid (4)

# PUZZLE 240

**Across**
**1** Syntactically correct (11)
**7** Dark stain (4)
**8** Background actors (6)
**9** Weighty (5)
**10** Heaps (5)
**13** Cluttered (5)
**15** Opposite of white (5)
**17** Relating to the nervous system (6)
**18** Provoke (4)
**19** Revise (11)

**Down**
**2** Soothe (7)
**3** Reasons for doing things (7)
**4** Malt beverages (4)
**5** Christmas song (5)
**6** Continues; persists (5)
**11** Forbidden by law (7)
**12** Bewitch (7)
**13** Large country house (5)
**14** Pack full (5)
**16** Top tournament, in tennis (4)

# PUZZLE 241

**Across**
**3** Mends (5)
**6** Bitterly cold (7)
**7** Surprised: 'taken ___' (5)
**8** Scottish border river (5)
**9** Soaked (3)
**11** Timpani, eg (5)
**13** Reveals (5)
**15** Number of sides on a dice (3)
**18** Tennis surface (5)
**19** Widely recognized (5)
**20** Transparency film (7)
**21** Will (5)

**Down**
**1** Not so fast (6)
**2** Shrieks (7)
**3** Tongues of fire (6)
**4** Airport scan (1-3)
**5** Behalf (4)
**10** Windpipe entrances (7)
**12** Cue (6)
**14** Affection; kindness (6)
**16** Snow blades (4)
**17** Famous painting, ___ *Lisa* (4)

# PUZZLE 242

**Across**
**1** In open view (6)
**4** Loon (4)
**6** Male or female (6)
**7** Common household pets (4)
**8** Uncanny (6)
**11** Spherical bodies (4)
**12** Court order (4)
**13** Special reduced prices (6)
**16** Company image (4)
**17** Slander (6)
**18** Precious stones (4)
**19** Say again (6)

**Down**
**1** Leaves of a book (5)
**2** Guitar-family instrument (5)
**3** Indian flavouring (5,6)
**4** Initiate proceedings (4,3)
**5** Halloween month (7)
**9** Aim (7)
**10** Choices (7)
**14** Remove all traces of (5)
**15** Perspire (5)

# PUZZLE 243

**Across**

**1** No matter the result (4,4,3)
**6** Borders (6)
**7** Clothes (4)
**8** City area (5)
**11** Undo a dress, perhaps (5)
**12** Grave (5)
**13** Snowman decoration? (5)
**17** *Back to the Future* bully, Tannen (4)
**18** Assistance (6)
**19** In the same way (11)

**Down**

**1** Paparazzi target (5)
**2** 'No. 5', for Lou Bega (5)
**3** Piece of chaff (4)
**4** Of very great size (7)
**5** Madder (7)
**9** Riga resident (7)
**10** Cautious (7)
**14** March/April zodiac sign (5)
**15** Largest UK bank note (5)
**16** Administer a medicine (4)

# PUZZLE 244

**Across**

**3** Edged (5)
**6** God (7)
**7** Live (5)
**8** Massive (5)
**9** iPhone purchase (3)
**11** Artist's protective wear (5)
**13** Pond scum (5)
**15** Donation to a waiter (3)
**18** Put on (5)
**19** Synthetic clothing material (5)
**20** Sticks (7)
**21** Purchase all of (3,2)

**Down**

**1** Lighter-than-air gas (6)
**2** Join together (7)
**3** Tibetan mountaineer (6)
**4** Weak, ineffectual person (4)
**5** Small round marks or spots (4)
**10** Graph output device (7)
**12** Abduct (6)
**14** Tries to persuade of something (6)
**16** Cold-shoulder (4)
**17** Choke up (4)

# PUZZLE 245

**Across**
1 Dependableness (11)
7 Manners in which (4)
8 Department (6)
9 Discerns by sight (5)
10 Go and get (5)
13 Hits repeatedly (5)
15 Single figure (5)
17 Multiply by two (6)
18 Chopped (4)
19 Visually striking (3-8)

**Down**
2 Model (7)
3 Look at closely (7)
4 Moves up and down on water (4)
5 Unmoving (5)
6 Young person (5)
11 'In memoriam' words (7)
12 Add a point of view (5,2)
13 Change opinion (5)
14 Make someone laugh (5)
16 Become more loving (4)

# PUZZLE 246

**Across**
1 Idolization (4-7)
7 Double-reeded instrument (4)
8 Of a population subgroup (6)
9 Edible seed container (5)
10 Notable descendant (5)
13 Rugged (5)
15 Spiral-shelled mollusc (5)
17 Summing (6)
18 Gemstone (4)
19 Association (11)

**Down**
2 Official trade ban (7)
3 Conforming (7)
4 Draught animals (4)
5 Delhi language (5)
6 Walnut-like nut (5)
11 Bans (7)
12 Paper-folding art (7)
13 Vagrant (5)
14 Beneath (5)
16 Nasty person (4)

# PUZZLE 247

**Across**

**1** Beyond belief (10)
**6** Full of anxiety (6)
**7** Stick with a hook for fishing (4)
**10** Litter (7)
**12** Tool for piercing leather (3)
**13** 'That's it!' (3)
**14** Vivid (7)
**15** Drinks mixer (4)
**18** Welsh, Breton or Manx, eg (6)
**19** Fortified (10)

**Down**

**1** Late in paying money (2,7)
**2** Stiff paper (9)
**3** Leaving (7)
**4** Catch (3)
**5** Santa's helper? (3)
**8** Indifferent (9)
**9** Vitamin B9 (5,4)
**11** Dismissal (5-2)
**16** Your and my (3)
**17** *Arabian Nights* character, Baba (3)

# PUZZLE 248

**Across**

**1** Claims (7)
**5** Relief player (3)
**7** Scold (3)
**8** Former Saracen Africa (7)
**9** Average (2-2)
**10** Me (6)
**12** Sloping font (6)
**13** Clinton's VP, Al (4)
**15** Ludicrous (7)
**16** Two-wheeled carriage (3)
**17** *Homo sapiens* (3)
**18** Mutt (7)

**Down**

**1** Belief in nothing beyond what is material (11)
**2** Set of laws (11)
**3** Small fish with sucker (4)
**4** Squirts (6)
**5** Someone who spreads frightening rumours (11)
**6** Where the Ganges flows to (3,2,6)
**11** One who has suffered harm (6)
**14** Devotional painting (4)

# PUZZLE 249

**Across**

**1** Swamped (7)
**5** Hit the slopes? (3)
**7** Citing (11)
**8** Stimulate; spur (4)
**10** Discuss (6)
**12** Acquire (6)
**13** Siamese (4)
**15** Ridiculous person (6,2,3)
**17** Mafia boss, perhaps (3)
**18** LPs (7)

**Down**

**1** Flame-retardant (11)
**2** Inoperative (3)
**3** Dreadful (4)
**4** Moves to music (6)
**5** Dark green, leafy vegetable (7)
**6** Recipe components (11)
**9** Eight-sided shape (7)
**11** Reflecting surface (6)
**14** Ancient Gallic neck ornament (4)
**16** In support of (3)

# PUZZLE 250

**Across**

**1** Lack of knowledge (9)
**8** Element with symbol Xe (5)
**9** Roofing slabs (5)
**10** Exertion (6)
**12** Low-pitched musical instrument (4)
**14** Good fortune (4)
**15** 'I've solved it!' (6)
**17** Not a soul (2,3)
**18** Individual leaf of paper (5)
**20** Dissembler (9)

**Down**

**2** Card game (3)
**3** Possessors (6)
**4** Singing voice (4)
**5** Conspire (7)
**6** First-rate (9)
**7** Powered stairs (9)
**11** Place of manufacturing (7)
**13** Train-stopping piston (6)
**16** Software trial (4)
**19** Tennis replay (3)

# PUZZLE 251

**Across**

**1** Financial obligations (11)
**7** Autobiography (6)
**8** Territory governed by Hamas (4)
**9** Doe's mate (4)
**10** Working as a thespian (6)
**13** Prickly plant (6)
**16** Strong desire (4)
**17** Baby napkins (4)
**18** Wheeled (6)
**19** Make room for (11)

**Down**

**2** Subject of Newton's first law (7)
**3** Conveyed, as in an item (7)
**4** Immature insect stage (5)
**5** Mesopotamian, nowadays (5)
**6** Informal language (5)
**11** Untidy, as in hair (7)
**12** Disregard (7)
**13** Type of poisonous snake (5)
**14** Third-degree, in maths (5)
**15** Antitoxin (5)

# PUZZLE 252

**Across**

**1** Extreme fear of water (11)
**7** No score (3)
**8** Shapes with four equal sides (7)
**9** Formally confer a rank (6)
**10** Murders (4)
**13** Tightly curled hairstyle (4)
**14** Dwarf tree (6)
**16** Written condition (7)
**18** Pasture (3)
**19** Wanted poster message (4,2,5)

**Down**

**1** Disabled (11)
**2** Hand over (7)
**3** Dominate the thoughts of someone (6)
**4** Sixty minutes (4)
**5** Prevent entry to (3)
**6** Kill someone important (11)
**11** Spiral-shaped pasta pieces (7)
**12** Circle of light (6)
**15** Car driven by a chauffeur (4)
**17** Egg cells (3)

# PUZZLE 253

**Across**

**1** Feeling shame (11)
**7** Golfing average (3)
**8** North American reindeer (7)
**9** Conceits (4)
**10** 'My brother' in an Elton John song (6)
**13** Six-legged creature (6)
**14** Trendy (4)
**16** Immature frog (7)
**18** Brazilian port (3)
**19** Organizes (11)

**Down**

**1** Using indirect expressions (11)
**2** Temporarily takes (7)
**3** Instrument of torture (4)
**4** Overseas (6)
**5** Bawl (3)
**6** Betray (6-5)
**11** Receive from your parents (7)
**12** Repeated back (6)
**15** Existed (4)
**17** Couple (3)

# PUZZLE 254

**Across**

**1** Proponents (10)
**7** Lean and muscular (6)
**8** Game, '_ ___ with my little eye' (1,3)
**9** Particular washing machine cycle (5)
**11** Pallid; blanched (5)
**13** Visitors to a website (5)
**14** Pile (5)
**16** Lash (4)
**18** Ploy (6)
**20** Deter (10)

**Down**

**2** Integrates (7)
**3** Segment from a chart? (3)
**4** Sunbeams (4)
**5** Clear (7)
**6** Small mouthful (3)
**10** Screenplays (7)
**12** Fastening (7)
**15** First modern Greek king (4)
**17** Used to have (3)
**19** Rogue (3)

# PUZZLE 255

**Across**
**3** Business (5)
**6** Sovereign (7)
**7** Horse straps (5)
**8** Sports result (5)
**9** Cleopatra's nemesis (3)
**11** Chocolate substitute pod (5)
**13** Brings on board (5)
**15** Cat breed with very fine, short fur (3)
**18** Heavily built (5)
**19** Course (5)
**20** Antiseptic (7)
**21** Stove light (5)

**Down**
**1** 'You fell for it!' (6)
**2** Soldier (7)
**3** Flog (6)
**4** Opposite of alkaline (4)
**5** Orient (4)
**10** Cinema film (7)
**12** Personal request (6)
**14** Is the same as (6)
**16** Cover in paper (4)
**17** At capacity (4)

# PUZZLE 256

**Across**
**1** Size (9)
**8** Journos (5)
**9** Be cyclical (5)
**10** Spoons for serving liquids (6)
**12** Amend (4)
**14** Pile (4)
**15** Forgive (6)
**17** Second (5)
**18** Sign of a fire (5)
**20** Election nominee (9)

**Down**
**2** Part of a circle's edge (3)
**3** Placed inside another object (6)
**4** Grassed earth (4)
**5** Decrypted (7)
**6** Pre-adult times (9)
**7** Feigned (9)
**11** Former Greek monetary unit (7)
**13** Elapsed (6)
**16** Walked along (4)
**19** Cereal species grown for its seeds (3)

# PUZZLE 257

**Across**

**1** Pain-relief needle technique (11)
**7** Leaf-gathering, perhaps (6)
**8** *Road Runner* company (4)
**9** Wide open in amazement (5)
**11** Gush forth (5)
**13** Perfect (5)
**14** Decorate; embellish (5)
**16** Sitting around (4)
**18** Deadly (6)
**20** Eventually (2,3,6)

**Down**

**2** Altered (7)
**3** Penultimate Greek letter (3)
**4** Complains incessantly (4)
**5** Ensnared (7)
**6** Edge of an object (3)
**10** Flat part of a curve (7)
**12** Inspects again (7)
**15** Former communist states, the Eastern ___ (4)
**17** Dull brown (3)
**19** The letter after sigma (3)

# PUZZLE 258

**Across**

**1** Radically (11)
**7** Cast figure (6)
**8** Bovine animals (4)
**9** Neat and tidy (5)
**11** Conjecture (5)
**13** Book of maps (5)
**14** Detective's breadcrumbs (5)
**16** Stuffed, fried tortilla (4)
**18** Have sufficient money for (6)
**20** Rear vistas (11)

**Down**

**2** Withdrawal of forces (7)
**3** Ready (3)
**4** Frozen (4)
**5** Regular receipt of money (7)
**6** Universal truth (3)
**10** Show-off (7)
**12** Drove a car (7)
**15** Two equal things (4)
**17** Actress, Gardner (3)
**19** Winter bug (3)

# PUZZLE 259

**Across**
**1** Lets down (11)
**7** Thespians (6)
**8** Gives money for goods (4)
**9** Extracted from the earth (5)
**11** Targeted (5)
**13** Castle refuges (5)
**14** Buffoons (5)
**16** Flat, round type of bread (4)
**18** Relating to the stars (6)
**20** Communicates via letter (11)

**Down**
**2** Slant (7)
**3** Back in time (3)
**4** Pain-in-the-neck (4)
**5** Suggests (7)
**6** Tinker (3)
**10** Less full (7)
**12** Green jewel (7)
**15** Gaping animal throats (4)
**17** Lennon's Yoko (3)
**19** Confucian path of virtuous conduct (3)

# PUZZLE 260

**Across**
**1** Knocks down (10)
**7** Pre-Christmas period (6)
**8** Counterpart to columns (4)
**9** Slow, lazy speech (5)
**11** Eucalyptus-eater (5)
**13** Sceptic (5)
**14** Overwhelmingly (2,3)
**16** Large bag (4)
**18** Finis (3,3)
**20** Barrel organ, informally (5-5)

**Down**
**2** Advanced in years (7)
**3** Naturally occurring mineral aggregate (3)
**4** Very small quantity (4)
**5** Consensus (7)
**6** Stitch (3)
**10** Beard hair (7)
**12** Erudite (7)
**15** Live somewhere temporarily (4)
**17** Volcanic material (3)
**19** Largest native Australian bird (3)

# PUZZLE 261

**Across**
1 Undercover name (3,2,6)
7 Designed to be lived in (11)
8 Type of complex that makes you feel small (11)
13 Lack of due respect (11)
18 Borrowed reading material (7,4)
20 Infantryman (4,7)

**Down**
2 Huge expanse of water (5)
3 Propel (5)
4 Thousand dollars (US slang) (3)
5 Go in (5)
6 Respond (5)
9 Fuzz (3)
10 Spin an engine (3)
11 Scull (3)
12 Hostel (3)
14 Money (archaic slang) (5)
15 Member of the heron family (5)
16 Receded (5)
17 Reproduce exactly (5)
19 Greek letter similar to 'P' (3)

# PUZZLE 262

**Across**
1 Benefit; worth (10)
7 Refrain (6)
8 Ova (4)
9 Angled punctuation symbol (5)
11 One more time (5)
13 Mix of yellow and blue (5)
14 Passing remark (5)
16 iPad, perhaps? (4)
18 Loosen a shirt, perhaps (6)
20 Precautions (10)

**Down**
2 Student (7)
3 Type of conifer (3)
4 Speech defect (4)
5 Appears (7)
6 Sink downwards (3)
10 Marshal (7)
12 Brought on (7)
15 Respiratory organ (4)
17 Twelfths of a foot (abbr.) (3)
19 Liqueur, ___ Maria (3)

# PUZZLE 263

**Across**

**1** Mutual association (11)
**6** Evacuates from a pilot's seat (6)
**7** At an earlier time (archaic) (4)
**8** Listens to (5)
**11** Metalworker (5)
**12** Grossly overweight (5)
**13** Disparages (5)
**17** Edible Pacific tuber (4)
**18** Noisy grass insect (6)
**19** Level, as in a race (4,3,4)

**Down**

**1** Prague resident, perhaps (5)
**2** *Carmen*, eg (5)
**3** Corrode (4)
**4** Relating to heat (7)
**5** Tourist (7)
**9** Hug (7)
**10** Provide fresh supplies (7)
**14** Practice (5)
**15** Cheerless (5)
**16** Check for irregularities (4)

# PUZZLE 264

**Across**

**7** Imaginable (11)
**8** Less transparent (7)
**9** Computer-menu opener (3)
**10** Group of nine people (5)
**12** Crest (5)
**13** It's mostly oxygen and nitrogen (3)
**14** Indigenous inhabitants (7)
**16** Difficult (11)

**Down**

**1** Financial-reporting profession (11)
**2** Preconquest American (4)
**3** Sullenly (11)
**4** Replacing a computer file with a different one (11)
**5** Within a train (6)
**6** SMS communication (4,7)
**11** William the Conqueror, eg (6)
**15** Egotistical (4)

# PUZZLE 265

**Across**

**1** Reporters (11)
**6** Chilliest (6)
**7** George Orwell's real name (4)
**8** Taut (5)
**11** Liquid (5)
**12** Heats up (5)
**13** Ride a bike (5)
**17** V, to a Roman (4)
**18** Plan of things to be done (6)
**19** Wasteful (11)

**Down**

**1** Roasting meat (5)
**2** Operating, as in machinery (5)
**3** Industrious insects (4)
**4** In a perfect world (7)
**5** Insignificant (7)
**9** Tehran resident (7)
**10** Masculine pronoun (7)
**14** Light, narrow, paddled boat (5)
**15** Speak highly of (5)
**16** Country whose capital is Bamako (4)

# PUZZLE 266

**Across**

**1** Forfeit (9)
**7** Feet coverings (5)
**8** One who steals (5)
**10** Elliptical (4)
**11** Ringed planet (6)
**14** Money earned (6)
**15** internet connection type (2-2)
**17** Appellations (5)
**19** Nourishing substances (5)
**20** Concealing (9)

**Down**

**2** Antiquated (7)
**3** Stand up (4)
**4** Rich big shot (3,3)
**5** Twenty-second Greek letter (3)
**6** Finnic language (8)
**9** Most amusing (8)
**12** Mythical one-horned animal (7)
**13** Makes laugh (6)
**16** Miles away (4)
**18** Musical, *Five Guys Named ___* (3)

# PUZZLE 267

**Across**

**1** May be eaten (10)
**7** Begins (6)
**8** Youths (4)
**9** Steer (5)
**11** White piano keys were once made of this (5)
**13** Wonky (5)
**14** Assume (5)
**16** Butter used in Indian cooking (4)
**18** Add to the start (6)
**20** Initiative (10)

**Down**

**2** Exclusions (3-4)
**3** Gentleman (3)
**4** Soft, pulpy substance (4)
**5** Dearest (7)
**6** Objective (3)
**10** Least shallow (7)
**12** Responds (7)
**15** Prompt (4)
**17** Gardening tool (3)
**19** Musical ability (3)

# PUZZLE 268

**Across**

**1** The study of weather (11)
**7** Large marine mammals (6)
**8** Workout centres (4)
**9** Hard to please (5)
**11** Ends (5)
**13** Tablet pens (5)
**14** Attempts (5)
**16** Twirl (4)
**18** Newest (6)
**20** Comprehends (11)

**Down**

**2** Fatigue (7)
**3** Elongated fish (3)
**4** Race around too quickly (4)
**5** Igniter (7)
**6** Chewy sweet? (3)
**10** 'Be quiet!' (7)
**12** Gratified (7)
**15** Dutch-disease-prone trees (4)
**17** God of flocks and herds (3)
**19** Earl Grey, eg (3)

# PUZZLE 269

**Across**

**1** Knick-knack (4-1-4)
**7** Less (5)
**8** Bare (5)
**10** Untruths (4)
**11** Statements of belief (6)
**14** Sycophant (3-3)
**15** *Star Trek* android (4)
**17** Correct (5)
**19** Had title to (5)
**20** Environs (9)

**Down**

**2** Depicts artistically (7)
**3** Edge; verge (4)
**4** Base two (6)
**5** Biblical vessel (3)
**6** Boss (8)
**9** Throws away (8)
**12** Emptied (7)
**13** Pancake mix (6)
**16** Vegetarian ingredient (4)
**18** Large antelope (3)

# PUZZLE 270

**Across**

**1** For no reason (10)
**7** Display surface (6)
**8** Knock (4)
**9** Take by force (5)
**11** Banquet (5)
**13** Unnerve: ___ out (5)
**14** Paces (5)
**16** Opposite of pro (4)
**18** Source (6)
**20** Biology branch dealing with living organisms (10)

**Down**

**2** Forgives (7)
**3** Female roe (3)
**4** Highest European volcano (4)
**5** School study area (7)
**6** Tropical edible root (3)
**10** Correct (7)
**12** Young tree (7)
**15** Centres of activity (4)
**17** Snooze (3)
**19** Afflicted (3)

# PUZZLE 271

**Across**

**1** A complete lack of truth (1,4,2,4)
**7** Test (3-3)
**8** Pottery material (4)
**9** A short measure of length (4)
**10** New emigrant settlement (6)
**13** Aromatic ointment (6)
**16** Blows away (4)
**17** Crippled (4)
**18** Lingo (6)
**19** Retreating (11)

**Down**

**2** Carnivorous South American fish (7)
**3** Togs (7)
**4** Relating to vision (5)
**5** Inuit dwelling (5)
**6** Coyly (5)
**11** Of little intellectual interest (7)
**12** Maternity-ward baby (7)
**13** Beneath (5)
**14** Boundary (5)
**15** Significant (5)

# PUZZLE 272

**Across**

**1** For an instant (11)
**7** Rummage (6)
**8** Baby powder (4)
**9** Comedians (4)
**10** Aim (6)
**13** Reveries (6)
**16** Mischievous children (4)
**17** Geriatric (4)
**18** Sated (4,2)
**19** Groups with the power to make decisions (11)

**Down**

**2** Al fresco (4,3)
**3** It spans from Portugal to China (7)
**4** As one, in music (5)
**5** Fuming (5)
**6** Sailing boat (5)
**11** Three of a kind (7)
**12** The eighth planet (7)
**13** Roman moon goddess (5)
**14** Upright (5)
**15** More secure (5)

# PUZZLE 273

**Across**
**1** Courteous (11)
**7** Repairs (6)
**8** Promises (4)
**9** Dribbles (5)
**11** Snide, critical comments (5)
**13** Tally (3,2)
**14** Action words (5)
**16** Transpose (4)
**18** Pressure (6)
**20** Diminuendo (11)

**Down**
**2** Kicked the bucket (7)
**3** Common article (3)
**4** See at a glance (4)
**5** Move forward (7)
**6** Depressed (3)
**10** Chubbier (7)
**12** Construct again (7)
**15** Egyptian goddess (4)
**17** Sorrow (3)
**19** Cereal grass (3)

# PUZZLE 274

**Across**
**1** Unmoving (6)
**4** Defective (4)
**6** Go back (6)
**7** Lower-arm bone (4)
**8** College treasurer (6)
**11** Sovereign (4)
**12** Archaic pronoun (4)
**13** Refuses to admit (6)
**16** Young sheep (4)
**17** Select (6)
**18** Limit (4)
**19** In a lively way (6)

**Down**
**1** Bush (5)
**2** Sacrificial block (5)
**3** States the opposite (11)
**4** Intoxicated (7)
**5** Monetary resources (7)
**9** Not listened to (7)
**10** Trip (7)
**14** Humorous incongruity (5)
**15** Grotty (5)

# PUZZLE 275

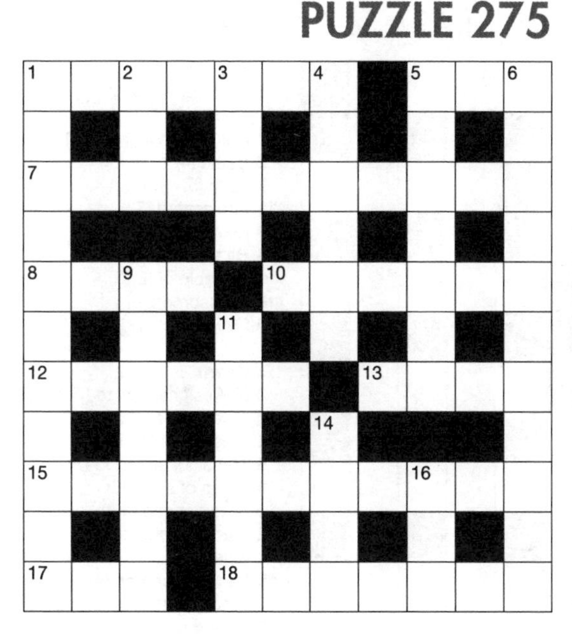

**Across**

**1** Kettledrums (7)
**5** Capture; arrest (slang) (3)
**7** Inevitably (11)
**8** Cross with a looped upper arm (4)
**10** Popular pastry (6)
**12** Temporary apprentice (6)
**13** Bloke (4)
**15** Increase in function (11)
**17** Prattle (3)
**18** Tobacco consumers (7)

**Down**

**1** Cautiously (11)
**2** PC competitor (3)
**3** And (4)
**4** Kind of (2,1,3)
**5** Irish social dance (7)
**6** Violent, mentally ill people (11)
**9** Tomato sauce (7)
**11** Injuries (6)
**14** Forbid (4)
**16** Small metal loop (3)

# PUZZLE 276

**Across**

**1** Ninth zodiac sign (11)
**7** Monet tree (6)
**8** Patron saint of sailors (4)
**9** Conceal in the hand (4)
**10** Northern European sea (6)
**13** South American woollen garment (6)
**16** Check (4)
**17** They're used to row a boat (4)
**18** Culmination (6)
**19** End racial separation (11)

**Down**

**2** Tropical evergreen tree (7)
**3** Relating to the Muslim religion (7)
**4** Beat strongly (5)
**5** Coastal opening (5)
**6** Showing no emotion (5)
**11** Permitting (7)
**12** Immediate (7)
**13** Self-satisfied (5)
**14** Geeks (5)
**15** Arise (5)

# PUZZLE 277

**Across**
1 Member of *homo sapiens* (5,5)
7 Call attention; refer (6)
8 Baths (4)
9 Hard (5)
11 Intoxicated (5)
13 Established (5)
14 Hit violently (5)
16 Capable of (2,2)
18 Crossbreed (6)
20 Overcome; endure (3,7)

**Down**
2 Makes changes to (7)
3 Vote of assent (3)
4 Fragments (4)
5 Transitional period (7)
6 Lump of slime (3)
10 At top speed (4,3)
12 Placing inside a larger object (7)
15 Iranian monarch (4)
17 Small, snub-nosed dog (3)
19 Sibling (3)

# PUZZLE 278

**Across**
1 Competitor; contributor (11)
6 Lots and lots (6)
7 Rents out (4)
8 Deluge (5)
11 Babies' beds (5)
12 Groups of eight binary digits (5)
13 Virtue (5)
17 Prefix meaning 'before' (4)
18 Rotten; foul (6)
19 With ease (11)

**Down**
1 Evidence (5)
2 Broadcast audio (5)
3 Large, round container (4)
4 North Star (7)
5 Remarkable (7)
9 Give a piece of your mind to (3,4)
10 Alone, by ___ (7)
14 Rub vigorously (5)
15 Just before tomorrow (5)
16 Stout pole on a ship (4)

# PUZZLE 279

**Across**

3 Animal compartment (5)
6 Biblical betrayer (7)
7 Fool's Day month (5)
8 Massage (5)
9 Comic screech (3)
11 Opposite of 'heads' (5)
13 Impressionist, Edgar (5)
15 Australian electronic travel document (init.) (3)
18 Jet (5)
19 Secret lover (5)
20 Seated on a horse (7)
21 Support structures? (5)

**Down**

1 Organ rupture (6)
2 Act of God (7)
3 Influenced (6)
4 Expresses publicly (4)
5 Break in the action (4)
10 Retaining (7)
12 Turmoils (6)
14 Exploited (6)
16 Spike (4)
17 Police (4)

# PUZZLE 280

**Across**

1 Overcoming (11)
7 Packed tightly (6)
8 Mallow plant with long, ridged seed pods (4)
9 Small chess piece (4)
10 Showered (6)
13 Reconstruct (6)
16 Mines (4)
17 Neocon (4)
18 Tours (6)
19 Commercial workers (11)

**Down**

2 Ignorant (7)
3 Keepsake (7)
4 Cow's mammary gland (5)
5 Go over with a pen (3,2)
6 Protect (5)
11 Brings about by authority (7)
12 Give a right to (7)
13 Addict's recovery time (5)
14 Baby deer (5)
15 Motion picture (5)

# PUZZLE 281

**Across**

**3** A decimal division (5)
**6** Severely criticize (3,4)
**7** Nobles (5)
**8** Bullet firings (5)
**9** Not hesitate (3)
**11** Outdo (5)
**13** Closes (5)
**15** Director, Mendes (3)
**18** Shyly (5)
**19** Keyboard instrument (5)
**20** Reported (7)
**21** One of Snow White's helpers (5)

**Down**

**1** Loftier (6)
**2** Affected individuals (7)
**3** Themes (6)
**4** Christmas (4)
**5** 'Be quiet' (4)
**10** Via (7)
**12** Yield good results (3,3)
**14** Spoke (6)
**16** Careered (4)
**17** Temptations song, ___ *was a Rollin' Stone* (4)

# PUZZLE 282

**Across**

**1** Flips over (7)
**5** Backing (3)
**7** Contact number (abbr.) (3)
**8** Enduring artistic work (7)
**9** Peel (4)
**10** Circus tent (3,3)
**12** Masticated (6)
**13** Cried (4)
**15** Jewish-state resident (7)
**16** *Numero* ___, the best (3)
**17** Deity (3)
**18** Hits (7)

**Down**

**1** Taking part with other people (11)
**2** Offered (11)
**3** Starchy food grain (4)
**4** Equilibrium (6)
**5** Not take the blame (4,3,4)
**6** Jobs (11)
**11** Alludes (6)
**14** Fibber (4)

# PUZZLE 283

**Across**

**1** Ruthlessly (2,4,5)
**7** Implants (6)
**8** Pre-Roman inhabitant of Europe (4)
**9** Not very clever (5)
**11** Horse (5)
**13** Lens opening setting (1-4)
**14** Flower of the daisy family (5)
**16** Brake part (4)
**18** Choose not to participate (3,3)
**20** Social event (3-8)

**Down**

**2** Figures (7)
**3** Twelve months old (3)
**4** Platter (4)
**5** Places (7)
**6** Opposite of a lark? (3)
**10** Tardiest (7)
**12** Perform, as in instructions (7)
**15** Bell chime (4)
**17** Shade (3)
**19** Mild sound of rebuke (3)

# PUZZLE 284

**Across**

**1** Ending (11)
**7** Arachnid (6)
**8** Deities (4)
**9** Brusque (5)
**11** Hard, solid rock (5)
**13** Key (5)
**14** Many-headed legendary snake (5)
**16** Among (4)
**18** Piece of grassland (6)
**20** Basic intelligence (6,5)

**Down**

**2** Overseas trades (7)
**3** Really annoyed; angry (3)
**4** Usual rule (4)
**5** Firmly (7)
**6** Head movement (3)
**10** Liberty (7)
**12** Apprehensive (7)
**15** 'So be it' (4)
**17** Cow's low (3)
**19** Mature (3)

# PUZZLE 285

**Across**

**3** Devotee (5)
**6** Effective (2,5)
**7** Titled (5)
**8** Ethical (5)
**9** Arachnid's trap (3)
**11** Japanese poem (5)
**13** Metal pin (5)
**15** Tolkien tree creature (3)
**18** Scrub hard (5)
**19** Fencing used to train samurai (5)
**20** Helps (7)
**21** Lukewarm (5)

**Down**

**1** Spanish racket game (6)
**2** Bar-based singing activity (7)
**3** More drawn-out (6)
**4** Temptress (4)
**5** Travel on (4)
**10** A cookie, eg (7)
**12** Discharge cargo (6)
**14** Consider identical (6)
**16** Parody (4)
**17** Crocodile clasp? (4)

# PUZZLE 286

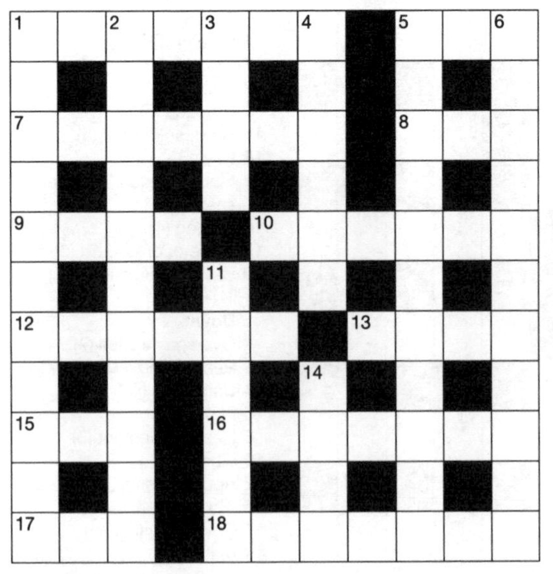

**Across**

**1** Before birth (2,5)
**5** Resort based around a spring (3)
**7** Passage (7)
**8** Punch lightly (3)
**9** Verve (4)
**10** Relating to the mail (6)
**12** Accepts (6)
**13** *Frozen* Disney princess (4)
**15** Tidal retreat (3)
**16** End-of-line stations (7)
**17** Adversary (3)
**18** 16th-century German portraitist (7)

**Down**

**1** Following (2,3,4,2)
**2** Not obtainable (11)
**3** Threat, 'Do this or ___!' (4)
**4** Choice (6)
**5** Considerable (11)
**6** Name (11)
**11** Swap (6)
**14** Taken through the mouth (4)

# PUZZLE 287

**Across**
- **3** Daft (5)
- **6** Not native (7)
- **7** Artist's support (5)
- **8** Girl's item of clothing (5)
- **9** Jamaican musical style (3)
- **11** Firm and crunchy (5)
- **13** Seeking damages (5)
- **15** Go (3)
- **18** Large-scale brawls (5)
- **19** 'No. 5', for Lou Bega (5)
- **20** Drop away (4,3)
- **21** Window material (5)

**Down**
- **1** Employee (6)
- **2** Thaw something out (7)
- **3** Creeps up (6)
- **4** Succulent (4)
- **5** Local-business review site (4)
- **10** Loud enough to be heard (7)
- **12** Trial prints (6)
- **14** Inform (6)
- **16** Complacent (4)
- **17** Jane Austen novel (4)

# PUZZLE 288

**Across**
- **1** Convulsive muscle twitch (3)
- **7** Conquers (9)
- **8** Lie down and tan (3)
- **9** Soft, cuddly toy (5,4)
- **11** Abolition (11)
- **12** Diversion (9)
- **15** WALL-E's love (3)
- **16** To do with voting (9)
- **17** 'I agree' (3)

**Down**
- **1** Thin wrapping sheet (6,5)
- **2** Adds (11)
- **3** Repair (4)
- **4** Suffering from pains (4)
- **5** At once (11)
- **6** Stargazers (11)
- **10** Jean, perhaps (5)
- **13** Has dinner (4)
- **14** European currency (4)

# PUZZLE 289

**Across**
**1** Unit of electric charge (7)
**5** Dunk (3)
**7** Predicted (7)
**8** For one (3)
**9** Epochs (4)
**10** Two-piece swimwear (6)
**12** Something of little value (6)
**13** Dry ravine (4)
**15** Even so (3)
**16** The United States (7)
**17** Top-left computer key (3)
**18** Unusual (7)

**Down**
**1** Low, living-room furniture (6,5)
**2** Deluded (11)
**3** Drive out; expel (4)
**4** Formal neckwear (3,3)
**5** Repetition (11)
**6** Enter, as in an event (11)
**11** At all times (6)
**14** Small dam (4)

# PUZZLE 290

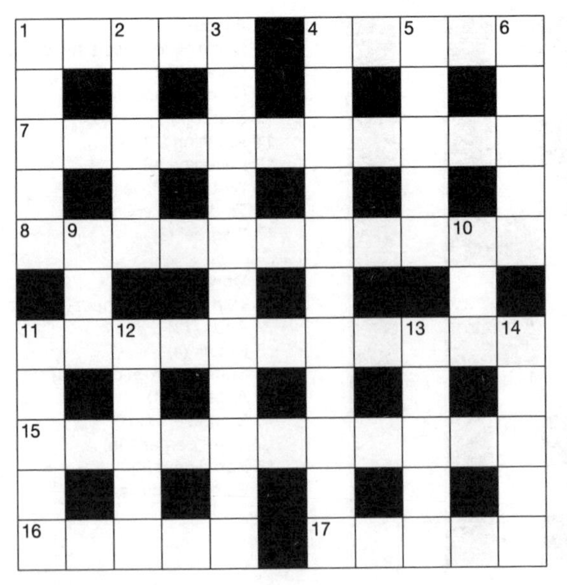

**Across**
**1** Loud, jarring sound (5)
**4** Finals, eg (5)
**7** Requested sale value (6,5)
**8** Booking (11)
**11** For no good reason (11)
**15** The Pope's religion (11)
**16** Accomplishments (5)
**17** Fashionable (5)

**Down**
**1** Seat (5)
**2** Egyptian crosses (5)
**3** Multiple family groupings (11)
**4** Justification (11)
**5** Proof of being elsewhere (5)
**6** Authoritarian (5)
**9** Be incorrect (3)
**10** Vegetable or palm, eg (3)
**11** Rainbow-shaped (5)
**12** Immerse in liquid so as to clean (5)
**13** Simpleton (5)
**14** 'Delicious!' (5)

# PUZZLE 291

**Across**
1 Valiant (7)
5 Fluid pouch in an animal (3)
7 Literally (3)
8 Maths equations in general (7)
9 Consented (6)
10 Clench the teeth (4)
12 Maybe: '___ depends' (4)
13 Critique (6)
15 Ceremony for a deceased person (7)
16 A goal or target (3)
17 Place (3)
18 Sweet age? (7)

**Down**
1 Unpleasant (11)
2 Doubt (11)
3 Paradise (6)
4 Cartoon bear (4)
5 Of a lower rank (11)
6 Female artisan (11)
11 Automatic reaction (6)
14 Upper body limbs (4)

# PUZZLE 292

**Across**
1 Roofed and walled structures (9)
8 Coral ridges (5)
9 Quotes (5)
10 Loathing (6)
12 Pitcher (4)
14 Small child (4)
15 Nairobi resident? (6)
17 Current craze (5)
18 Robot (5)
20 Attributes (9)

**Down**
2 Consume (3)
3 Coming last, perhaps (6)
4 Hankering (4)
5 Escape (7)
6 Bans (9)
7 The study of space (9)
11 Vivid graphic representation (7)
13 Mass times gravity (6)
16 Worshipped statue (4)
19 Pulitzer Prize winner, Harper (3)

# PUZZLE 293

**Across**

**1** Build (9)
**8** Location (5)
**9** Varieties (5)
**10** Give up work for good (6)
**12** Hindu dress (4)
**14** Belonging to us (4)
**15** Snack legume, often roasted or salted (6)
**17** Solemn bell ring (5)
**18** Lucifer (5)
**20** Throat lozenge (5,4)

**Down**

**2** Personal (3)
**3** Curses (6)
**4** Charge per unit (4)
**5** Team leader (7)
**6** Fails to notice (9)
**7** Helper (9)
**11** Underwater missile (7)
**13** Made untidy, with 'up' (6)
**16** Stopper (4)
**19** Likewise (3)

# PUZZLE 294

**Across**

**1** Bone filling (6)
**4** Immoral habit (4)
**6** Winter, eg (6)
**7** Lightly cooked, if meat (4)
**8** Oblige (6)
**11** Used in fluorescent lamps (4)
**12** Grizzly or polar, eg (4)
**13** Has a desire (6)
**16** Calf-length skirt (4)
**17** Emerged (6)
**18** Full of excitement (4)
**19** Expunges (6)

**Down**

**1** Melodious sounds (5)
**2** Provide with weapons again (5)
**3** Crumbly white cheese (11)
**4** Porch (7)
**5** Animated drawing (7)
**9** Gap (7)
**10** Analysing (7)
**14** Dangers (5)
**15** Falls without trace (5)

# PUZZLE 295

**Across**

**1** Exactly (9)
**7** Conduits (5)
**8** Established truth (5)
**10** On a grand scale (4)
**11** Unneeded extras (6)
**14** Small firearm (6)
**15** Wight or Man, eg (4)
**17** Type of footwear (5)
**19** Cooked in hot oil (5)
**20** Engrossing (9)

**Down**

**2** Coneys (7)
**3** Throw a fishing line (4)
**4** Postage tokens (6)
**5** Floral offering (3)
**6** Tries (8)
**9** Scans some text incorrectly (8)
**12** From Moscow, eg (7)
**13** Main Japanese island (6)
**16** Touch-and-go (4)
**18** Evil elf (3)

# PUZZLE 296

**Across**

**1** Circular music storage device (7,4)
**7** West Indian state (3)
**8** Ex-celebrity (3-4)
**9** Large-scale artistic work (4)
**10** Mixed cereal breakfast (6)
**13** Type of salad (6)
**14** Cut (4)
**16** Lack of experience (7)
**18** Spree (3)
**19** Lack of equilibrium (11)

**Down**

**1** Intelligentsia (11)
**2** Quantified amount (7)
**3** Pallid (4)
**4** Absorbent paper (6)
**5** Fury (3)
**6** Uniformity (11)
**11** Five-grid sudoku (7)
**12** SLR, eg (6)
**15** Fresh-food shop (4)
**17** All the details: ___ and outs (3)

# PUZZLE 297

**Across**

**1** Accurately (9)
**7** Gave way (5)
**8** Metaphorical expression (5)
**10** Bookworm (4)
**11** Overhaul (6)
**14** Half the diameter (6)
**15** Ibuprofen target (4)
**17** Due (5)
**19** Searches (5)
**20** Lacking flavour (9)

**Down**

**2** Sent away for (7)
**3** Frees (4)
**4** Large towns (6)
**5** Leonardo, familiarly (3)
**6** Artistic setting (8)
**9** Strong, black coffee (8)
**12** Speech patterns (7)
**13** Monetary fund (6)
**16** Biblical epistle (abbr.) (4)
**18** Wilhelmina, informally (3)

# PUZZLE 298

**Across**

**1** Order a drug (9)
**8** Strong feeling of annoyance (5)
**9** Assisted (5)
**10** Complain about (6)
**12** Old Italian monetary unit (4)
**14** The ___ of March (4)
**15** Causing great distress (6)
**17** Arise from bed (3,2)
**18** Prone (5)
**20** Redirecting (9)

**Down**

**2** Floor covering (3)
**3** Taking place in succession (6)
**4** A large quantity (4)
**5** Auction process (7)
**6** English university city (9)
**7** Proceeding (9)
**11** Famous conductors (7)
**13** Radiating light (6)
**16** Church recess (4)
**19** Small truck (3)

# PUZZLE 299

**Across**

**1** Surgical routines (10)
**7** Rise (6)
**8** Guitar speakers (4)
**9** Biblical king of Judea (5)
**11** Moves in a steady stream (5)
**13** Common black tea (5)
**14** Sacred song (5)
**16** Mongolian and Chinese desert (4)
**18** Mend (6)
**20** Sweet milk dessert (10)

**Down**

**2** Own (7)
**3** Mourn; repent (3)
**4** Fuss (2-2)
**5** Ancient Greek fortune tellers (7)
**6** Sample a liquid (3)
**10** Simple wind instrument (7)
**12** Ready and eager (7)
**15** Caiman's cousin (4)
**17** Sphere (3)
**19** Edible, spherical green seed (3)

# PUZZLE 300

**Across**

**1** Disagreeable (9)
**8** Goddess of love (5)
**9** Passenger ship (5)
**10** Attempting to beat (6)
**12** Faux pas (2-2)
**14** Steals from (4)
**15** Desktop arrow (6)
**17** Crook (5)
**18** Trades (5)
**20** Emanate (9)

**Down**

**2** Mother superior, eg (3)
**3** Relieving (6)
**4** Bistro (4)
**5** Reflects (7)
**6** Bank account deficit (9)
**7** False profession of a belief (9)
**11** One who mends shoes (7)
**13** Load (6)
**16** Drawback (4)
**19** Subjective subject (3)

# PUZZLE 301

**Across**

**3** All-night parties (5)
**6** Be granted (7)
**7** Canonized person (5)
**8** In motion, as in a process (5)
**9** Commercial messages (3)
**11** Decision-making power (3-2)
**13** Keen (5)
**15** Evening wear (3)
**18** Cholesterol, eg (5)
**19** Mayhem (5)
**20** Removes impurities (7)
**21** Olympic athletic event (5)

**Down**

**1** Former Spanish currency (6)
**2** Something that is asked for (7)
**3** Dwell (6)
**4** Concealing shroud (4)
**5** Takes an exam (4)
**10** Relating to parody (7)
**12** Clamour (6)
**14** Went out (6)
**16** Burn (4)
**17** Very, very bad (4)

# PUZZLE 302

**Across**

**1** Classic poison element (7)
**5** Pastry dish (3)
**7** Prune (3)
**8** Incomplete (7)
**9** Restraint (4)
**10** Be part of a group (6)
**12** Exchanged (6)
**13** Baptism receptacle (4)
**15** Acorn-bearing plant (3,4)
**16** Female bird (3)
**17** Alcohol addict (3)
**18** Wiped (7)

**Down**

**1** Quotas (11)
**2** Large food store (11)
**3** Opposite of yep (4)
**4** Large rug (6)
**5** Thinker (11)
**6** Educated (11)
**11** Consisting of verses (6)
**14** Something you might pass on to a child (4)

# PUZZLE 303

**Across**

**1** Eager disposition (11)
**7** Turfs out (6)
**8** Cameo stone (4)
**9** Medications (5)
**11** Drink with a sucking sound (5)
**13** Relating to Eastern countries (5)
**14** Treatise (5)
**16** Sell via a machine (4)
**18** Geronimo descendant (6)
**20** Type of fight involving toying with an opponent (3-3-5)

**Down**

**2** Wounds (7)
**3** French 'Luke' (3)
**4** Prone to snooping (4)
**5** Narrow strips of pasta (7)
**6** Reticent in company (3)
**10** Parent's father (7)
**12** Attains (7)
**15** Poet (4)
**17** *Hitch* actress, Mendes (3)
**19** Commotion (3)

# PUZZLE 304

**Across**

**1** Telling off (11)
**6** Large soup dish (6)
**7** Glasses frames (4)
**8** Odes (5)
**11** Form of oxygen (5)
**12** Demise (5)
**13** Joint above the foot (5)
**17** Concern (4)
**18** Send abroad (6)
**19** Company providing advice (11)

**Down**

**1** Misbehave (3,2)
**2** Become one (5)
**3** Charged atoms (4)
**4** Skyline (7)
**5** In name only (7)
**9** Aromatic culinary herb (7)
**10** Affairs (7)
**14** Famous (5)
**15** Way in (5)
**16** Basic unit of a living organism (4)

# PUZZLE 305

**Across**
**1** Common perception (10)
**7** Cling (6)
**8** A great deal (4)
**9** Lathers (5)
**11** Key bread ingredient (5)
**13** Cays (5)
**14** Nimble (5)
**16** Hindu teacher (4)
**18** Counsel (6)
**20** Expert (10)

**Down**
**2** Boring (7)
**3** Small deer (3)
**4** Follow orders (4)
**5** Large piece of wood burned at Christmas (4,3)
**6** East-African time zone (init.) (3)
**10** Take it (7)
**12** Unlatches (7)
**15** The Three Wise Men (4)
**17** Parcel delivery company (init.) (3)
**19** Irish singer, Doonican (3)

# PUZZLE 306

**Across**
**1** Spoke to (9)
**8** Rustic paradise (5)
**9** Does not include (5)
**10** Broke in to a computer system (6)
**12** Fellow (4)
**14** Iranian monetary unit (4)
**15** Top of the line (6)
**17** In what place? (5)
**18** Indirectly mocking (5)
**20** Releases (9)

**Down**
**2** Night's counterpart (3)
**3** Banks; depends (6)
**4** Make available for purchase (4)
**5** Keep out (7)
**6** Taken out (9)
**7** Gathers together in one place (9)
**11** French country house (7)
**13** Beats (6)
**16** Welt (4)
**19** Skating-rink surface (3)

# PUZZLE 307

**Across**

**1** Fantastically well (11)
**7** Plan (6)
**8** Jokes (4)
**9** Expectorate (5)
**11** Post (5)
**13** Code word for 'O' (5)
**14** Strangely (5)
**16** List of options (4)
**18** Bunny (6)
**20** Alternative massage therapy (11)

**Down**

**2** Guesses (7)
**3** Falsehood (3)
**4** Proposal (4)
**5** Made ineffective (7)
**6** Cut tree trunk (3)
**10** In small steps (7)
**12** Murdering (7)
**15** Main point (4)
**17** In advance of, poetically (3)
**19** Sound-level measure (3)

# PUZZLE 308

**Across**

**3** Weeps (5)
**6** Common ice-cream flavour (7)
**7** Governed (5)
**8** Deck crew (5)
**9** Prompt, as in memory (3)
**11** Biblical father of Joseph (5)
**13** Snare (5)
**15** Like hearts and diamonds (3)
**18** Vital bodily fluid (5)
**19** Juicy, tropical fruit (5)
**20** Mass books (7)
**21** Garden figure (5)

**Down**

**1** Cuban capital (6)
**2** Royal-family name (7)
**3** Organic chemistry element (6)
**4** In a lazy way (4)
**5** Team (4)
**10** Atheistic (7)
**12** Change into (6)
**14** Unhurriedly (6)
**16** Haze (4)
**17** Suspicious of (2,2)

# PUZZLE 309

**Across**
**1** Characterization (9)
**8** Propose (5)
**9** Low-lying, boggy ground (5)
**10** Dash (6)
**12** Embryo precursor (4)
**14** Possesses (4)
**15** Blood fluid (6)
**17** Fruit used for making wine (5)
**18** Prominent member of a field (5)
**20** At odds with something (9)

**Down**
**2** Blockhead (3)
**3** Rotated (6)
**4** Organized force (4)
**5** Reaches a destination (7)
**6** Experience (2,7)
**7** Sparkling wine (9)
**11** Indian language (7)
**13** Unpowered aircraft (6)
**16** Shorten, as in a sail (4)
**19** Longing (3)

# PUZZLE 310

**Across**
**1** The office of a domestic affairs manager (11)
**7** Sneaky, deceitful person (6)
**8** *The Lord of the Rings* actor, Bean (4)
**9** Help in crime (4)
**10** Acts dishonestly (6)
**13** Private club subscriber (6)
**16** Breathe hard (4)
**17** Roman attire (4)
**18** Medical centre (6)
**19** Investigatory (4-7)

**Down**
**2** Quiver (7)
**3** Clothes bucket (7)
**4** Holy memento (5)
**5** Laughing animal (5)
**6** Evergreen coniferous trees (5)
**11** Drained (7)
**12** Stress (7)
**13** Recurring melody (5)
**14** Conjuring (5)
**15** *The Addams Family* actress, Christina (5)

# PUZZLE 311

**Across**
1 Being made up of (10)
7 Twitch (6)
8 There are seven in a week (4)
9 The opposite of persona (5)
11 Pimpled (5)
13 Theatre seat guide (5)
14 Charred remains (5)
16 Soft cloth (4)
18 Woollen shawl (6)
20 Possessive mark (10)

**Down**
2 Positions (7)
3 A short pin or bolt (3)
4 Enjoying (4)
5 Brings on (7)
6 Tent rope (3)
10 Conductor (7)
12 Ocular cleansing lotion (7)
15 Skin growth (4)
17 Period of history (3)
19 Baby's first word? (3)

# PUZZLE 312

**Across**
1 Keyboard writing (6)
4 Ebay status (4)
8 Chic (7)
9 Coach (3)
10 Tilt (4)
11 Igloo-dweller (6)
13 Bad-tempered (6)
14 Platform from shore to water (4)
16 Stimulus (3)
17 Occurring (7)
18 Places down gently (4)
19 Scorched (6)

**Down**
1 Of religious beliefs (11)
2 Ahead of time (11)
3 Almost here (4)
5 Contributing to the cost of (11)
6 Dejected (11)
7 Store in a secret place (5)
12 Talk (5)
15 Multi-user online writing tool (4)

# PUZZLE 313

**Across**

**7** Changed; modified (11)
**8** Highest amount (7)
**9** Lamb's mother (3)
**10** Rage (5)
**12** Fits one inside another (5)
**13** Flat area of a seated person (3)
**14** Retrieve (7)
**16** Focus (11)

**Down**

**1** Extremely accurate timepiece (6,5)
**2** Stubby-tailed cat (4)
**3** Visual lacks of balance (11)
**4** Convey (11)
**5** Fireplace remainders (6)
**6** Antagonists (11)
**11** Add on (6)
**15** Tiny bottle (4)

# PUZZLE 314

**Across**

**1** Intriguing (11)
**7** Proceedings (6)
**8** Opposite of columns (4)
**9** Money substitute (5)
**11** Devoutness (5)
**13** Colourless with dread (5)
**14** Stared at longingly (5)
**16** Biblical 'you' (4)
**18** Skilful (6)
**20** Tropical seabird (7,4)

**Down**

**2** Beginners (7)
**3** 1,000,000,000 years (3)
**4** Piece of cake (4)
**5** Naming (7)
**6** Unused (3)
**10** Polar menace (7)
**12** Even more minuscule (7)
**15** Type of whisky (4)
**17** Not him... (3)
**19** Meat cut (3)

# PUZZLE 315

**Across**
3 Small plant cutting (5)
6 Early 20th-century art movement (7)
7 Flows like treacle (5)
8 Fault (5)
9 Semite (3)
11 Creep and cringe (5)
13 Milk processor (5)
15 Archery wood (3)
18 Genuinely (5)
19 Compadre (5)
20 Precipitating (7)
21 A gonad, medically (5)

**Down**
1 Space free of matter (6)
2 Art exhibition room (7)
3 Had a cigarette (6)
4 Tear down (4)
5 Sudden blast of wind (4)
10 Justify (7)
12 Recollection (6)
14 Governing (6)
16 Circle of light (4)
17 Famous female opera singer (4)

# PUZZLE 316

**Across**
1 Most recent previous date (9)
7 'Yippee!' (5)
8 Improvise (2-3)
10 Forbid (4)
11 Man's formal headgear (3,3)
14 Start to confide (4,2)
15 Before long (4)
17 Ingested (5)
19 Desert watering holes (5)
20 Moans (9)

**Down**
2 Improve (7)
3 System of weights for precious metals (4)
4 Logic (6)
5 Be sick (3)
6 Type of disease? (8)
9 Plant specialist (8)
12 Actual; real (5-2)
13 Be destroyed by heat (4,2)
16 Travelling folk (4)
18 Noah's per-species limit (3)

# PUZZLE 317

**Across**

**1** Spread rapidly (11)
**7** Musical staff sign (4)
**8** Vinegary, eg (6)
**9** Foundation (5)
**10** Ruin (5)
**13** Pale, sandy colour (5)
**15** Sharp cutting tool (5)
**17** Mammary duct opening (6)
**18** Parsley or sage (4)
**19** Store vendor (11)

**Down**

**2** Let go of something (7)
**3** Raising (7)
**4** Young horse (4)
**5** Sound (5)
**6** Do very well (5)
**11** Large, black leopard (7)
**12** Dante's hell (7)
**13** Financial institutions (5)
**14** Drive; urge (5)
**16** Aid (4)

# PUZZLE 318

**Across**

**1** Withdraw from confrontation (4,3)
**5** UK-founded processor design company (3)
**7** Late (7)
**8** Type of lettuce (3)
**9** Fall in drops (4)
**10** Be thrifty (6)
**12** Peerless (6)
**13** Cylinder to wind film onto (4)
**15** Large, ornamental carp (3)
**16** Native of former Indian province (7)
**17** Sunbeam (3)
**18** Not adhere to a plan (2,5)

**Down**

**1** A leech or mosquito, eg (11)
**2** Reputation (11)
**3** Opposite of evens (4)
**4** Romance language (6)
**5** Island chain (11)
**6** Not using properly (11)
**11** Baloney (6)
**14** Have learnt (4)

# PUZZLE 319

**Across**
1 Flickering (9)
7 Greeting letters (5)
8 Welsh breed of dog (5)
10 Sheet of paper (4)
11 Judge (6)
14 Complete (6)
15 Metal filament (4)
17 Ledge (5)
19 Roof overhangs (5)
20 Without question (9)

**Down**
2 Vertical (7)
3 Work item (4)
4 Best-ever achievement (6)
5 Word used with 'neither' (3)
6 Wrecks; thwarts (8)
9 Go up (8)
12 Crooks (7)
13 Modular house (6)
16 Repeated sound of laughter (4)
18 Self-image (3)

# PUZZLE 320

**Across**
1 Demolition (11)
7 Become unhappy (6)
8 Ceases (4)
9 Permit (5)
11 Stench (5)
13 Type of poplar (5)
14 Rewrites (5)
16 Competent (4)
18 Division (6)
20 Disreputable but attractive quality (11)

**Down**
2 Provides the means for (7)
3 To a small extent (3)
4 Tea or coffee dispensers (4)
5 Took out to dinner, eg (7)
6 Funny (3)
10 In a normal state of mind (7)
12 Observes (7)
15 Long-legged wading bird (4)
17 Barnyard sound (3)
19 Mitt Romney's wife (3)

# PUZZLE 321

**Across**

**1** Public declaration of intent (9)
**7** Ruse (5)
**8** Pugilist (5)
**10** Major periods of geological time (4)
**11** Hydrated calcium sulphate (6)
**14** Abrupt (6)
**15** Tiny biting fly (4)
**17** Rolled rice dish (5)
**19** Pivotal (5)
**20** Gallery art (9)

**Down**

**2** Set in correct relative positions (7)
**3** Irritates; annoys (4)
**4** Womb resident (6)
**5** Formal wear (3)
**6** Unbelievers (8)
**9** At a far distance (8)
**12** Transmitting (7)
**13** Not harmful (6)
**16** Vehicle for hire (4)
**18** Aegean, eg (3)

# PUZZLE 322

**Across**

**1** In addition to (5,4)
**7** Small nails (5)
**8** Woolly ruminant (5)
**10** Flour grinder (4)
**11** Book user (6)
**14** Putting in a horizontal position (6)
**15** Greatly (4)
**17** A rather unintelligent person (5)
**19** Natural elevations (5)
**20** Nonsense (9)

**Down**

**2** In the vicinity (7)
**3** Used for smelling (4)
**4** Bathed, perhaps (6)
**5** Casual shirt (3)
**6** Tripped (8)
**9** Bought item (8)
**12** Four-player tennis match (7)
**13** Bury (6)
**16** French 'dear' (4)
**18** Fifth month, in French (3)

# PUZZLE 323

**Across**
3 Cautions (5)
6 Quandary (7)
7 New (5)
8 In a deceitful way (5)
9 Implore (3)
11 Playground seat on chains (5)
13 Sketches (5)
15 Tree with rough, serrated leaves (3)
18 Sudden downwards glide (5)
19 Head coverings (5)
20 Communicates with gestures (7)
21 Sturdy (5)

**Down**
1 Night-time cushion (6)
2 Refuse (7)
3 Wished for (6)
4 All-night dance party (4)
5 River sediment (4)
10 Expanding (7)
12 Highly polished (6)
14 Entirely (6)
16 Persian emperor (4)
17 Wild pig (4)

# PUZZLE 324

**Across**
1 Doing away with (11)
7 Reproduces on a press (6)
8 Indic language closely related to Hindi (4)
9 Muscular (5)
11 Binge (5)
13 Mixes liquid (5)
14 Excessively theatrical (5)
16 Vertical stone semicircle (4)
18 Avoids (6)
20 Rude lack of thanks (11)

**Down**
2 Biggest (7)
3 Board-game playing pieces (3)
4 A bird's home (4)
5 Brass instrument (7)
6 Kate Winslet husband, Rocknroll (3)
10 Also (7)
12 Intellectual (7)
15 Soot particle (4)
17 Sprinted (3)
19 Be seated (3)

# PUZZLE 325

**Across**
- **7** Organizer (11)
- **8** End result (7)
- **9** Female hare (3)
- **10** Slogan (5)
- **12** Steakhouse order (1-4)
- **13** Unpleasant and prolonged noise (3)
- **14** Copy (7)
- **16** Restorative; healing (11)

**Down**
- **1** Make room for (11)
- **2** Plunder (4)
- **3** Based on a set of beliefs (11)
- **4** Amused (11)
- **5** Single-room apartment (6)
- **6** Lack of due respect (11)
- **11** Coloured (6)
- **15** Creative activities (4)

# PUZZLE 326

**Across**
- **1** An official statement (11)
- **7** Male bovine (4)
- **8** Men's hairdresser (6)
- **9** Quality beef cut (5)
- **10** Urge (5)
- **13** Talks to a god (5)
- **15** Capital of Tunisia (5)
- **17** Try out (6)
- **18** Requests (4)
- **19** Contact list (7,4)

**Down**
- **2** Earth's midriff? (7)
- **3** Bedtime song (7)
- **4** Red jewel (4)
- **5** Permeate (5)
- **6** Standards (5)
- **11** Large-leaved edible plant (7)
- **12** Continue doing (5,2)
- **13** Spaghetti, eg (5)
- **14** Ready to fight (5)
- **16** Small barrels (4)

# PUZZLE 327

**Across**

**1** Take for granted (6)
**4** Small fish with sucker (4)
**6** Relating to milk (6)
**7** Demand (4)
**8** Insight (6)
**11** Easy and pleasant (4)
**12** Stitched garment join (4)
**13** Cloister (6)
**16** Pop or folk, perhaps (4)
**17** Not rough (6)
**18** Lyric poems on a particular subject (4)
**19** Nun (6)

**Down**

**1** Luminous (5)
**2** Cults (5)
**3** Includes (11)
**4** Non-specific (7)
**5** Sanctified (7)
**9** Freezing (3-4)
**10** Lawsuit compensation (7)
**14** Approximately (5)
**15** Early anaesthetic (5)

# PUZZLE 328

**Across**

**1** Expects (11)
**7** Camel's protuberance (4)
**8** Develop (6)
**9** Cash registers (5)
**10** Reconnaissance soldier (5)
**13** Spirit or apparition (5)
**15** Type of reptile (5)
**17** Be rude (6)
**18** Behaving uncontrollably (4)
**19** Compelling (11)

**Down**

**2** Provide with healthy food (7)
**3** Pierces with a weapon (7)
**4** Surefooted wild goat (4)
**5** Central body part (5)
**6** Tidied with a brush (5)
**11** Touch (7)
**12** Not familiar (7)
**13** Sorrow (5)
**14** Desert waterhole (5)
**16** Stupefy (4)

# PUZZLE 329

**Across**
**1** Fete (6,5)
**7** Solemn act (4)
**8** Literary term for England (6)
**9** Tolerate (5)
**10** Assists in wrongdoing (5)
**13** Fixes (5)
**15** Look forward to (5)
**17** Coterie (6)
**18** Exertion (4)
**19** Boy or girl in full-time education (11)

**Down**
**2** Friendly (7)
**3** Much feared (7)
**4** Undiluted (4)
**5** Pay increase (5)
**6** Americans, informally (5)
**11** Enthral (7)
**12** Superficial (7)
**13** Staffs of office (5)
**14** Horse's whinny (5)
**16** Narrate (4)

# PUZZLE 330

**Across**
**1** Combining (11)
**7** Straight (4)
**8** Zealously enthusiastic (4-2)
**9** Cleanse (5)
**10** Fittingly (5)
**13** Emotionally insecure (5)
**15** Church songs (5)
**17** Least friendly (6)
**18** Pay attention to (4)
**19** The flow of electrons (11)

**Down**
**2** Cherish (7)
**3** Appeared (7)
**4** Puts sails on a boat (4)
**5** Metal block (5)
**6** Soft and sticky (5)
**11** Seer (7)
**12** Lax (7)
**13** Overly trusting (5)
**14** Banishment (5)
**16** Excitement (4)

# PUZZLE 331

**Across**

1 Chinese philosophy (6)
4 Quick, sharp knocks (4)
6 Inhaler target (6)
7 Aquatic vertebrate (4)
8 Chinese martial art (4,2)
11 Arab military commander (4)
12 A permanent mark (4)
13 Feeding (6)
16 Thwart (4)
17 Morals (6)
18 Slip (4)
19 Drum and bass genre (6)

**Down**

1 Express gratitude (5)
2 Frequently (5)
3 A sampled extent (11)
4 Mirror (7)
5 Fervour (7)
9 Expose (7)
10 Scrambled (7)
14 Celtic language (5)
15 Zest (5)

# PUZZLE 332

**Across**

3 Information (5)
6 Non-fractional value (7)
7 Enter (5)
8 Custom (5)
9 Small, social insect (3)
11 Battle line (5)
13 Performing (5)
15 Female pronoun (3)
18 Lumps of earth (5)
19 Hold responsible (5)
20 Plant also known as lucerne (7)
21 Healthy vegetable dish? (5)

**Down**

1 Not just (6)
2 Quits a job (7)
3 Buddy (6)
4 Handle a situation (4)
5 Position (4)
10 Row of on-screen buttons (7)
12 Yarn (6)
14 Flake out (3,3)
16 Tidal outflows (4)
17 Become less appealing (4)

# PUZZLE 333

**Across**

**1** Kitchen cooking appliance (9)
**7** Cottage (5)
**8** Rubbish (5)
**10** Sleeveless cloak (4)
**11** Religious festival (6)
**14** Warm again (6)
**15** Hawaiian skirt (4)
**17** Refined (5)
**19** May, eg (5)
**20** Puts too much into (9)

**Down**

**2** Highly detailed (2,5)
**3** Mother of Zeus (4)
**4** Surrounded by (6)
**5** By means of (3)
**6** Dynamic; thrilling (8)
**9** Cranial pain (8)
**12** Rendered senseless (7)
**13** Mariner (6)
**16** Gun munitions (4)
**18** West Indian cricketer, Richards (3)

# PUZZLE 334

**Across**

**1** Birthright (11)
**6** Silent-film successor (6)
**7** Podiatrist's expertise (4)
**8** Frown (5)
**11** Indian staple (5)
**12** Regretful (5)
**13** Celestial orbs (5)
**17** Deep breath of relief or sadness (4)
**18** Rich, moist cake (6)
**19** Finishing blow (4,2,5)

**Down**

**1** Tiny bits (5)
**2** Greeting (5)
**3** News article (4)
**4** Culpable (2,5)
**5** Less obscure (7)
**9** Spicy pork sausage (7)
**10** Glorify (7)
**14** Sports stadium (5)
**15** Liquid condiment (5)
**16** Fever (4)

# PUZZLE 335

**Across**

**1** Blue semi-precious stone (5,6)
**7** Original surname (3)
**8** Tuscan red wine (7)
**9** Greek rainbow goddess (4)
**10** Rum cocktail (3,3)
**13** Oily (6)
**14** Audacity (4)
**16** Large retail outlets (7)
**18** Actress, Hurley (3)
**19** Suggested (11)

**Down**

**1** Aircraft wheels (7,4)
**2** Proposition (7)
**3** Ill (4)
**4** Brute (6)
**5** Coffee dispenser (3)
**6** Set up (11)
**11** Followed (7)
**12** Hindu retreat (6)
**15** Tempo (4)
**17** Snapshot (3)

# PUZZLE 336

**Across**

**1** Add to; make complete (10)
**7** Continuous, gradually tightening curve (6)
**8** Message sent to a phone (4)
**9** Polled (5)
**11** Journalistic slant (5)
**13** Small, poisonous snake (5)
**14** Biochemical test (5)
**16** Lampang currency (4)
**18** Erasable writing tool (6)
**20** As predicted (4,6)

**Down**

**2** Against (7)
**3** Average score (3)
**4** Morays, eg (4)
**5** Prolongs (7)
**6** Burden (3)
**10** Voter (7)
**12** Inclination (7)
**15** Blunted fencing weapon (4)
**17** Tough, rigid plastic (init.) (3)
**19** Prefix meaning a revived form (3)

# PUZZLE 337

**Across**

**1** Pay-off (6)
**4** Short burst of wind (4)
**6** Feeling (6)
**7** Not pleasant to look at (4)
**8** Shine brightly and obscure sight (6)
**11** Freezes over (4)
**12** Pageantry (4)
**13** Fourscore (6)
**16** New Zealand bird (4)
**17** Large, chirruping insect (6)
**18** Bully (4)
**19** Slips (6)

**Down**

**1** Fanatical (5)
**2** Formal ballroom dance (5)
**3** Points of contention (11)
**4** Taking a break (7)
**5** Hazel tree (7)
**9** Get rid of (7)
**10** Moving suddenly and rapidly (7)
**14** Got wind of (5)
**15** 'A very long time' (5)

# PUZZLE 338

**Across**

**1** Recalling (11)
**7** Brought about (6)
**8** Is the right size (4)
**9** Tapered roll of tobacco (5)
**11** Give out (5)
**13** Stares lecherously (5)
**14** Concede (5)
**16** Slender woody shoot (4)
**18** Get back (6)
**20** Principal actress (7,4)

**Down**

**2** Deleting (7)
**3** Aurora's Greek equivalent (3)
**4** Chums (4)
**5** Declined (7)
**6** The Web (3)
**10** Exacted retribution (7)
**12** Amalgamated (7)
**15** Pieces of grain husk (4)
**17** Misfortune (3)
**19** Imperial unit of volume (abbr.) (3)

# PUZZLE 339

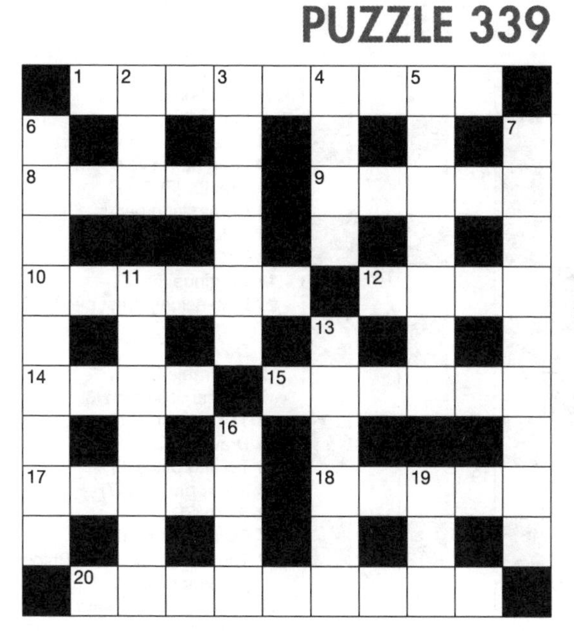

**Across**

**1** Roof apartment (9)
**8** Sibling's daughter (5)
**9** Chief town dignitary (5)
**10** Chooses (6)
**12** Young bovine (4)
**14** Used to secure a door (4)
**15** Paper wallet (6)
**17** Pursue (5)
**18** Sound through the mouth (5)
**20** Marks by using pressure (9)

**Down**

**2** Only just obtain (3)
**3** A score (6)
**4** Units represented by an omega (4)
**5** Towards the heavens (7)
**6** Mental powers (9)
**7** Liked better (9)
**11** Shout out (7)
**13** Figures out (6)
**16** Erode (4)
**19** *South Park* baby (3)

# PUZZLE 340

**Across**

**1** Silhouette (6)
**4** Rear of the human body (4)
**6** The East (6)
**7** Raised floor for a high table (4)
**8** Woman graduate (6)
**11** Like some wines (4)
**12** Oscar-winning actress, Hathaway (4)
**13** Bothering (6)
**16** Penultimate match (4)
**17** Babble (6)
**18** Warm and comfortable (4)
**19** Musical dramas (6)

**Down**

**1** Leaf pore (5)
**2** Farewell (5)
**3** In hope of (4,1,4,2)
**4** Underlying stone (7)
**5** Domestic fowl (7)
**9** Portable lamp (7)
**10** Rendezvous (7)
**14** Deduce (5)
**15** Estimate (5)

# PUZZLE 341

**Across**
**1** Questioningly (11)
**7** Lobbed (6)
**8** Pipe (4)
**9** Long narrative poems (5)
**11** Creator (5)
**13** Committing perjury (5)
**14** Splotch (5)
**16** Keyboard slip-up (4)
**18** Continue (6)
**20** Low-height forest plants (11)

**Down**
**2** Miserable (7)
**3** Animal collection (3)
**4** Taverns (4)
**5** Draw in (7)
**6** Testing place (3)
**10** Xbox, perhaps (7)
**12** Snob (7)
**15** Escarpment (4)
**17** The feminine side, in Chinese philosophy (3)
**19** 'Great Leap Forward' instigator (3)

# PUZZLE 342

**Across**
**1** Shrill; extremely loud (3-8)
**7** *Swan Lake* attire (4)
**8** Son of Zeus (6)
**9** Gloomy and drab (5)
**10** Selects actors (5)
**13** Inheritors (5)
**15** Small fallen branch (5)
**17** Colouring materials (6)
**18** Red-wax-coated cheese (4)
**19** Having measurable length (11)

**Down**
**2** Personally offensive (7)
**3** Sink unblocker (7)
**4** Academic test (4)
**5** Does nothing (5)
**6** Enlarges (5)
**11** Influential 1920s and '30s style (3,4)
**12** Type of keyboard composition (7)
**13** Wished (5)
**14** Colloquialism (5)
**16** Consumes (4)

# PUZZLE 343

**Across**
3 Ronald Reagan's wife (5)
6 From Thailand (7)
7 Ceased (5)
8 Cascades (5)
9 High mountain (3)
11 Corkwood (5)
13 Computer bug (5)
15 Mole (3)
18 'Look happy!' (5)
19 Doctrine (5)
20 Letter; dispatch (7)
21 Hitchhiking gesture (5)

**Down**
1 Acacia tree with yellow flowers (6)
2 Affect favourably (7)
3 Sewing instrument (6)
4 Branching point, in a system (4)
5 *Star Wars* Jedi master (4)
10 Pledge (7)
12 Self-assurance (6)
14 Require (6)
16 Jazz singing style (4)
17 Fashionable young man (4)

# PUZZLE 344

**Across**
1 In the hope of being paid (2,4)
4 Video chats, colloquially (4)
6 A name formed from a name (6)
7 Zero (4)
8 Decorative clothing (6)
11 TV equivalent of an Oscar (4)
12 Entrance lobby (4)
13 Eventually (2,4)
16 Pelt (4)
17 CDEFGABC, perhaps (6)
18 Sums (4)
19 Group of six (6)

**Down**
1 Final Greek alphabet letter (5)
2 Tennis or football (5)
3 Rivals (11)
4 Satisfied (7)
5 Lowest value (7)
9 Expressed gratitude (7)
10 Isolated land masses (7)
14 Not suitable for the situation (5)
15 Chosen (5)

# PUZZLE 345

**Across**
**1** Sucrose (4,5)
**7** Apache abode (5)
**8** *The Metamorphosis* author (5)
**10** Former Rat Pack member, Martin (4)
**11** Leave (6)
**14** Chows down (6)
**15** Baltic Sea river (4)
**17** Flair (5)
**19** Old record (5)
**20** Sent to the printer, perhaps (9)

**Down**
**2** Entreaties (7)
**3** Just about made do (4)
**4** Conservation (6)
**5** Alfred, to his friends (3)
**6** Pupils (8)
**9** In spite of indications to the contrary (5,3)
**12** Firm, as in pasta (2,5)
**13** Happened to (6)
**16** Days before (4)
**18** Not me, but ___ (3)

# PUZZLE 346

**Across**
**1** Chief representative of a country (4,2,5)
**7** Bracket (11)
**8** Traditionally (11)
**13** Moved (11)
**18** Likelihood (11)
**20** Surplus to requirements (11)

**Down**
**2** Source of spam? (5)
**3** Works (5)
**4** Be of the right size and shape for (3)
**5** Eighth Greek letter (5)
**6** Turn around quickly (5)
**9** Quick __ _ flash (2,1)
**10** Female sibling (3)
**11** Pigeon sound (3)
**12** On fire (3)
**14** Perform again (5)
**15** Peer (5)
**16** Actor's parts (5)
**17** Diner (5)
**19** Hive worker (3)

# PUZZLE 347

**Across**
- **1** Scene (9)
- **7** Used a gun (5)
- **8** Be penny-pinching (5)
- **10** Roof overhang (4)
- **11** Small, crawling insect with pincers (6)
- **14** Glob (6)
- **15** Wooded valley (4)
- **17** Two lots of six (5)
- **19** Articles (5)
- **20** Weedkiller (9)

**Down**
- **2** Coming (7)
- **3** Things that fail to work properly (4)
- **4** Offhand (6)
- **5** Twenty-first Greek letter (3)
- **6** Transgressed (8)
- **9** Boxer (8)
- **12** Rest days (7)
- **13** Mix socially (6)
- **16** Metallic element found in brass (4)
- **18** Actress, Wanamaker (3)

# PUZZLE 348

**Across**
- **1** Affectedly self-important (7)
- **5** Steep in liquid (3)
- **7** Opposing social reform (11)
- **8** War-loving fantasy creatures (4)
- **10** Skit (6)
- **12** Treat poorly (6)
- **13** Shape into a curve or angle (4)
- **15** Primitive human (11)
- **17** Largest living deer (3)
- **18** Demonic (7)

**Down**
- **1** Concert (11)
- **2** Emu's extinct relative (3)
- **3** Reveals; exposes (4)
- **4** Offends (6)
- **5** Alarm (7)
- **6** Dazzlingly coloured (11)
- **9** Type of hat named after a Russian people (7)
- **11** Digressions (6)
- **14** Spoilt child (4)
- **16** Early Chinese dynasty (3)

# PUZZLE 349

**Across**
**1** Rising in value (10)
**7** Threefold (6)
**8** Drinks slowly (4)
**9** Like cloud fragments (5)
**11** Does not pass (5)
**13** Ornamental quartz (5)
**14** Learn bit by bit (5)
**16** 'Stop right away!' (4)
**18** Laudable (6)
**20** Courtesy (10)

**Down**
**2** Caring for (7)
**3** Gym unit (3)
**4** The highest point (4)
**5** Place into position (7)
**6** Aperture (3)
**10** Potential problem (7)
**12** Detests (7)
**15** Wally (4)
**17** Trendy (3)
**19** *Harry Potter* character, Weasley (3)

# PUZZLE 350

**Across**
**1** Polished (7)
**5** Email symbols (3)
**7** Start legal proceedings against (3)
**8** Bucket for scrubbing clothes (7)
**9** Of the same type (4)
**10** Coiffure (6)
**12** Acts as monarch (6)
**13** Historical (4)
**15** Louder (7)
**16** Actor, McKellen (3)
**17** Utter (3)
**18** Peculiarity (7)

**Down**
**1** Public eating places (11)
**2** Malleability (11)
**3** Small amphibian (4)
**4** Consternation (6)
**5** Substitute (11)
**6** Functions, in computing (11)
**11** Rainbow colour (6)
**14** Reared (4)

# PUZZLE 351

**Across**

**1** Vocational higher-education institute (11)
**7** Undesirable plant (4)
**8** South American woollen garment (6)
**9** Unmoving (5)
**10** Terrifying people (5)
**13** Fidgety (5)
**15** Vapours (5)
**17** Confusion (6)
**18** Sound from a vehicle horn (4)
**19** Panting (3,2,6)

**Down**

**2** Unfold (4,3)
**3** European Jewish language (7)
**4** Large showcase (4)
**5** More pleasant (5)
**6** Prepares hot food (5)
**11** Complaint (7)
**12** World's highest mountain (7)
**13** The start of a song (5)
**14** Celestial body with a tail (5)
**16** Thrust with a knife (4)

# PUZZLE 352

**Across**

**1** Competes against (7)
**5** Mechanical wheel (3)
**7** Wheeled vehicle (3)
**8** Large wild ox (7)
**9** Dried grape (6)
**10** Knowledgeable about (2,2)
**12** Issue (4)
**13** Most secure (6)
**15** Devour (7)
**16** Rocky peak (3)
**17** Former vocalist, ___ Vicious (3)
**18** Left office (7)

**Down**

**1** Happenings (11)
**2** Divided into regions (11)
**3** Suggest (6)
**4** Not hard (4)
**5** Mail to be sent on to multiple people (5,6)
**6** Affable (4-7)
**11** Evident (6)
**14** Low, continuous vibratory sound (4)

# PUZZLE 353

**Across**

**1** Large northern constellation (9)
**8** Extremely energetic (5)
**9** Not recently cleaned, perhaps (5)
**10** Device for boiling water (6)
**12** Sand ridge (4)
**14** Small amounts, eg of powder (4)
**15** Eavesdrop (6)
**17** Witchcraft (5)
**18** Tropical lizard (5)
**20** Musing (9)

**Down**

**2** Bite sharply (3)
**3** Very seldomly (6)
**4** Fashion or style (4)
**5** Revulsion (7)
**6** Drug bust, perhaps (9)
**7** Via (2,5,2)
**11** Plant of the genus *Nicotiana* (7)
**13** More immense (6)
**16** Hairless (4)
**19** Metal food container (3)

# PUZZLE 354

**Across**

**1** Get into trouble (4,7)
**7** Act as a substitute (4,2)
**8** Comply with (4)
**9** Superman, maybe (4)
**10** Intense dislike (6)
**13** Of the north (6)
**16** Letters (4)
**17** Sea-based armed service (4)
**18** Feature (6)
**19** Self-contained (11)

**Down**

**2** Out and about (2,3,2)
**3** Burst violently (7)
**4** One before tenth (5)
**5** Dark, yellowish-brown colour (5)
**6** Attuned (5)
**11** Enticed (7)
**12** Release (7)
**13** Hindu forehead decoration (5)
**14** Spouted gibberish (5)
**15** Soup spoon (5)

# PUZZLE 355

**Across**

**1** Fit and healthy (4-6)
**7** Tropical forest (6)
**8** Feeling; sensation (4)
**9** Finger bands (5)
**11** Bordered (5)
**13** Cry out loudly (5)
**14** Proficient (5)
**16** Audio repetition (4)
**18** Makes fresh again (6)
**20** Priest's house (10)

**Down**

**2** Bestial (7)
**3** Breakfast item (3)
**4** Crier's cry (4)
**5** Attacked a country (7)
**6** Small amount (3)
**10** Sugar (7)
**12** Authorize (7)
**15** Seize (4)
**17** Bottle top (3)
**19** A word expressing negation (3)

# PUZZLE 356

**Across**

**3** Satan (5)
**6** Pasta envelopes (7)
**7** Suddenly changes course (5)
**8** Masters of ceremonies (5)
**9** Opposite of 'to'? (3)
**11** Eyelashes, eg (5)
**13** Moves like a wheel (5)
**15** Computer emulation (3)
**18** They're white when surrendering (5)
**19** Semiaquatic beaver-like rodent (5)
**20** Schulz comic strip (7)
**21** Fails at (5)

**Down**

**1** Triangular Indian snack (6)
**2** Female siblings (7)
**3** Cause to change course (6)
**4** Competes (4)
**5** Without (4)
**10** Silhouette (7)
**12** Ab crunch exercises (3-3)
**14** Hours of darkness (6)
**16** Crust covering a wound (4)
**17** Stabilizing device (4)

# PUZZLE 357

**Across**
**1** Sway (9)
**8** Called (5)
**9** Relating to a sovereign (5)
**10** Subsequent part (6)
**12** 'Right away!' in hospital (4)
**14** Sad to say (4)
**15** Roman god of fire (6)
**17** Supple (5)
**18** Type of letter (5)
**20** Using (9)

**Down**
**2** Classic object-taking game (3)
**3** Women of good social position (6)
**4** Is mistaken (4)
**5** Puzzling (7)
**6** Remarkably (9)
**7** Openly and unashamedly (9)
**11** A discrete amount of energy (7)
**13** Supply (6)
**16** Remove the skin from (4)
**19** Came first in a race (3)

# PUZZLE 358

**Across**
**3** God or goddess (5)
**6** Italian potato dumplings (7)
**7** Orchestral stringed instrument (5)
**8** Private educator (5)
**9** Dedicated verse (3)
**11** Glow; glimmer (5)
**13** Principle (5)
**15** Garment (3)
**18** Conceals in paper (5)
**19** Jewish teacher (5)
**20** Hotel availability (7)
**21** Slow down (5)

**Down**
**1** One-shot plant (6)
**2** Circus performer (7)
**3** Separate (6)
**4** Hard, magnetic metal (4)
**5** Beijing money (4)
**10** Everlasting (7)
**12** Reason for an action (6)
**14** Effect (6)
**16** Seaside rock pool animal (4)
**17** *Mamma Mia* songwriters (4)

# PUZZLE 359

**Across**
**1** Home confinement (5,6)
**7** Complex projects (11)
**8** Not able to be lessened (11)
**13** Allegations (11)
**18** With awe (11)
**20** Establishing (11)

**Down**
**2** Possessor (5)
**3** Landscape (5)
**4** Installable software (3)
**5** Healing-hands therapy (5)
**6** Bulge (5)
**9** Bird of myth (3)
**10** Type of hacker attack (init.) (3)
**11** Army bed (3)
**12** The story of someone's life (3)
**14** Jester (5)
**15** Below (5)
**16** Grecian column style (5)
**17** Tights material (5)
**19** 'Far out!' (3)

# PUZZLE 360

**Across**
**1** Ceilidh, eg (4,5)
**8** Chief (5)
**9** Arrives (5)
**10** Underground railway (6)
**12** Long song for one voice (4)
**14** Perpetually (4)
**15** Shiny Christmas decoration (6)
**17** Urban areas smaller than cities (5)
**18** Camouflages (5)
**20** Conveyed (9)

**Down**
**2** Entirely (3)
**3** Standard (6)
**4** Moves with a curving trajectory (4)
**5** Photographic equipment (7)
**6** Outlooks (9)
**7** Found (9)
**11** Hive-building material (7)
**13** Things to see (6)
**16** Exploiter (4)
**19** Payable (3)

# PUZZLE 361

**Across**
**3** Not yet grown up (5)
**6** Settle (7)
**7** Burdened (5)
**8** Composed (5)
**9** Maize head (3)
**11** Dork (5)
**13** Popular gadget magazine (5)
**15** Do something bad (3)
**18** Straighten up (5)
**19** Competition reward (5)
**20** Filled, as in a gap (7)
**21** Strolls (5)

**Down**
**1** Semitic language (6)
**2** Glass containers (7)
**3** Fade with age (6)
**4** Revert a computer action (4)
**5** Firing weapons (4)
**10** The study of living organisms (7)
**12** Arm muscles (6)
**14** Large birds of prey (6)
**16** Vomit (4)
**17** Cause the death of (4)

# PUZZLE 362

**Across**
**1** Handsome (4-7)
**7** Rolled tortilla dish (4)
**8** Admission coupon (6)
**9** Massive (5)
**10** Accessory device (3-2)
**13** Loses a layer of skin (5)
**15** Soaked (5)
**17** Not out (2,4)
**18** Spotted-skin disease (4)
**19** A difference from what is expected (11)

**Down**
**2** Feeling great (2,1,4)
**3** Submerged in water (7)
**4** A sworn promise (4)
**5** Miffed (5)
**6** Make progress (3,2)
**11** Large museum scene (7)
**12** Naturally grown (7)
**13** Stretch of short grass (5)
**14** Spiritual character of a group (5)
**16** Selection of hot and cold plates (4)

# PUZZLE 363

**Across**
**1** US pretrial decisions panel (5,4)
**7** Loathes (5)
**8** System of rules (5)
**10** Horrible (4)
**11** Bicycle seat (6)
**14** Unification (6)
**15** An unspoilt paradise (4)
**17** Small, parasitic insect (5)
**19** Oven shelves (5)
**20** Size (9)

**Down**
**2** Codes of ceremonies (7)
**3** Promontory (4)
**4** Gregorian precursor, in terms of calendars (6)
**5** Outfit (3)
**6** Reproachful (8)
**9** Purest (8)
**12** Inferred (7)
**13** Be in power (6)
**16** Formal legal instrument (4)
**18** *Kill Bill* actress, Thurman (3)

# PUZZLE 364

**Across**
**1** Broadcasts (9)
**7** Acknowledged (5)
**8** Chucked (5)
**10** Egyptian river (4)
**11** Sickness (6)
**14** Cushioned (6)
**15** Portent (4)
**17** Knight's weapon (5)
**19** Draws parallel lines (5)
**20** Norms (9)

**Down**
**2** Agitated (7)
**3** Without clothing (4)
**4** Reciprocal (6)
**5** Sailor (3)
**6** Gin-like alcoholic drink (8)
**9** Lack of strength (8)
**12** Tasted (7)
**13** Involving the front of a vehicle (4-2)
**16** Small, black-and-white whale (4)
**18** Habitually, in verse (3)

# PUZZLE 365

**Across**

**7** Overstates (11)
**8** Surface rock formation (7)
**9** Buddy (3)
**10** Repeat in summary (5)
**12** Highways (5)
**13** Large container (3)
**14** Seat with storage within (7)
**16** Regions (11)

**Down**

**1** Weightlessness (4,7)
**2** Role in a play (4)
**3** Fear of open areas (11)
**4** Formulation (11)
**5** Paradise (6)
**6** Lack of ability (11)
**11** Provides a supply of food (6)
**15** Cause permanent damage (4

# PUZZLE 366

**Across**

**3** Worked at a trade (5)
**6** Playful composition (7)
**7** All set (5)
**8** Construct (5)
**9** Stitch an edge (3)
**11** Taken to the air (5)
**13** Jumped into water (5)
**15** Use a needle (3)
**18** VII, to the Romans (5)
**19** Bring down (5)
**20** Luggage (7)
**21** Amusing (5)

**Down**

**1** Real (6)
**2** Senior college members (7)
**3** Transferred (6)
**4** Mosque prayer leader (4)
**5** Segments of the week (4)
**10** Distance travelled (7)
**12** Close at hand (6)
**14** Elan (6)
**16** Dilatory (4)
**17** Smack an insect (4)

# PUZZLE 367

**Across**
**1** Dubious (11)
**7** Modernize (6)
**8** Platform projecting into the sea (4)
**9** City famous for its leaning tower (4)
**10** Chewy sweet (6)
**13** Many-tiered temple (6)
**16** Animal's claw (4)
**17** Authorize (4)
**18** Scottish highland language (6)
**19** Subduing (11)

**Down**
**2** Exact copy (7)
**3** Bluster (7)
**4** Incident (5)
**5** One who steals (5)
**6** Bend (5)
**11** Hand appendages (7)
**12** Omission (7)
**13** Small lakes (5)
**14** Seize (5)
**15** Unwanted pond covering (5)

# PUZZLE 368

**Across**
**1** Figured out (6)
**4** Natural chamber in a cliff (4)
**6** North Pole area (6)
**7** Bottle stopper (4)
**8** Principal taxonomic category (6)
**11** Gaudy (4)
**12** Understood (4)
**13** Almost (6)
**16** Float in the sky (4)
**17** Dickens's Dodger? (6)
**18** Breeding stallion (4)
**19** Pines for something (6)

**Down**
**1** Acute (5)
**2** Fortunate (5)
**3** Factual TV show (11)
**4** Spiral ear cavity (7)
**5** In effect, though not actually (7)
**9** Spend time relaxing (4,3)
**10** Decreased (7)
**14** Send on (5)
**15** Squeals (5)

# PUZZLE 369

**Across**

**1** Celebrity signature, perhaps (9)
**8** Change (5)
**9** Steepness of a roof (5)
**10** Erase (6)
**12** Mouth edges (4)
**14** Single; solitary (4)
**15** Distort; mutilate (6)
**17** Owned person (5)
**18** Endured (5)
**20** Occupiers (9)

**Down**

**2** Hawaiian guitar, informally (3)
**3** Peculiarity (6)
**4** Mature (4)
**5** Placing (7)
**6** Defacing of property, eg (9)
**7** Spoken quietly (9)
**11** Connection (7)
**13** Decorative streaked stone (6)
**16** Bigfoot's cousin? (4)
**19** Tell tales, with 'on' (3)

# PUZZLE 370

**Across**

**1** Mainly (9)
**7** Middle Eastern minced-meat ball (5)
**8** Summoned via a PA system (5)
**10** Young girl (4)
**11** College grounds (6)
**14** Spoke (6)
**15** An equal (4)
**17** Sunset to sunrise (5)
**19** Unhealthily pale (5)
**20** Next to (9)

**Down**

**2** Thumbs down (7)
**3** Alcoholic honey drink (4)
**4** Revoke a law (6)
**5** Captain's journal (3)
**6** Human bones (8)
**9** Wrecks (8)
**12** Pushed down (7)
**13** Hammered (6)
**16** Healthy mineral springs (4)
**18** Apply styling cream to hair (3)

# PUZZLE 371

**Across**

**1** Considerable (11)
**7** Smoothed some shirts, perhaps (6)
**8** Japanese wheat noodles (4)
**9** Seaweed jelly (4)
**10** Corsair (6)
**13** Unwanted pets (6)
**16** Harsh (4)
**17** Relating to water (4)
**18** Respiratory condition (6)
**19** Egyptian symbols (11)

**Down**

**2** Vertically stringed piano (7)
**3** Spanish punch (7)
**4** Work out the total (3,2)
**5** New Delhi country (5)
**6** Thrust (5)
**11** Correctly (7)
**12** Victory (7)
**13** Break (5)
**14** Apply again (5)
**15** Jargon (5)

# PUZZLE 372

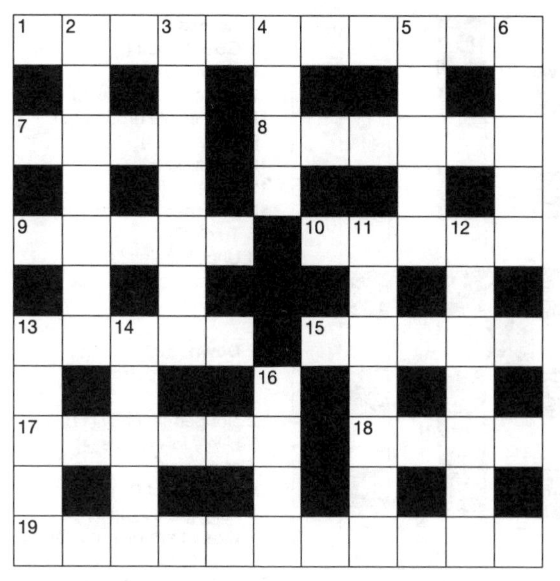

**Across**

**1** Things that cannot be done (11)
**7** Zone (4)
**8** Least wild (6)
**9** Plain rings (5)
**10** Behaved (5)
**13** Fop (5)
**15** Jab (5)
**17** Solicitor (6)
**18** Put footwear on a horse (4)
**19** Visual lacks of balance (11)

**Down**

**2** Final Buddhist goal (7)
**3** Trademarked, eg (7)
**4** Delayed (4)
**5** Ham-fisted (5)
**6** Positioned (5)
**11** Leisure yacht (7)
**12** Surround (7)
**13** River mouth (5)
**14** Not any chance (2,3)
**16** Mild, creamy cheese (4)

# PUZZLE 373

**Across**

**1** Book with a flexible cover (9)
**7** Plunges into water (5)
**8** Subject (5)
**10** Light and breezy (4)
**11** Highly seasoned Italian sausage (6)
**14** Spectacle (6)
**15** Dance unit (4)
**17** Remnant (5)
**19** Females (5)
**20** T-800's mission (9)

**Down**

**2** Hostile (7)
**3** Freedom from worries (4)
**4** Computer graphic (6)
**5** Sporting prize (3)
**6** Next-door (8)
**9** Newspaper snippet (8)
**12** Try (7)
**13** Building with historical exhibits (6)
**16** Graceful, white waterbird (4)
**18** Familiar version of Abraham (3)

# PUZZLE 374

**Across**

**1** Goes to bed (7)
**5** Hound (3)
**7** Brit, to an Aussie (3)
**8** As a single group (2,5)
**9** Capacity (4)
**10** Dropped (6)
**12** Speaker (6)
**13** Unarmed combat sport (4)
**15** Track (7)
**16** Uncertainties (3)
**17** Asian cooking sauce (3)
**18** Nitpickers (7)

**Down**

**1** Bodies of performers' work (11)
**2** Not permanently (11)
**3** Lively folk dance (4)
**4** Monkey (6)
**5** Disenchant (11)
**6** Fully glazed buildings (11)
**11** Close-harmony rock and roll style (3-3)
**14** Coloured some hair, perhaps (4)

# PUZZLE 375

**Across**
**7** Armed police force (11)
**8** Generally (7)
**9** Waggishness (3)
**10** Coronet (5)
**12** Higher (5)
**13** Gear (3)
**14** Sore (7)
**16** Concentrates on a particular area (11)

**Down**
**1** Non-committal attitude (11)
**2** Just the one time (4)
**3** Ice-cream dessert (6,5)
**4** Unlikely (11)
**5** 'Act your age!' (4,2)
**6** Completely plain (11)
**11** Reasoned (6)
**15** Disturb or disconcert (4)

# PUZZLE 376

**Across**
**1** Secret sequences (9)
**8** A photo, eg (5)
**9** Sleazeball (5)
**10** Nefarious computer user (6)
**12** Large, luxury car (4)
**14** Unable to feel (4)
**15** Ensnarl (6)
**17** Gent, informally (5)
**18** Truncated (5)
**20** Conveys an opinion (9)

**Down**
**2** Programming language for critical systems (3)
**3** Filters (6)
**4** 'That hurts!' (4)
**5** Judging (7)
**6** Tool for gutting cod, eg (4,5)
**7** Foes (9)
**11** Complicated (7)
**13** Low singers (6)
**16** Outdoor event with rides (4)
**19** Be in arrears to (3)

# PUZZLE 377

**Across**
**1** Travelling around (11)
**6** Workable; possible (6)
**7** Selects, with 'for' (4)
**8** Stays in a tent (5)
**11** Otherwise known as (5)
**12** Airborne insects (5)
**13** Written with keys (5)
**17** Stare (4)
**18** Spud (6)
**19** Quarrelsome (11)

**Down**
**1** Municipal (5)
**2** Domain (5)
**3** Right to a property to cover a debt (4)
**4** Wheeled shopping cart (7)
**5** Crazy person (7)
**9** At a brisk speed, in music (7)
**10** Current (7)
**14** Instrument with black and white keys (5)
**15** Portals (5)
**16** At the time of (4)

# PUZZLE 378

**Across**
**3** Earnings (5)
**6** Portuguese island (7)
**7** On no occasion (5)
**8** Vacant (5)
**9** Game official (3)
**11** Advertising text (5)
**13** Splits (5)
**15** Common banknote value (3)
**18** Official decree (5)
**19** Polynesian language (5)
**20** Abase (7)
**21** Pointed a light (5)

**Down**
**1** Warm-blooded vertebrate (6)
**2** Go from the beginning again (7)
**3** Roam (6)
**4** Looseness (4)
**5** Browse the Web (4)
**10** Docking cushions (7)
**12** Not relevant to (6)
**14** Come to a conclusion (6)
**16** December holiday, informally (4)
**17** Single-handed (4)

# PUZZLE 379

**Across**
**3** Dense (5)
**6** Obstacle (7)
**7** Backstreet (5)
**8** Better-trained (5)
**9** Zip (3)
**11** Disinterested in your current activity (5)
**13** Existences (5)
**15** It may be alto or tenor (3)
**18** Western Slavic language (5)
**19** Eva Perón (5)
**20** Stumped (7)
**21** Off-limits through social convention (5)

**Down**
**1** The fastest-growing grass (6)
**2** Stays absolutely still (7)
**3** Movement (6)
**4** Troubles (4)
**5** Map legends (4)
**10** Flair (7)
**12** From the top, in music (2,4)
**14** Go beyond (6)
**16** Following straight after (4)
**17** Large tree branch (4)

# PUZZLE 380

**Across**
**3** Stories (5)
**6** Less noisy (7)
**7** Wooden frames for oxen (5)
**8** Type of artichoke (5)
**9** Whichever (3)
**11** Diminutive person (5)
**13** Groove-cutting chisel (5)
**15** Daughter's opposite? (3)
**18** Contemptuous remark (5)
**19** Bracelet attachment (5)
**20** By the time mentioned (7)
**21** Large wall painting (5)

**Down**
**1** Robber; bandit (6)
**2** People in a group (7)
**3** Attempting (6)
**4** Facebook action (4)
**5** Sliding window frame (4)
**10** Not so old (7)
**12** Not casual (6)
**14** Avaricious (6)
**16** Cheat (4)
**17** Whisker (4)

# PUZZLE 381

**Across**

**1** Ascribe (9)
**7** Worn out (5)
**8** Washed out (5)
**10** Motorway junction (4)
**11** Female graduate (6)
**14** Enrol (4,2)
**15** Round handle (4)
**17** Because (5)
**19** Shade of violet (5)
**20** Tens of hundreds (9)

**Down**

**2** Rotating (7)
**3** Fairground amusement (4)
**4** Confuse (6)
**5** Edward, informally (3)
**6** Emphasizes (8)
**9** Hitch (8)
**12** Ruined; spoiled (7)
**13** Writing desk with drawers (6)
**16** Pond organism (4)
**18** Utmost, with 'degree' (3)

# PUZZLE 382

**Across**

**1** Hypnotized (10)
**7** Targeting views (6)
**8** Agrees with the head (4)
**9** Collared garment (5)
**11** Broker (5)
**13** Explosion (5)
**14** Declare (5)
**16** Interrogative question (4)
**18** Retreat (2,4)
**20** Smugly virtuous person (5-5)

**Down**

**2** Intoxicating drink (7)
**3** Soft, flat hat (3)
**4** Excessively curious (4)
**5** This evening (7)
**6** Faulty (3)
**10** An Italian meal made from rice (7)
**12** Saw (7)
**15** Like an omelette, eg (4)
**17** Crone (3)
**19** *Monsters, Inc.* girl (3)

# PUZZLE 383

**Across**
1 Usual behaviours (11)
7 Alcoholic malt drink (4)
8 Gentle (6)
9 Thoughts (5)
10 Metal fastener (5)
13 Trivial (5)
15 Water-raising devices (5)
17 Pleasantly (6)
18 Hue (4)
19 Completely settled (3,3,5)

**Down**
2 Late (7)
3 Different version (7)
4 Catches a fish (4)
5 Command (5)
6 Scatter around (5)
11 Sales table (7)
12 Cost (7)
13 Relating to ancient Carthage (5)
14 Implied (5)
16 Looked at closely (4)

# PUZZLE 384

**Across**
1 Magazine (9)
8 Taxes (5)
9 Loud, in music (5)
10 Grain container (6)
12 500 sheets of paper (4)
14 Sweet, uncovered pie (4)
15 Winter, eg (6)
17 Purchase amount (5)
18 Visual groove (5)
20 Powerlessness (9)

**Down**
2 Liable (3)
3 Sample food (6)
4 Details (4)
5 Planted areas (7)
6 Very typical example (9)
7 Apparently (9)
11 Piece (7)
13 Spoken (6)
16 Parsley or sage (4)
19 Spot (3)

# PUZZLE 385

**Across**

**1** Informative (11)
**7** Plea (6)
**8** Animal skin (4)
**9** Repeating program code (4)
**10** Participant in a game (6)
**13** Woven fibres (6)
**16** Empty space (4)
**17** Fragrant, prickly flower (4)
**18** Tiled picture (6)
**19** Confine; imprison (11)

**Down**

**2** Certificate (7)
**3** Less expensive (7)
**4** Colourful spring flower (5)
**5** Destitute (5)
**6** 'Bye for now' (5)
**11** Counsellor (7)
**12** Snob (7)
**13** Modern Persian tongue (5)
**14** Computer language (5)
**15** Humorous (5)

# PUZZLE 386

**Across**

**1** Become wider (6)
**4** Infant (4)
**6** Rumour (6)
**7** Painful toe problem (4)
**8** Second-largest continent (6)
**11** Article on someone who has just died (4)
**12** Inner being; personality (4)
**13** Deed (6)
**16** The heavenly kingdom (4)
**17** Lots and lots (6)
**18** Eras (4)
**19** Once per annum (6)

**Down**

**1** Doctrine (5)
**2** Cutting light (5)
**3** Descriptive (11)
**4** Withdraw (4,3)
**5** Filled tortilla (7)
**9** Liberating (7)
**10** Very young children (7)
**14** Sluggard (5)
**15** Cruel (5)

# PUZZLE 387

**Across**

**1** Hugely (9)
**7** One hundredth of a rial (5)
**8** Poisonous (5)
**10** Young child's bed (4)
**11** Immobilized (6)
**14** Cleans (6)
**15** Become dim (4)
**17** Step (5)
**19** Call off (5)
**20** Set of working machine parts (9)

**Down**

**2** Humanity (7)
**3** 'Be all ___', to listen eagerly (4)
**4** Lampoon (6)
**5** California airport (init.) (3)
**6** Teaches (8)
**9** Internals (8)
**12** Fervent (7)
**13** Fireside (6)
**16** Notify of danger (4)
**18** Had dinner (3)

# PUZZLE 388

**Across**

**1** Collected body of work (9)
**8** Type of letter-based numeral (5)
**9** Classical language (5)
**10** Space free of matter (6)
**12** Scissor action (4)
**14** Passionate desire (4)
**15** Augustus or Julius (6)
**17** Elegance (5)
**18** Exhibited (5)
**20** Essential (9)

**Down**

**2** Symbol for voltage over current (3)
**3** It's used for licking (6)
**4** Nocturnal birds of prey (4)
**5** Means (7)
**6** Special benefit (9)
**7** Stimulating (9)
**11** Waterfall (7)
**13** Analyses word-by-word (6)
**16** No more than (4)
**19** Available for purchase (3)

# PUZZLE 389

**Across**

**1** Divide into parts (5,4)
**8** Rowing boat crew (5)
**9** Water-park attraction (5)
**10** Measuring the duration of (6)
**12** Above (4)
**14** Astrological transition point (4)
**15** Wry (6)
**17** Glossy (5)
**18** Call (5)
**20** Button press (9)

**Down**

**2** Old piece of cloth (3)
**3** Become receptive (6)
**4** Fine, dry powder (4)
**5** Penned (7)
**6** Whit Sunday (9)
**7** Admired (9)
**11** Extremely large (7)
**13** Grumbling person (6)
**16** Cheats (4)
**19** Acorn-bearing tree (3)

# PUZZLE 390

**Across**

**1** Amendments (11)
**7** Petty quarrel (4)
**8** Surroundings (6)
**9** Gush forth (5)
**10** Expels large quantities of (5)
**13** Sweep (5)
**15** Amplify (5)
**17** Take for granted (6)
**18** Connected (4)
**19** Spectacular (11)

**Down**

**2** In writing (2,5)
**3** Serve responses (7)
**4** Arrived (4)
**5** Small, black, oval fruit (5)
**6** Becomes acidic (5)
**11** Schemed (7)
**12** Cowboy film (7)
**13** Curtain call cry (5)
**14** Overturn (5)
**16** Very large; huge (4)

# PUZZLE 391

**Across**
3 Bogs down (5)
6 Flowering bedding plant (7)
7 Radioactive gas (5)
8 Type of couch (5)
9 *Sound of Music* actress, Karath (3)
11 Insignificant (5)
13 Train tracks (5)
15 Web-browser page view (3)
18 Abhorrence (5)
19 Go and fetch (5)
20 Antagonistic (7)
21 Jobs (5)

**Down**
1 Salt component (6)
2 Fail to fulfil an obligation (7)
3 Kill because of a person's religion (6)
4 Counterpart to 'undo' (4)
5 Crooned (4)
10 Authorization (7)
12 Jokes (6)
14 At a high volume (6)
16 Be next to (4)
17 Pelvic projections (4)

# PUZZLE 392

**Across**
3 Scope (5)
6 Drop away (4,3)
7 Ignites (5)
8 Plain-living US sect (5)
9 Very skilled person (3)
11 Spy (5)
13 Leaves (5)
15 Opposite of min (3)
18 Male admirers (5)
19 Small European island nation (5)
20 Give orders (7)
21 Musical manuscript lines (5)

**Down**
1 Material wealth (6)
2 Flower on a fruit tree (7)
3 Place of business (6)
4 Hide underground (4)
5 'Poppycock!' (4)
10 Degrees (7)
12 Procession of people (6)
14 Reliable (6)
16 Flightless Australian birds (4)
17 Jumping insect that attaches itself to dogs and cats (4)

# PUZZLE 393

**Across**
1 Need (11)
7 Ruffian (4)
8 Domed, spongy cake (6)
9 Barely enough (5)
10 Spotted (5)
13 Engages in fun (5)
15 Expensive (5)
17 Nullify (6)
18 Legatee (4)
19 Confidence in oneself (4-7)

**Down**
2 Above board (7)
3 Insistence (7)
4 Uncastrated male sheep (4)
5 Pixie-like (5)
6 Adjusted pitch (5)
11 Get the latest news, perhaps (5,2)
12 Mournful (7)
13 Kicks (5)
14 Celestial being (5)
16 'Look this way!' (4)

# PUZZLE 394

**Across**
3 Fish displays (5)
6 Not listen accurately (7)
7 Not silently or in a whisper (5)
8 Eagerly sought-after object (5)
9 Writing fluid (3)
11 Thin, flaky biscuit (5)
13 Type of Arctic owl (5)
15 Meat joint (3)
18 Monks' building (5)
19 Unbroken (5)
20 Feel aversion to (7)
21 Pious (5)

**Down**
1 NATO phonetic 'S' (6)
2 Wrinkle without moisture (7)
3 Locomotives (6)
4 Shielded recess (4)
5 Lather (4)
10 Lumpy (7)
12 Put right (6)
14 Broken ships (6)
16 Burglar's booty (4)
17 Off the market (4)

# PUZZLE 395

**Across**

**1** Flight of steps (9)
**8** Additional (5)
**9** A period of time (5)
**10** More experimental, artistically (6)
**12** Voice characteristic (4)
**14** Bedouin (4)
**15** Stupefy (6)
**17** Clock's hourly sound (5)
**18** Pancakes served with sour cream (5)
**20** Model (9)

**Down**

**2** Small amount of alcohol (3)
**3** Likenesses (6)
**4** Hooded monk's habit (4)
**5** Rident (7)
**6** Aptness (9)
**7** Pleasing in appearance (9)
**11** Slow-moving mass of ice (7)
**13** Conflict (6)
**16** A hundredth of a euro (4)
**19** Rascal (3)

# PUZZLE 396

**Across**

**1** Muslim spiritual leader (6)
**4** Shade of dark red (4)
**6** Adoring (6)
**7** Harvest a crop (4)
**8** Cornflakes, eg (6)
**11** Squid juices (4)
**12** Yearn (4)
**13** Teams (6)
**16** In excess of (4)
**17** Two-way switch (6)
**18** Circular movement of water (4)
**19** Clear a river bed (6)

**Down**

**1** Severe abdominal pain (5)
**2** Blood-filter organ (5)
**3** Made visually prominent (11)
**4** Elaborate, columned porch (7)
**5** Burst into laughter (5,2)
**9** Developed (7)
**10** With enthusiasm (7)
**14** Exhorted (5)
**15** Stockholm resident (5)

# PUZZLE 397

**Across**

**1** Emitting light (11)
**7** Persian or Arabian, eg (4)
**8** Haphazard (6)
**9** Fruit liquid (5)
**10** Covered with fine, soft hair (5)
**13** Brief, bright light (5)
**15** Bone framework enclosing the brain (5)
**17** Sufficient (6)
**18** Complain; whinge (4)
**19** Assigning (11)

**Down**

**2** Abnormal (7)
**3** Contaminates (7)
**4** Be worthy of (4)
**5** Senior (5)
**6** Stomach (5)
**11** Dishevelled (7)
**12** Become aware of again (7)
**13** Paddock (5)
**14** Nuclei and electrons (5)
**16** At what time? (4)

# PUZZLE 398

**Across**

**1** Poignant (9)
**8** Glorify (5)
**9** Daily news journal (5)
**10** *Zelda* currency (6)
**12** Advantages (4)
**14** Lion's sound (4)
**15** More plentiful (6)
**17** Gaze fixedly (5)
**18** 'L'-size clothing (5)
**20** Foolishness (9)

**Down**

**2** 'Give __ _ break!' (2,1)
**3** Names (6)
**4** Accident exclamation (4)
**5** Garments (7)
**6** One who maims and kills for a cause (9)
**7** Maintains (9)
**11** Rustic labourer (7)
**13** Beamed (6)
**16** Jump (4)
**19** Long and deep track (3)

# PUZZLE 399

**Across**

**1** Misfortunes (11)
**7** Very short hairstyle (4)
**8** Mix-up (6)
**9** Persistent worry (5)
**10** States firmly (5)
**13** Touch or taste (5)
**15** Source of rain (5)
**17** Not clever (6)
**18** Eden resident? (4)
**19** Without any question (6,5)

**Down**

**2** Drive insane (7)
**3** Reveals (7)
**4** Cesspool (4)
**5** Not belonging to a major label (5)
**6** Plants grow from them (5)
**11** Lava emitter (7)
**12** Background actor's noise (7)
**13** Small firework (5)
**14** Freshly (5)
**16** Often, with 'to' (4)

# PUZZLE 400

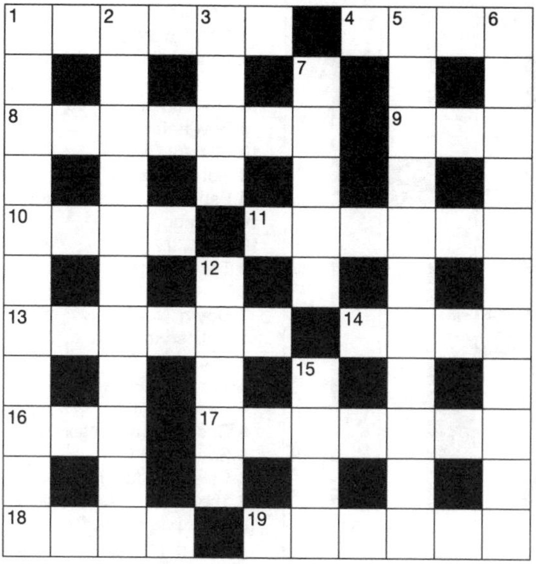

**Across**

**1** Workers' groups (6)
**4** Bend the ___, to submit (4)
**8** Ended (3,4)
**9** Chafe (3)
**10** Shrub (4)
**11** Sire (6)
**13** Nepalese soldier (6)
**14** 'Tee hee' (2,2)
**16** Elect (3)
**17** Timetable units (7)
**18** Chutzpah (4)
**19** Biochemical tests (6)

**Down**

**1** Clear (11)
**2** Exemplifies (11)
**3** Main body of a basilica (4)
**5** Its capital is Bismarck (5,6)
**6** Discomfits (11)
**7** Anomalous (5)
**12** Sales outlets (5)
**15** Mineral-rich rocks (4)

# PUZZLE 401

**Across**

**1** Pointing in the right direction (11)
**7** Painful emotion (4)
**8** Depressed area (6)
**9** Gimmick (5)
**10** Fragment (5)
**13** Outer part of bread (5)
**15** Precipice (5)
**17** Positive aspect of a situation (6)
**18** Feeling; atmosphere (4)
**19** Burials (11)

**Down**

**2** Nuclear power generator (7)
**3** Motors (7)
**4** Pulls (4)
**5** Entomb (5)
**6** Gather (5)
**11** Montage (7)
**12** To start with (2,5)
**13** Principle to be committed to (5)
**14** Not yet hardened (5)
**16** Action word (4)

# PUZZLE 402

**Across**

**1** Magic word (11)
**7** London theatre, The Old ___ (3)
**8** From an Eastern continent (7)
**9** Bow notch (4)
**10** Ship (6)
**13** Not uniform (6)
**14** Band travel, perhaps (4)
**16** Exterior (7)
**18** Punt (3)
**19** Technical (11)

**Down**

**1** Inclined to explore (11)
**2** Use again (7)
**3** Outdoor garment (4)
**4** Chauffeur (6)
**5** Cricketing essential (3)
**6** Sped up (11)
**11** Celebrity life (7)
**12** The Twins constellation (6)
**15** Back part of the foot (4)
**17** Foot digit (3)

# PUZZLE 403

**Across**

**1** Bulging (11)
**6** Cloister (6)
**7** Explosive munition (4)
**8** Requirements (5)
**11** Domestic servants (5)
**12** Not as good (5)
**13** Compassion (5)
**17** Credit-card provider (4)
**18** Emotional shock (6)
**19** Store vendor (11)

**Down**

**1** Sow (5)
**2** Happen (5)
**3** Taught alongside birds? (4)
**4** Enclosing wall of the chest (7)
**5** Wandering (7)
**9** Imported curios (7)
**10** Slip-up (7)
**14** Utterly defeats (5)
**15** Feel wistful (5)
**16** Cease (4)

# PUZZLE 404

**Across**

**1** Like countryside drives (6)
**4** Remunerated (4)
**6** Deadly (6)
**7** Resentment (4)
**8** Five-star (6)
**11** Gross; unpleasant (4)
**12** Cans (4)
**13** Not quite (6)
**16** Having an acid taste (4)
**17** Large tropical lizard (6)
**18** Responsibility (4)
**19** Works of fiction (6)

**Down**

**1** Vends (5)
**2** Clear your plate (3,2)
**3** Party (11)
**4** Insurance payment (7)
**5** Conjures up (7)
**9** Mythical one-horned animal (7)
**10** Guarantees (7)
**14** Egg-shaped (5)
**15** Groups of players (5)

# PUZZLE 405

**Across**

**1** Minor part in a drama (4-2)
**4** Ski equipment (4)
**6** Jabber (6)
**7** Globes (4)
**8** Release from anxiety (6)
**11** Observe (4)
**12** Messed around (4)
**13** Indulgence (6)
**16** Bring bad luck on (4)
**17** Someone assembling a film (6)
**18** Bradley, to his friends (4)
**19** Olfacts (6)

**Down**

**1** Bet (5)
**2** Identifying piece of paper (5)
**3** A state of requiring help (11)
**4** Legendary bird (7)
**5** Marine crustacean (7)
**9** Less full (7)
**10** Catalogued (7)
**14** Before (5)
**15** Fenced areas (5)

# PUZZLE 406

**Across**

**1** Persuasive speech (9)
**8** Gentle push (5)
**9** He lives in a lamp (5)
**10** Tore (6)
**12** Flat-topped hill, in the US (4)
**14** Terrible fate (4)
**15** Displacement (6)
**17** Hearten (5)
**18** Robbery (5)
**20** Lawyers (9)

**Down**

**2** Preceded (3)
**3** Canada's oldest city (6)
**4** This being the case (4)
**5** Admit to (7)
**6** Acquaint (9)
**7** Wreak havoc on (9)
**11** Defend (7)
**13** Woollen shawl (6)
**16** Triumvirate (4)
**19** Evergreen climbing plant (3)

# PUZZLE 407

**Across**

**1** Temporary framework (11)
**7** Soothing, as of sound (6)
**8** Cougar (4)
**9** Hence (4)
**10** Refreshed (6)
**13** Lie in an ungainly way (6)
**16** Tuber (4)
**17** Extremely large (4)
**18** Accept as true (6)
**19** Exciting (11)

**Down**

**2** Expel from the lungs (5,2)
**3** Pendulous ornamental shrub (7)
**4** Semiaquatic weasel (5)
**5** Eskimo (5)
**6** Stately (5)
**11** A large snake (7)
**12** Gradual destruction (7)
**13** Rescues (5)
**14** Swiss grated potatoes dish (5)
**15** Handy pub (5)

# PUZZLE 408

**Across**

**1** Approach (6)
**4** Jedi outfit? (4)
**6** Assassin (6)
**7** Head-louse eggs (4)
**8** Pope's envoy (6)
**11** What can be seen right now (4)
**12** Division of a school year (4)
**13** Imperilled (2,4)
**16** 'Z' in radio communication (4)
**17** Force through (6)
**18** Sheet of ice (4)
**19** Unpleasant sounds (6)

**Down**

**1** Memento (5)
**2** Punctuation mark (5)
**3** Company (11)
**4** Exceed (3,4)
**5** Pesters (7)
**9** Not the same (7)
**10** Calculate (7)
**14** Statues of gods (5)
**15** Kicks with the middle of the leg (5)

# PUZZLE 409

**Across**

**1** Roughly correct (11)
**6** Mass prayer (6)
**7** Something that shouldn't be done (2-2)
**8** Historical period (5)
**11** Consent (5)
**12** Fantastic (5)
**13** Copper and zinc alloy (5)
**17** Division of an educational course (4)
**18** The thing in question (6)
**19** Experts (11)

**Down**

**1** Disagree (5)
**2** Real-life picture (5)
**3** Bag examination (1-3)
**4** Boss (7)
**5** Digs a passageway (7)
**9** Cream-coloured root vegetable (7)
**10** Disordered (7)
**14** Regions (5)
**15** Secure deposit boxes (5)
**16** Code word for the letter 'L' (4)

# PUZZLE 410

**Across**

**3** Grand dances (5)
**6** North-west African country (7)
**7** Better informed (5)
**8** Rigid (5)
**9** Drinking vessel (3)
**11** Muffler (5)
**13** Edible, freshwater fish (5)
**15** Ungainly boat (3)
**18** Horse (5)
**19** Relating to the ear (5)
**20** Simplest (7)
**21** Arrange in tiers (5)

**Down**

**1** Resembling verse (6)
**2** Solace (7)
**3** Withdraw from a role (3,3)
**4** Defeat (4)
**5** Father (4)
**10** Meat, fish or dairy (7)
**12** More complete (6)
**14** On edge (6)
**16** Lock up for a crime (4)
**17** Worship (4)

# PUZZLE 411

**Across**

**1** Bounded (6)
**4** Collections (4)
**6** Sea forces (6)
**7** Flirtatious girl (4)
**8** Musical speed reversion (1,5)
**11** Animal flank (4)
**12** Mend by stitching (4)
**13** Madden (6)
**16** Garden party (4)
**17** Encroach upon (6)
**18** Farewells (4)
**19** Malodorous (6)

**Down**

**1** Government after a coup (5)
**2** Film (5)
**3** Revelations (11)
**4** Having a resemblance (7)
**5** Providing care (7)
**9** Calamity (7)
**10** Long-tailed primates (7)
**14** Take advantage of (5)
**15** All possible (5)

# PUZZLE 412

**Across**

**1** Poor excuse (3-3)
**4** Deep, round dish (4)
**6** In a dormant state (6)
**7** Viscous fuel liquids (4)
**8** Agriculturist (6)
**11** Cupid's Greek counterpart (4)
**12** Fissure (4)
**13** Sixteenths of a pound (6)
**16** British singer who duetted with Eminem (4)
**17** Damage (6)
**18** Hair colourers (4)
**19** Financial returns (6)

**Down**

**1** Worthless leftovers (5)
**2** Arctic, eg (5)
**3** Most important (3,8)
**4** Relating to binary algebra (7)
**5** Greeting (7)
**9** Skill (7)
**10** Techniques (7)
**14** Barbaric (5)
**15** Appears (5)

# PUZZLE 413

**Across**

1 Winning all 13 tricks, in bridge (5,4)
8 Garret (5)
9 Perfect interval, in music (5)
10 Admission (6)
12 Land measure (4)
14 Be a couch potato (4)
15 Part of a larger group (6)
17 Exit (5)
18 Breakfast strip (5)
20 Painting (9)

**Down**

2 Baloney (3)
3 Most pleasant (6)
4 Secure storage box (4)
5 Influences (7)
6 Analogous things (9)
7 Jeopardizes (9)
11 Sort (7)
13 Amount (6)
16 Gripped (4)
19 Gyp (3)

# PUZZLE 414

**Across**

1 Ask questions (11)
7 Involving vocal parts (4)
8 Small laugh (6)
9 Series of links (5)
10 Worries (5)
13 Traditional stories (5)
15 Scam (5)
17 Nonsense (6)
18 Parched (4)
19 System of analysis (11)

**Down**

2 Disobedient, as a child (7)
3 What this is written in (7)
4 Great anger (4)
5 Prophet (5)
6 Levels (5)
11 Type of international post (7)
12 Avoiding, as in danger (7)
13 PC–phone interface (5)
14 Turnabout (5)
16 Clothed (4)

# PUZZLE 415

**Across**
**1** Fawning (11)
**6** Highest point (6)
**7** Spanish carmaker (4)
**8** Jab (5)
**11** Small fairy (5)
**12** Worship (5)
**13** Pare (5)
**17** Large plant with a trunk (4)
**18** Irrational aversion (6)
**19** Think about (11)

**Down**
**1** Bog (5)
**2** Appoint someone king or queen (5)
**3** Long-handled gardening tools (4)
**4** More horrible (7)
**5** Roman or Milanese, eg (7)
**9** Experience (7)
**10** 'Right answer' (7)
**14** Dark sunspot centre (5)
**15** Uplift (5)
**16** Tinned meat product (4)

# PUZZLE 416

**Across**
**3** Lower-value banknote (5)
**6** Aerial (7)
**7** Overlaid map enlargement (5)
**8** Be deserving of (5)
**9** Elderly (3)
**11** 'Things' (5)
**13** Adolescence (5)
**15** Realize (3)
**18** Tempest (5)
**19** Stallion (5)
**20** Acutely (7)
**21** Combat engagement (5)

**Down**
**1** Pump in (6)
**2** Notions (7)
**3** Evenly (6)
**4** It may be bulletproof? (4)
**5** 'Dash!' (4)
**10** Physicians (7)
**12** Least (6)
**14** Hard-shelled sea animal (6)
**16** Professional cook (4)
**17** Two-masted square-rigged ship (4)

# PUZZLE 417

**Across**
**1** Yearly celebration (11)
**7** Small piece of cloud (4)
**8** Metal used in wires (6)
**9** Belonging to them (5)
**10** Examines closely (5)
**13** Quality rating (5)
**15** Bodily sacs (5)
**17** Handkerchief alternative (6)
**18** Horse's gait (4)
**19** 'That was easy' (5,2,4)

**Down**
**2** Not the one nor the other (7)
**3** Tacit (7)
**4** Every one (4)
**5** Brightest star in a constellation (5)
**6** Threads (5)
**11** Type of crossword (7)
**12** The internet, eg (7)
**13** Style of dress (3-2)
**14** Type of aeroplane seat (5)
**16** Nevada gambling resort (4)

# PUZZLE 418

**Across**
**1** Intense beams of light (6)
**4** Go against (4)
**6** Handy (6)
**7** Beat (4)
**8** Noble (6)
**11** Is indebted to (4)
**12** Worry incessantly (4)
**13** Baby (6)
**16** Opposite of manual (4)
**17** Less tough (6)
**18** Sunday to Saturday (4)
**19** Primary painting colour (6)

**Down**
**1** React to a joke, perhaps (5)
**2** Sully (5)
**3** With careful discrimination (11)
**4** Step away (4,3)
**5** Involve (7)
**9** On the way (2,5)
**10** Microsoft email application (7)
**14** Pivotal (5)
**15** Hurl (5)

# PUZZLE 419

**Across**

**1** Display explosives (9)
**8** Internal (5)
**9** Toy named after Theodore Roosevelt (5)
**10** Quoting (6)
**12** Free from wind (4)
**14** Attention-gaining interjection (4)
**15** Dusk (6)
**17** Hand covering (5)
**18** Mushrooms, eg (5)
**20** Collaborate (9)

**Down**

**2** Charged molecule (3)
**3** Prone to mistakes (6)
**4** Cereal commonly used for food (4)
**5** Abducts (7)
**6** Acquittal (9)
**7** The same on both sides (9)
**11** Wavering singing effect (7)
**13** Feel pain (6)
**16** Central tower of a castle (4)
**19** Fruit with a hard shell (3)

# PUZZLE 420

**Across**

**1** Attainment (11)
**7** Charity for the poor (4)
**8** Hazy and polluted (6)
**9** Once and then again (5)
**10** Located (5)
**13** Traverse (5)
**15** Young dog (5)
**17** Each of two (6)
**18** Waiter's carrier (4)
**19** Making a copy of (11)

**Down**

**2** Former Soviet bloc hostilities (4,3)
**3** Bugs (7)
**4** Jar for holding flowers (4)
**5** Boundaries (5)
**6** Played, as in with an idea (5)
**11** Marine (7)
**12** Justify (7)
**13** Obvious (5)
**14** Readily available (2,3)
**16** Cartoon character, Flintstone (4)

# PUZZLE 421

**Across**

3 Bubbly (5)
6 Briefer (7)
7 Dissolve (5)
8 Breezy (5)
9 Trigonometry function (abbr.) (3)
11 Loud kiss (5)
13 Square or circle (5)
15 Bronze (3)
18 Posts (5)
19 Tablets (5)
20 Practical, not theoretical (7)
21 Captures (5)

**Down**

1 Church-rite oil (6)
2 Result of multiplication (7)
3 Painting borders (6)
4 Area (4)
5 Cry out (4)
10 Tattily (7)
12 Dorothy's home (6)
14 Hauled (6)
16 Small mark (4)
17 Strong criticism (4)

# PUZZLE 422

**Across**

1 Remaining joined together (11)
6 Fertilized ovum (6)
7 Those people (4)
8 Elements (5)
11 Zagreb native (5)
12 Propose (5)
13 No longer a child (5)
17 Knitted covering for the hand (4)
18 Italian sandwiches (6)
19 Unfriendly (3-8)

**Down**

1 Unfasten (5)
2 Darling (5)
3 Again (4)
4 Changed (7)
5 Examine up close (7)
9 Avoiding group interactions (7)
10 Contorted (7)
14 Constituent items (5)
15 Bronze medal position (5)
16 Monkeys (4)

# PUZZLE 423

**Across**
**1** Measure of data flow (9)
**7** Sets of cards (5)
**8** Contorts (5)
**10** Thick string (4)
**11** Mistreats (6)
**14** Ocular (6)
**15** High-water mark; climax (4)
**17** Tortilla-chip topping (5)
**19** Covered on the inside (5)
**20** Skill (9)

**Down**
**2** Agrees to (7)
**3** Fading evening light (4)
**4** Drink (6)
**5** Heavy unit of weight (3)
**6** Authorizes (8)
**9** Bars temporarily (8)
**12** Additional helpings (7)
**13** Be in charge of (6)
**16** Conspire (4)
**18** Unit of illumination (3)

# PUZZLE 424

**Across**
**1** Leaping (9)
**7** Snap (5)
**8** Fix software (5)
**10** Coupled (4)
**11** Christ's teaching (6)
**14** Morals (6)
**15** University teacher (4)
**17** Entice (5)
**19** Clues (5)
**20** Large musical group (9)

**Down**
**2** Ancient Egyptian king (7)
**3** Pen-stained (4)
**4** Male child sponsored at a baptism (6)
**5** Central point (3)
**6** Critical trial step (4,4)
**9** Common decorative carp (8)
**12** Associate (7)
**13** Put an end to (6)
**16** Not that, but ___ (4)
**18** Disfigure (3)

# PUZZLE 425

**Across**

1 Oversight (11)
6 South American river (6)
7 New Testament book (4)
8 Vapour (5)
11 Drinking tube (5)
12 Stumbles (5)
13 Stranger (5)
17 Heroic tale (4)
18 It neutralizes an acid (6)
19 Limitations (11)

**Down**

1 Chairs and benches (5)
2 Time without war (5)
3 Transport vehicles (4)
4 Initiated (7)
5 Appalling act (7)
9 Whirlwind (7)
10 Emerges (7)
14 Careworn (5)
15 Debris (5)
16 Den (4)

# PUZZLE 426

**Across**

1 Pulls away (9)
8 Municipal chief (5)
9 Non-reflective paint finish (5)
10 Amend (6)
12 Excite (4)
14 Gradient (4)
15 Rubber (6)
17 Contemptible person (5)
18 Not as many (5)
20 Assembly (9)

**Down**

2 Frigid (3)
3 Religious dissent (6)
4 Pantheon home (4)
5 Portable timepieces (7)
6 Make self-conscious (9)
7 College teachers (9)
11 Kingston's island (7)
13 Like better (6)
16 Engage a gearwheel (4)
19 Success (3)

# PUZZLE 427

| | 1 | 2 | | 3 | | 4 | | 5 | | |
|---|---|---|---|---|---|---|---|---|---|---|
| 6 | | | | | | | | | | |
| 7 | | | | | | 8 | | | | 9 |
| | | | | | | | | | | |
| 10 | | | | | 11 | | | 12 | | |
| | | | | 13 | | | | | | |
| 14 | | | | | | | 15 | | | |
| | | | | | | 16 | | | | |
| 17 | | 18 | | | | 19 | | | | |
| | | | | | | | | | | |
| | 20 | | | | | | | | | |

**Across**

**1** Sweetener (9)
**7** Temporary hold (5)
**8** Swindle (5)
**10** Ornamental church partition (4)
**11** Smart (6)
**14** Flavours (6)
**15** Layer of dirt (4)
**17** Automaton (5)
**19** Desktop graphics (5)
**20** Depot (9)

**Down**

**2** Brain cells (7)
**3** Flat and smooth (4)
**4** Take on (6)
**5** Struggle for superiority (3)
**6** User (8)
**9** Italian dessert (8)
**12** Mindless (7)
**13** Type of flying insect (6)
**16** Thousandth of a tonne (4)
**18** Deadly snake (3)

# PUZZLE 428

| 1 | | 2 | | | 3 | | 4 | | 5 | |
|---|---|---|---|---|---|---|---|---|---|---|
| | | | | | | | | | | |
| 6 | | | | | | | 7 | | | |
| | | | | | | | | | | |
| 8 | 9 | | 10 | | | 11 | | | | |
| | | | | | | | | | | |
| 12 | | | | | | 13 | | 14 | | 15 |
| | | | | | 16 | | | | | |
| 17 | | | | | 18 | | | | | |
| | | | | | | | | | | |
| 19 | | | | | | | | | | |

**Across**

**1** Unable to hear a thing (4,2,1,4)
**6** Repeatedly pester (6)
**7** Out of town (4)
**8** Burning stick (5)
**11** Insolent (5)
**12** Get up from sitting (5)
**13** Prolonged pain (5)
**17** Belonging to the reader (4)
**18** Pestilent disease (6)
**19** Not joined (11)

**Down**

**1** Opposite of credit (5)
**2** Common birch-family tree (5)
**3** Feudal slave (4)
**4** Talking to a god (7)
**5** Hone (7)
**9** Obsolete (7)
**10** Play with vigour, musically (3,4)
**14** Is expected (5)
**15** Cede (5)
**16** Turned around quickly (4)

# PUZZLE 429

**Across**
- **3** Maddening (5)
- **6** Island in the Mediterranean (7)
- **7** Conceal (5)
- **8** Utter joy (5)
- **9** Strength-training muscle (3)
- **11** Caper (5)
- **13** Muse (5)
- **15** Work at, as a trade (3)
- **18** Indoor throwing game (5)
- **19** Self-evident truth (5)
- **20** Tedium (7)
- **21** Microsoft co-founder, Bill (5)

**Down**
- **1** Collapse, as a roof eg (4,2)
- **2** Adore (7)
- **3** Carton (6)
- **4** File a digital document (4)
- **5** Long, rambling story (4)
- **10** Defrauded (7)
- **12** Goes up a ladder (6)
- **14** Idea (6)
- **16** Suspend (4)
- **17** Present (4)

# PUZZLE 430

**Across**
- **3** Minded (5)
- **6** Proclaim (7)
- **7** Snoops (5)
- **8** Hirsute (5)
- **9** Public-transport vehicle (3)
- **11** Carrying out (5)
- **13** Bound edge of a book (5)
- **15** Talk at length (3)
- **18** Prolonged sleep (3-2)
- **19** Member of the camel family (5)
- **20** Underwater eye protection (7)
- **21** Emblem (5)

**Down**
- **1** Italian-style ice cream (6)
- **2** Staring with hostility (7)
- **3** Official population count (6)
- **4** Thorny-stemmed flower (4)
- **5** Short race (4)
- **10** Leaps quickly (7)
- **12** Building to park cars in (6)
- **14** Less experienced (6)
- **16** Smooth-tongued (4)
- **17** Extol (4)

# PUZZLE 431

**Across**
**1** Senior manager (9)
**8** Fertile desert area (5)
**9** Walked back and forth (5)
**10** Legally responsible (6)
**12** Sustained medical blackout (4)
**14** Sensible (4)
**15** Came to a halt (6)
**17** Filthy (5)
**18** Muslim body covering (5)
**20** Butt in (9)

**Down**
**2** Greek letter 'X's (3)
**3** Fortress (6)
**4** Upper clothing items (4)
**5** Aircraft courses (7)
**6** Globally (9)
**7** Post-Victorian (9)
**11** One who loses by some distance (4-3)
**13** One who belongs to a group (6)
**16** Pile of wood for burning a body (4)
**19** Criticize sharply (3)

# PUZZLE 432

**Across**
**1** In addition (11)
**7** Performs brilliantly (4)
**8** Hot spring that sprays upwards (6)
**9** Reinstall (5)
**10** Sorceress (5)
**13** Exodus plague (5)
**15** Oxygenating bodily fluid (5)
**17** One-off (6)
**18** Quiet; gentle (4)
**19** Biasing (11)

**Down**
**2** Not easy to see (7)
**3** Sampling (7)
**4** Nervous (4)
**5** Beginning (5)
**6** Ground (5)
**11** Relating to the Muslim religion (7)
**12** Draw near (5,2)
**13** Dowdy woman (5)
**14** Chilled (2,3)
**16** Bawdy (4)

# PUZZLE 433

**Across**

**1** Features (10)
**7** Basic (6)
**8** Immediately following (4)
**9** Least good (5)
**11** Bides (5)
**13** In accordance with (2,3)
**14** Befuddle (5)
**16** Out of control (4)
**18** Belonging to a foreign culture (6)
**20** Amount per hundred (10)

**Down**

**2** Clothes fitters (7)
**3** Tear in a piece of paper (3)
**4** Burst (4)
**5** Ale holder? (7)
**6** Half a dozen (3)
**10** One who is talking (7)
**12** Particularly revealing (7)
**15** Fantastical animal prefix (4)
**17** Plan (3)
**19** Very warm (3)

# PUZZLE 434

**Across**

**1** Defuse tension through honesty (5,3,3)
**6** Primarily (6)
**7** Coins and notes (4)
**8** Thespian (5)
**11** Central Las Vegas area (5)
**12** Grind teeth (5)
**13** Maxim (5)
**17** Pepsi rival (4)
**18** More horrible (6)
**19** With great importance (11)

**Down**

**1** Bottom half of a semicolon (5
**2** Expel (5)
**3** Lego and Barbie (4)
**4** Enthusiastic (7)
**5** Supplying (7)
**9** With motion, musically (3,4)
**10** Offensive (7)
**14** Vinegar and lemon juice (5)
**15** Primitive (5)
**16** Small clump of bushes (4)

# PUZZLE 435

**Across**

**1** Not specialized (11)
**7** The weight of something (4)
**8** Colourful hair accessory (6)
**9** Hurried (5)
**10** Snatches (5)
**13** Kitchen frothing device (5)
**15** Farewell (5)
**17** Reside in (6)
**18** Obsessive fad (4)
**19** Famous individual (11)

**Down**

**2** Mascara target (7)
**3** Lands (7)
**4** Away from the expected course (4)
**5** Horse-like African mammal (5)
**6** Feasts (5)
**11** Very different to the norm, as an opinion (7)
**12** Pamphlet (7)
**13** Cry of excitement (5)
**14** Become subject to (5)
**16** Religious song (4)

# PUZZLE 436

**Across**

**1** Rhythmic vibration (11)
**7** Hospital room (4)
**8** Dash (6)
**9** Representative (5)
**10** Skips over (5)
**13** Native of Bern (5)
**15** Pointed, as an angle (5)
**17** South-west European peninsula (6)
**18** Public official's cry (4)
**19** 'Start right away!' (3,8)

**Down**

**2** Type of songbird (7)
**3** Lookup tables (7)
**4** Strike with a whip (4)
**5** Hip bone (5)
**6** Musical sounds (5)
**11** Reveal (7)
**12** Template (7)
**13** Insect wound (5)
**14** Static (5)
**16** Hot molten rock (4)

# PUZZLE 437

**Across**

**1** Alarming; scary (4-7)
**6** Persons in general (6)
**7** Gesture without words (4)
**8** Dance music (5)
**11** Merry (5)
**12** Used up (5)
**13** Juicy, stoneless fruit (5)
**17** Henry VIII's final wife, Katherine (4)
**18** Came back down to earth (6)
**19** Fatty food substance (11)

**Down**

**1** Wished (5)
**2** Presses clothes (5)
**3** Greek god of war (4)
**4** This or that person (7)
**5** More spry (7)
**9** Charge with misconduct (7)
**10** Regulate (7)
**14** Aircraft detection system (5)
**15** Warble (5)
**16** Beers (4)

# PUZZLE 438

**Across**

**1** Gestation (9)
**8** More recent (5)
**9** Type of bodily sense (5)
**10** Without difficulty (6)
**12** After that (4)
**14** Earl Greys, perhaps (4)
**15** Hydrated calcium sulphate (6)
**17** Salt water (5)
**18** Commenced (5)
**20** Hobbies (9)

**Down**

**2** Brawl (3)
**3** Distort (6)
**4** Pretentious (4)
**5** Pressed-fruit drinks (7)
**6** Inflatable hose inside a tyre (5,4)
**7** Wonders (9)
**11** There is one on each edge in Monopoly (7)
**13** 'See you!' (3-3)
**16** 'All your base are belong to us', eg (4)
**19** Understand (3)

# PUZZLE 439

**Across**
7 Picking apart (11)
8 Large, flightless bird (7)
9 2001 film, *Shallow* ___ (3)
10 At the side of (5)
12 Roman marketplace (5)
13 Remained still (3)
14 Some different person (7)
16 Participation (11)

**Down**
1 Student grant (11)
2 Scottish dress skirt (4)
3 Furniture to eat at (6,5)
4 Nimble (5-6)
5 Better off (6)
6 Gather together (11)
11 A stanza of eight lines (6)
15 Shades (4)

# PUZZLE 440

**Across**
3 Circular (5)
6 Computer (7)
7 Malice (5)
8 Pixie (5)
9 Drink a mouthful (3)
11 'A long way' (5)
13 Wear away (5)
15 Artificial colour (3)
18 Carefully consider (5)
19 Playing card, perhaps (5)
20 Stir up (7)
21 Male admirers (5)

**Down**
1 Bush travel (6)
2 Enamoured (7)
3 Save (6)
4 What Linux is based on (4)
5 Fight between two people (4)
10 Vicars (7)
12 Grammar (6)
14 Fingers (6)
16 Freshwater, ray-finned fish (4)
17 Large celebration (4)

# PUZZLE 441

**Across**

**1** Similar, interchangeable items (11)
**6** Fluster (6)
**7** Essential email action (4)
**8** Assist a diner, maybe (5)
**11** Greek island (5)
**12** Glow (5)
**13** Modify (5)
**17** Supplication (4)
**18** Mummify (6)
**19** Translated (11)

**Down**

**1** Makes (5)
**2** Articulate (5)
**3** Nays' opposites (4)
**4** Guaranteed (7)
**5** Sleeveless pullover (4,3)
**9** Command level (7)
**10** Year of wine production (7)
**14** Separated by distance (5)
**15** Measured with a stopwatch (5)
**16** Non-permanent worker (4)

# PUZZLE 442

**Across**

**1** Financial protection (9)
**8** Measuring device (5)
**9** Child's toy figure (5)
**10** Itemized (6)
**12** Magical power (4)
**14** Long narrow strip of fabric (4)
**15** College treasurer (6)
**17** Imbibed (5)
**18** Sting (5)
**20** Has (9)

**Down**

**2** Louse's egg (3)
**3** Uncoil (6)
**4** Assists (4)
**5** Insensitive (7)
**6** Breadth; range (9)
**7** Dissembler (9)
**11** Highest singing voice (7)
**13** Visitors (6)
**16** Travels down a snowy hill, perhaps (4)
**19** Wide street (abbr.) (3)

# PUZZLE 443

**Across**
**1** Really badly (11)
**7** Woven container (6)
**8** Fill up (4)
**9** Halts (5)
**11** Student bar orders (5)
**13** Any old how (2,3)
**14** Unable to proceed (5)
**16** 'Scram!' (4)
**18** Opposite of input (6)
**20** Destroy (11)

**Down**
**2** Placed in the ground (7)
**3** Diving seabird (3)
**4** Plucked stringed instrument (4)
**5** Just beginning to exist (7)
**6** Auction item (3)
**10** Exasperate (7)
**12** Enrol (7)
**15** Microphone arm (4)
**17** Evil spell (3)
**19** Metallic element (3)

# PUZZLE 444

**Across**
**1** Emanating (11)
**6** Walk like a baby (6)
**7** Travel here and there (4)
**8** Cabs (5)
**11** Last testaments (5)
**12** Small, thin pieces (5)
**13** 'Balderdash!' (2,3)
**17** An unmarried woman (4)
**18** Llama relative (6)
**19** Improvement (11)

**Down**
**1** Group of eight things (5)
**2** Reference listing (5)
**3** Repeated refusals (4)
**4** Greatly frighten (7)
**5** An unfamiliar thing (7)
**9** Extremely stupid (7)
**10** Deadlock (7)
**14** Shirk (5)
**15** Precise (5)
**16** Creamy coleslaw ingredient (4)

# PUZZLE 445

**Across**

**1** Coders (11)
**7** Spanish Surrealist artist (4)
**8** Teat (6)
**9** Maltreat (5)
**10** Kept an engine running (5)
**13** Moves like a tree (5)
**15** Member of a travelling people (5)
**17** Walk softly (6)
**18** Was obligated to pay money (4)
**19** Failing to notice (11)

**Down**

**2** Colourful sky display (7)
**3** Extremely (7)
**4** Parent's sister (4)
**5** Evict (5)
**6** Splash cash, perhaps (5)
**11** Boat-repair site (3,4)
**12** Oriental (7)
**13** Get started with gusto (3,2)
**14** Popular computer manufacturer (5)
**16** Nothing (4)

# PUZZLE 446

**Across**

**1** Blamelessness (9)
**8** Insert (5)
**9** Belief system (5)
**10** Underline (6)
**12** Coffee (4)
**14** Not very big at all (4)
**15** Text format settings (6)
**17** Type of letter (5)
**18** Abba musical, ___ *Mia!* (5)
**20** Recipient (9)

**Down**

**2** The tip of a pen (3)
**3** Earliest (6)
**4** Mark a pattern onto glass (4)
**5** White pool sphere (3,4)
**6** Empathetic (9)
**7** And so on and so on (2,7)
**11** Rejuvenated (7)
**13** Impresses down upon (6)
**16** Make indistinct (4)
**19** Graduate education degree (init.) (3)

# PUZZLE 447

**Across**

**1** Depress (5,4)
**7** Publish (5)
**8** Fruit known as 'St John's bread' (5)
**10** Line about which a body rotates (4)
**11** Debt or obligation evader (6)
**14** Made a note of (6)
**15** Mentioned (4)
**17** Single figure (5)
**19** Arm joint (5)
**20** Concerning (2,7)

**Down**

**2** Destroying (7)
**3** Cuckoo (4)
**4** Medical professional (6)
**5** Armed conflict (3)
**6** Horrified (8)
**9** Destroy with fire (4,4)
**12** Snatched (7)
**13** Chesterfield (6)
**16** Actress, Catherine ___-Jones (4)
**18** Not a solid or liquid (3)

# PUZZLE 448

**Across**

**3** Measured (5)
**6** Handicap (7)
**7** Fatuous (5)
**8** Trust (5)
**9** Beverley, to her friends (3)
**11** Timber beam (5)
**13** Flower used for making chains (5)
**15** 'That's right' (3)
**18** Church council (5)
**19** Supply (5)
**20** Adolescent (7)
**21** Recreation areas (5)

**Down**

**1** Gilbert and Sullivan work, *The* ___ (6)
**2** Illusion (7)
**3** Grabbed (6)
**4** Ardour (4)
**5** Attracted (4)
**10** Altering (7)
**12** Entices (6)
**14** Lackey (6)
**16** Rope fibre (4)
**17** Cat sound (4)

# PUZZLE 449

**Across**

**1** Development (11)
**6** Bovine animals (6)
**7** Bearing; manner (4)
**8** Pledged (5)
**11** Tongue of fire (5)
**12** Goods-transport vehicle (5)
**13** Candid (5)
**17** Cool and funky (slang) (4)
**18** Blood vessel (6)
**19** Completely on-message official? (11)

**Down**

**1** Opts (5)
**2** Exceed (5)
**3** Vision organs (4)
**4** Less complex (7)
**5** Supply too many staff (7)
**9** Combat vessel (7)
**10** Type of soft cheese (7)
**14** First Hebrew letter (5)
**15** Light-framed Inuit boat (5)
**16** Polynesian shrub used for narcotics (4)

# PUZZLE 450

**Across**

**1** With free will (11)
**7** Waterways (6)
**8** Bawls (4)
**9** Gaze fixedly (5)
**11** Artist's protective wear (5)
**13** Instruct morally (5)
**14** Appended (5)
**16** Snowy, barn and long-eared, eg (4)
**18** Not these (6)
**20** A wish that is unlikely to come true (7,4)

**Down**

**2** Skipped (7)
**3** Native American tribe (3)
**4** Large, protruding tooth (4)
**5** Began again (7)
**6** Throw in a high arc (3)
**10** Rejection (7)
**12** Become brighter (5,2)
**15** Coarse, ill-mannered person (4)
**17** Seek the hand of (3)
**19** 'What?' (3)

# PUZZLE 451

**Across**

**1** Bouncing apparatuses (11)
**7** Available for business (4)
**8** Unborn offspring (6)
**9** Suspends (5)
**10** Hurt (5)
**13** Animal groups (5)
**15** Make law (5)
**17** Nasty person, informally (6)
**18** Full of fear (4)
**19** Non-existence (11)

**Down**

**2** Supersede (7)
**3** Coped (7)
**4** Cooking range (4)
**5** 'Upward' compass point (5)
**6** Knight's weapon (5)
**11** Incorporate (7)
**12** Surpasses (7)
**13** Sentient mammal (5)
**14** Severely reprimand (5)
**16** Gradually withdraw (4)

# PUZZLE 452

**Across**

**1** Dislike of everyone (11)
**6** Misgivings (6)
**7** Aim; desired result (4)
**8** Brief error (5)
**11** Navy (5)
**12** Trivial (5)
**13** Collide (5)
**17** Chicken (4)
**18** Bury (6)
**19** Wrongly (11)

**Down**

**1** Example (5)
**2** Baffle (5)
**3** USSR news agency (4)
**4** Usual (7)
**5** Musicians (7)
**9** Middle-Eastern horse (7)
**10** Soap for washing your hair (7)
**14** Roughly (5)
**15** Small falcon (5)
**16** Taunt (4)

# PUZZLE 453

**Across**

**1** Pennies, eg (5,6)
**7** Gradually develop, as an event (6)
**8** Teeny (4)
**9** Crazy (4)
**10** Without any detour (6)
**13** Grazing area (6)
**16** Adds, with 'up' (4)
**17** Fortifying ditch (4)
**18** In flames (6)
**19** Squeezing (11)

**Down**

**2** Banal (7)
**3** Large spotted cat (7)
**4** Encrypted (5)
**5** Clueless (5)
**6** Be alive (5)
**11** Baby toys (7)
**12** Inhabitant (7)
**13** Imitate (5)
**14** Warning sound (5)
**15** Large marine mammal (5)

# PUZZLE 454

**Across**

**1** Too expensive (10)
**7** Wrongdoings (6)
**8** Cattle (4)
**9** Before all the others (5)
**11** Exceptionally small (5)
**13** Bore (5)
**14** Purloin (5)
**16** Vessel (4)
**18** Stopped (6)
**20** Arrange to work together effectively (10)

**Down**

**2** Decision (7)
**3** Odd; peculiar (3)
**4** Go quickly; hurry (4)
**5** Most faithful (7)
**6** Number cube (3)
**10** Eighth sign of the zodiac (7)
**12** Least distance way (7)
**15** African country (4)
**17** Involuntary drunken sound (3)
**19** *Underworld* director, Wiseman (3)

# PUZZLE 455

**Across**

**1** Accusations (11)
**7** Storage tower (4)
**8** Feature (6)
**9** Bend (5)
**10** Poetic lament (5)
**13** Large animal (5)
**15** Grim (5)
**17** Thinly dispersed (6)
**18** Small loaf of bread (4)
**19** Assume control (4,3,4)

**Down**

**2** Relaxation (7)
**3** Develops (7)
**4** Assistant to someone of import (4)
**5** Speak (5)
**6** Briny (5)
**11** Precise (7)
**12** Powerful ape, found in central Africa (7)
**13** Plague (5)
**14** Towards the rear (archaic) (5)
**16** 'All right, then' (4)

# PUZZLE 456

**Across**

**1** Victims (9)
**7** Flow control (5)
**8** Greek sorceress (5)
**10** Affluent (4)
**11** Long-legged wading bird (6)
**14** No specific people (6)
**15** Head and shoulders sculpture (4)
**17** Get pleasure from (5)
**19** Wept (5)
**20** Parsing again (9)

**Down**

**2** Unfortunate (7)
**3** Touch (4)
**4** Take away (6)
**5** Divest (3)
**6** Succeeded in dealing with (8)
**9** Height (8)
**12** Warning (7)
**13** Amylase or protease, eg (6)
**16** Defeated with a serve (4)
**18** Coffee (slang) (3)

# PUZZLE 457

**Across**
1 Russian sub-machine gun (11)
6 Tooth covering (6)
7 Discontinued (4)
8 Cattle-catching noose (5)
11 Thick slice of meat (5)
12 Military unit (5)
13 Writes with a keyboard (5)
17 Abrupt, high-pitched ring (4)
18 Citrus fruit (6)
19 Cardiac arrest (5,6)

**Down**
1 Prepare to pray, perhaps (5)
2 Lots (5)
3 Cease moving (4)
4 Unsuitably (7)
5 Run (7)
9 Obtain (7)
10 Lurch (7)
14 Black-and-white, bear-like animal (5)
15 Move furtively (5)
16 Bright star (4)

# PUZZLE 458

**Across**
1 Groundwork (11)
6 Extent (6)
7 Animal doctors (4)
8 Old Ottoman title (5)
11 Bank official (5)
12 Transport (5)
13 Telephone ring sounds (5)
17 Relinquish (4)
18 Exaggerate (6)
19 Choices (11)

**Down**
1 Had enough; frustrated (3,2)
2 Encourages (5)
3 Claim (4)
4 Entail (7)
5 Without artificial additives (7)
9 Non-professional (7)
10 That woman, personally (7)
14 Poetic (5)
15 Reduces speed (5)
16 Dispense a liquid (4)

# PUZZLE 459

**Across**
1 Via unknown means (7)
5 Mouse antagonist? (3)
7 Mire (3)
8 Recipe (7)
9 Same-aged sibling (4)
10 Shoves (6)
12 Clans (6)
13 Medical torpor (4)
15 Table support (7)
16 Beer (3)
17 Morse-code symbol (3)
18 Lacking (7)

**Down**
1 Exchanged (11)
2 Glorious (11)
3 Express petty annoyance (4)
4 Prepare for exercise (4,2)
5 Idle TV watcher (5,6)
6 Clear (11)
11 Confer (6)
14 Attractively well-shaped, as a body part (4)

# PUZZLE 460

**Across**
1 Exaggerated theatrics (9)
7 Spoken (5)
8 Item (5)
10 Info (slang) (4)
11 Complete disaster (6)
14 Fall asleep (3,3)
15 Conflicted (4)
17 Obliterate (5)
19 Not tails (5)
20 Judgements (9)

**Down**
2 Broke free (7)
3 Greasy (4)
4 The sale of goods (6)
5 Me, in French (3)
6 Proof (8)
9 Virtue (8)
12 Holding space (7)
13 Result (6)
16 The face below the mouth (4)
18 Bowl over (3)

# PUZZLE 461

**Across**

**1** Emphasizing (11)
**6** Imperfect (6)
**7** Large amount of material (4)
**8** Educate (5)
**11** Desiccated (5)
**12** Fisherman's bait? (5)
**13** Wind instrument (5)
**17** Window ledge (4)
**18** Looks forward to (6)
**19** Inexplicable (11)

**Down**

**1** Not suitable (5)
**2** Play (5)
**3** Metallic vein (4)
**4** Figure (7)
**5** Most prying (7)
**9** Strong feeling (7)
**10** Intricate (7)
**14** Merger (5)
**15** Abated (5)
**16** High (4)

# PUZZLE 462

**Across**

**1** Realizing (11)
**6** Place of worship (6)
**7** Distillery drums (4)
**8** Cheerful (5)
**11** Small, quick meal (5)
**12** Insane (5)
**13** Minds (5)
**17** A Yucatán Indian (4)
**18** Less at ease (6)
**19** Of the late 16th century (11)

**Down**

**1** Relating to the Netherlands (5)
**2** Repeat the main points (3,2)
**3** Sudden direction change (4)
**4** Retaliation (7)
**5** Observed (7)
**9** Type of international post (7)
**10** Flair; glamour (7)
**14** Horse's whinny (5)
**15** Alluring but dangerous woman (5)
**16** 'Doing' part of speech (4)

# PUZZLE 463

**Across**

**1** Pledge (11)
**6** Soil (6)
**7** A simple wooden structure (4)
**8** Move rhythmically (5)
**11** Military exercise (5)
**12** Nut from an oak tree (5)
**13** Fully aligned (5)
**17** Child's word for their mother (4)
**18** Map key (6)
**19** Accept (11)

**Down**

**1** Exhorted (5)
**2** Submerge (5)
**3** Neat (4)
**4** Small falcon (7)
**5** Sewing tools (7)
**9** Antiquated (7)
**10** Sure (7)
**14** Flip over (5)
**15** Equivocate, perhaps (5)
**16** Travelled through the air (4)

# PUZZLE 464

**Across**

**1** Amount permitted (9)
**8** Suggest (5)
**9** Food product made by bees (5)
**10** Bikes (6)
**12** Second Greek letter (4)
**14** Tea, ___ Grey (4)
**15** Black magic (6)
**17** Connected hotel rooms (5)
**18** US marsh (5)
**20** European nobleman (5,4)

**Down**

**2** Edge (3)
**3** Breathing gas (6)
**4** Hurting all over (4)
**5** Vie (7)
**6** Head honcho (3,6)
**7** Jewish house of worship (9)
**11** Bearer (7)
**13** Prohibit (6)
**16** Embroidered (4)
**19** Talk persistently (3)

# PUZZLE 465

**Across**

**1** Serving error in tennis (6,5)
**6** Revolve (6)
**7** Spring-loaded bouncing pole (4)
**8** Enquire (5)
**11** Tall tree with shiny bark (5)
**12** Nail-file material (5)
**13** Not fresh, perhaps (5)
**17** Brief written message (4)
**18** Elaborately ornamental style (6)
**19** Essentially (11)

**Down**

**1** Classic column style (5)
**2** Disentangle (5)
**3** Shepherd's women? (4)
**4** Assign (7)
**5** Reasoned (7)
**9** Masculine pronoun (7)
**10** Deteriorate (7)
**14** Positive electrode (5)
**15** Black piano-key wood (5)
**16** Mild expression of annoyance (4)

# PUZZLE 466

**Across**

**1** Periodical's sales (11)
**7** Relating to the eyes (6)
**8** 10th- to 12th-century Chinese dynasty (4)
**9** Rough whirring sound (4)
**10** Rarely encountered (6)
**13** A direction and magnitude (6)
**16** Dispatched (4)
**17** Shower (4)
**18** Angry mood (6)
**19** Making too full (11)

**Down**

**2** Comprise (7)
**3** Guilty person (7)
**4** Lies in wait (5)
**5** Less friendly (5)
**6** Not a single person (2,3)
**11** Supposed (7)
**12** Doom (7)
**13** Sixth zodiac sign (5)
**14** Serious wrongdoing (5)
**15** Proportion (5)

# PUZZLE 467

**Across**
**1** Complainant (9)
**8** Searches (5)
**9** Wrong (5)
**10** Nailed (6)
**12** Perplex with a problem (4)
**14** Buddy (4)
**15** Inexpensive restaurant (6)
**17** External toilet (5)
**18** Distasteful riches (5)
**20** Take to task (5,4)

**Down**
**2** Unisex first name (3)
**3** Releases (6)
**4** Upper-class twit (4)
**5** Complete (4,3)
**6** Duplicate piece of paper (9)
**7** Evolved (9)
**11** Messenger (7)
**13** Eliminated (6)
**16** Free passes, in sport (4)
**19** Harsh bird cry (3)

# PUZZLE 468

**Across**
**3** Rescued (5)
**6** Below (7)
**7** Frosting (5)
**8** Wander (5)
**9** Beer cask (3)
**11** Bride's counterpart (5)
**13** Discount events (5)
**15** Veto (3)
**18** Shy (5)
**19** Walk (5)
**20** Parts (7)
**21** Christmas-card adjective (5)

**Down**
**1** Superior (6)
**2** Ten-sided polygon (7)
**3** Glows (6)
**4** Futile (4)
**5** Uses a spade, perhaps (4)
**10** Region of ancient Palestine (7)
**12** Noon (6)
**14** Removes from a property (6)
**16** Elemental particle (4)
**17** Grizzly or polar, eg (4)

# PUZZLE 469

**Across**
3 Registered (5)
6 Sun umbrella (7)
7 Continuing for ages (2,3)
8 Ancient Roman language (5)
9 'Definitely!' (3)
11 Adult girl (5)
13 Follow after (5)
15 Covering (3)
18 Involuntary muscle contraction (5)
19 Ascend (5)
20 Book-lending location (7)
21 Steered a car (5)

**Down**
1 Repeat from the start, in music (2,4)
2 Washington DC, eg (7)
3 A piece of cauliflower (6)
4 Welsh national emblem (4)
5 Ineffectual people (4)
10 Get ready (7)
12 Agile (6)
14 Put in (6)
16 Move fast, like clouds (4)
17 Hello; goodbye (4)

# PUZZLE 470

**Across**
1 Relating to government by men (11)
7 Oxtail, eg (4)
8 Thin cotton cloth (6)
9 Priest (5)
10 Unfolds (5)
13 Thorax (5)
15 Large, soft feather (5)
17 Instructed (6)
18 Basis for cheese (4)
19 Study of digital circuits (11)

**Down**
2 Do away with (7)
3 Says again (7)
4 Military force (4)
5 Split in two (5)
6 Brings in (5)
11 Large-billed waterbird (7)
12 Made up of digits (7)
13 Attractive young woman (5)
14 Evade (5)
16 Celebrity (4)

# PUZZLE 471

**Across**
1 All people (9)
7 Double-deckers, eg (5)
8 Melodies (5)
10 Catches in the act (4)
11 Like a movie (6)
14 Excessively (6)
15 Run away (4)
17 Meagre (5)
19 Odd (5)
20 Suggest (9)

**Down**
2 Perceptible (7)
3 Healthy-looking, as skin (4)
4 Interrupt (4,2)
5 Put on (3)
6 Deserts (8)
9 Follows (8)
12 A thousand thousand (7)
13 Very drunk (slang) (6)
16 Moved in the sea (4)
18 Copy (3)

# PUZZLE 472

**Across**
3 Incensed (5)
6 Ancient city on the Euphrates (7)
7 Offspring (5)
8 Sheep's cry (5)
9 Small bang (3)
11 Terror (5)
13 Buckles (5)
15 Waterless (3)
18 Not quite right (5)
19 Plant barb (5)
20 Advice (7)
21 Expanse of sand (5)

**Down**
1 Spanish rice dish (6)
2 Ancient Egyptian monument (7)
3 All over the place (6)
4 Larva (4)
5 Indian style of meditation (4)
10 Money given for goods (7)
12 Biscuit-eating sound (6)
14 Shoved (6)
16 Stump (4)
17 Common soft drink (4)

# PUZZLE 473

**Across**
**1** Deletion key (9)
**8** Burdened (5)
**9** Windscreen cleaner (5)
**10** Wired-up (6)
**12** Tablet (4)
**14** Ship (4)
**15** Motto (6)
**17** Become less tense (5)
**18** Christian writings (5)
**20** Disclosing (9)

**Down**
**2** Conjunction word (3)
**3** Dog shelter (6)
**4** Church benches (4)
**5** Repeating (7)
**6** Dark-plumaged songbird (9)
**7** Extended (9)
**11** Writing for the blind (7)
**13** Worldwide (6)
**16** Rod through the centre of a wheel (4)
**19** Storage container (3)

# PUZZLE 474

**Across**
**1** Bias (9)
**8** Wanderer (5)
**9** Type of cereal plant (5)
**10** Undiscovered (6)
**12** Pursue on horseback, perhaps (4)
**14** Train that runs along roads (4)
**15** Dwellings (6)
**17** Nastier (5)
**18** Myanmar (5)
**20** Peak viewing period (5,4)

**Down**
**2** Butt (3)
**3** Deems (6)
**4** Soft and lustrous, as skin (4)
**5** Angels (7)
**6** Instinctive (9)
**7** Skilled, elder politician (9)
**11** Not as big (7)
**13** Bear-like, burrowing marsupial (6)
**16** Small shot of spirits (4)
**19** Periphery (3)

# PUZZLE 475

**Across**
1 Formal meetings (11)
7 Stellar (6)
8 Gaelic language (4)
9 Greek letter following alpha (4)
10 Basically; plainly (6)
13 Imperfection (6)
16 Far side (4)
17 Just (4)
18 Commendation (6)
19 Advancing (11)

**Down**
2 Offensive (7)
3 Prohibited (7)
4 Functions (5)
5 Muscle pain (5)
6 Threescore (5)
11 Human beings (7)
12 Contact (7)
13 Sag (5)
14 Page number in a printed book (5)
15 Native American tent (5)

# PUZZLE 476

**Across**
1 Habit (6)
4 Former Venetian magistrate (4)
6 Large Asian sheep (6)
7 Core of a being (4)
8 Brewing crockery (6)
11 Travelled by horse (4)
12 Agile (4)
13 Secure against possible loss (6)
16 Exclamation of surprise (4)
17 Ask to an event (6)
18 Meander (4)
19 Avaricious (6)

**Down**
1 Plot (5)
2 Mathematical summation symbol (5)
3 Preserving (11)
4 Wants (7)
5 Fail as a business (2,5)
9 Burst violently (7)
10 Full of anticipation (7)
14 Join (5)
15 The other side (5)

## PUZZLE 477

**Across**
- **1** Oddly (9)
- **8** Fits of anger (5)
- **9** Musical style (5)
- **10** Foil (6)
- **12** Japanese syllabic writing system (4)
- **14** A die, eg (4)
- **15** Film theatre (6)
- **17** Metal point (5)
- **18** Biblical tower (5)
- **20** Know again (9)

**Down**
- **2** Label (3)
- **3** Claim (6)
- **4** Binds the mouth of (4)
- **5** Ancestry (7)
- **6** Disapproval (9)
- **7** Open to question (9)
- **11** internet service (7)
- **13** London clock tower (3,3)
- **16** Danish toy company (4)
- **19** Top-level business domain (3)

## PUZZLE 478

**Across**
- **1** Ecclesiastic chess piece (6)
- **4** Confront (4)
- **6** Skin image (6)
- **7** Chemistry work areas (4)
- **8** Perform (6)
- **11** Fat (4)
- **12** Instructive notice (4)
- **13** Combined (6)
- **16** Lots (4)
- **17** Variant chemical arrangement (6)
- **18** Company; flock (4)
- **19** Slick (6)

**Down**
- **1** Snapping animal, perhaps (5)
- **2** Type of silky material (5)
- **3** Scheduling (11)
- **4** Be fooled by (4,3)
- **5** Garden vegetable (7)
- **9** Personification (7)
- **10** Ming or Qing (7)
- **14** *Pac-Man* and *Mario Bros* (5)
- **15** Unclean (5)

# PUZZLE 479

**Across**
1 Quest (6)
4 Huge (4)
6 Materialize (6)
7 Wave for a taxi (4)
8 Deliver a sermon (6)
11 Upper-case letters (4)
12 Deal; covenant (4)
13 Fashions (6)
16 Existence (4)
17 Together (2,4)
18 Swindles (4)
19 Unpowered aircraft (6)

**Down**
1 Payment on an envelope (5)
2 Plentiful (5)
3 Pulling no punches (4-7)
4 Car or aeroplane (7)
5 Dispatched (7)
9 Without hesitation (7)
10 Relevance (7)
14 Well-known (5)
15 First-rate (5)

# PUZZLE 480

**Across**
1 Daughter of Henry VIII (9)
7 Fermented grape juice drinks (5)
8 Brush (5)
10 Work hard (4)
11 Salt counterpart (6)
14 Impressive golf scores, perhaps (6)
15 Active person (4)
17 More secure (5)
19 Celebration (5)
20 Trademark (5,4)

**Down**
2 Joining (7)
3 Grated orange peel (4)
4 Strikes hard (6)
5 Office neckwear (3)
6 Chirrups (8)
9 Represents (8)
12 Computer software (7)
13 Nerve cell (6)
16 Duration (4)
18 Razor target (3)

# PUZZLE 481

**Across**
**1** Infinitesimally small (6)
**4** Physical piece of money (4)
**6** Improve (6)
**7** Musical, ___ *and Dolls* (4)
**8** Money case (6)
**11** Compatriot (4)
**12** Noticed (4)
**13** Violation (6)
**16** Buck (4)
**17** Consecrate a priest (6)
**18** Go against (4)
**19** Things to see (6)

**Down**
**1** Shot from a bow (5)
**2** Waste from a carcass (5)
**3** End up fighting (4,2,5)
**4** Related (7)
**5** Peaceful and picturesque (7)
**9** Overhead projector sheet (7)
**10** Prolonged (7)
**14** Embarrass (5)
**15** Finger holders? (5)

# PUZZLE 482

**Across**
**1** Dissimilarly (11)
**7** Fairly (6)
**8** Cover (4)
**9** Jumps a rope (5)
**11** Tally (5)
**13** Common European viper (5)
**14** Employing (5)
**16** Wireless internet (2-2)
**18** Gain (6)
**20** Series of road junctions (11)

**Down**
**2** Conjured up (7)
**3** Amusement (3)
**4** Shafts of light (4)
**5** Beginners (7)
**6** Hawaiian floral garland (3)
**10** Exact (7)
**12** Overseeing, as a company (7)
**15** *The Odyssey*, eg (4)
**17** Former cricketer, Botham (3)
**19** Eggs (3)

# PUZZLE 483

**Across**
**1** Knowledgeable people (11)
**7** Meadow (3)
**8** Evolve (7)
**9** Conceal (4)
**10** Champagne and juice drink (6)
**13** Helping (6)
**14** Judo ranking item (4)
**16** Contacts (7)
**18** PC exit key (3)
**19** Anxiety-causing (11)

**Down**
**1** Lacking warmth and affection (4-7)
**2** Protected (7)
**3** Probabilities (4)
**4** Give way under pressure (4,2)
**5** Nada (3)
**6** Not realistic (11)
**11** Alone, by ___ (7)
**12** Object dropped by a ship in port (6)
**15** Questions (4)
**17** Good moments (3)

# PUZZLE 484

**Across**
**1** Indian spice mix (6)
**4** Manager (4)
**6** Awful (6)
**7** Type of gemstone (4)
**8** Island containing Tokyo (6)
**11** Dunce (4)
**12** Former Indian coin (4)
**13** Casts (6)
**16** Fleshy cheek (4)
**17** Ordinary (6)
**18** Sudden impact (4)
**19** Was audibly wistful (6)

**Down**
**1** Fire starter (5)
**2** Give rise to (5)
**3** Bookkeepers (11)
**4** Wider (7)
**5** Drink some liquid (7)
**9** Score against yourself, in soccer (3,4)
**10** Lacking depth (7)
**14** Zing (5)
**15** Not liquid or gaseous (5)

# PUZZLE 485

**Across**

**1** Indigestion pain in the chest (9)
**8** Those currently logged on (5)
**9** Slightly falsify (5)
**10** Photo collections (6)
**12** A mark from a wound (4)
**14** Prompted an actor (4)
**15** Chase (6)
**17** Bread maker (5)
**18** Falsely implicate in a crime (5)
**20** Still the same (9)

**Down**

**2** Afore, poetically (3)
**3** Continue (6)
**4** Yellowish-beige colour (4)
**5** Shortens (7)
**6** Tea sweetener (5,4)
**7** Fetches (9)
**11** Burglary (5-2)
**13** Small, cup-shaped cake (6)
**16** Bend into a curve (4)
**19** Lincoln, colloquially (3)

# PUZZLE 486

**Across**

**1** Backless sofa that doubles as a bed (6,5)
**7** Clothing fastener (6)
**8** Metallic vein (4)
**9** Witchcraft (5)
**11** Open-jawed (5)
**13** Celestial orbs (5)
**14** Exactly right (5)
**16** Someone who looks down on others (4)
**18** Seemed (6)
**20** Inconsiderate (11)

**Down**

**2** Visitor (7)
**3** Top of an 'i'? (3)
**4** Has (4)
**5** Duty-bound (7)
**6** Knave (3)
**10** Large North American deer (7)
**12** Mercury and Venus (7)
**15** Tedious and lengthy (4)
**17** Refusal, slangily (3)
**19** Grease (3)

# PUZZLE 487

**Across**

**1** Sequence (10)
**7** Incite (4,2)
**8** 1975 Spielberg film (4)
**9** Finally understands (5)
**11** Fast 'French' food (5)
**13** Competing (5)
**14** Revises (5)
**16** Iranian king (4)
**18** Warrant (6)
**20** Someone who can't cope (6,4)

**Down**

**2** Completely (7)
**3** Mongrel (3)
**4** Ninth month (abbr.) (4)
**5** Wounded (7)
**6** At this time (3)
**10** Jabs (7)
**12** Contest submissions (7)
**15** Feature of church architecture (4)
**17** USB splitter (3)
**19** Giant bird of legend (3)

# PUZZLE 488

**Across**

**1** Elaborate (11)
**7** Influence (6)
**8** Hopping amphibian (4)
**9** Sharp (5)
**11** Carries (5)
**13** Seize by force (5)
**14** Accepted practice (5)
**16** Asian language (4)
**18** People of courage (6)
**20** Solemnity (11)

**Down**

**2** Workplaces (7)
**3** Circular chart type (3)
**4** Expressing movement to an interior (4)
**5** Hunter's wall trophy (7)
**6** A long period of history (3)
**10** End points (7)
**12** Laments (7)
**15** You (archaic) (4)
**17** Weeding implement (3)
**19** Went for a fast jog (3)

# PUZZLE 489

**Across**

**1** Creating a distinctive mood (11)
**7** Conditional clauses (3)
**8** Intrinsic (5-2)
**9** Act as a substitute (4,2)
**10** 'Go away!' (4)
**13** Prying (4)
**14** Hindu principle of cosmic order (6)
**16** Microblogging service (7)
**18** Water vessel (3)
**19** Distorted (11)

**Down**

**1** Forever (2,9)
**2** Contractile tissues (7)
**3** Present for consideration (6)
**4** Wig material (4)
**5** Go bad (3)
**6** Encumbered (11)
**11** Closed electrical path (7)
**12** Sung by a group (6)
**15** At the highest point (4)
**17** Lodge (3)

# PUZZLE 490

**Across**

**1** Sets of equipment (11)
**7** *Give Peace a Chance* singer (3)
**8** Strong blue cheese (7)
**9** Sulk (4)
**10** Ethiopian neighbour (6)
**13** Magic chants (6)
**14** Yoga expert (4)
**16** Fine, light rain (7)
**18** Folk tale hero, Baba (3)
**19** Lookout (11)

**Down**

**1** Instead of (2,7,2)
**2** Create (7)
**3** Hazard (4)
**4** Maker of suits (6)
**5** Rest on a chair (3)
**6** Concern about other people's feelings (11)
**11** Guacamole ingredient (7)
**12** Sports jacket (6)
**15** Former Megadrive maker (4)
**17** Helpful contacts? (3)

# PUZZLE 491

**Across**
**1** Intransigent (10)
**6** Handle (6)
**7** Cause damage (4)
**10** Pulled (7)
**12** Rocky height (3)
**13** Suitable (3)
**14** Difficult decision (7)
**15** Per person (4)
**18** Type of alcoholic cocktail (3,3)
**19** Old-fashioned person (5-5)

**Down**
**1** Instant (9)
**2** Extremely good (9)
**3** Betrothed (7)
**4** Expression of bad temper (3)
**5** Not be perfect (3)
**8** Tried (9)
**9** Death rate (9)
**11** A slow person (7)
**16** *Home and Away* diner owner (3)
**17** Concealed (3)

# PUZZLE 492

**Across**
**1** Rude (3-8)
**7** Workout muscles (3)
**8** Collects (7)
**9** Handheld device (4)
**10** Miniature tree (6)
**13** Naval standard (6)
**14** Soft body powder (4)
**16** Diva's voice effect (7)
**18** Twenty-third Greek letter (3)
**19** Result (11)

**Down**
**1** Not genuine (11)
**2** Teachings (7)
**3** Piece of pond plankton (4)
**4** Thought (6)
**5** Novel, *The Catcher in the* ___ (3)
**6** Characteristic (11)
**11** Focus (7)
**12** Skip over (6)
**15** Bean curd (4)
**17** Geologist's time measure (3)

# PUZZLE 493

**Across**

**1** How movable something is (11)
**7** Pigeonholed (11)
**8** Include within (11)
**13** Lacking in significance (11)
**18** The state of being a subject of a country (11)
**20** In the way petitioned (2,9)

**Down**

**2** A lot (5)
**3** Trunk of a statue (5)
**4** Life story (3)
**5** Stratum (5)
**6** Larceny (5)
**9** Greek letter 'X' (3)
**10** Pull apart with force (3)
**11** Relating to us (3)
**12** White ___ ghost (2,1)
**14** Metal fasteners (5)
**15** Interference pattern (5)
**16** Exams (5)
**17** Loud, non-musical sound (5)
**19** Large Australian bird (3)

# PUZZLE 494

**Across**

**1** Hindrance (11)
**7** Return to an earlier state (6)
**8** Does not forbid (4)
**9** Personnel (5)
**11** Heavenly messenger (5)
**13** Court official (5)
**14** Something of value (5)
**16** Fishing spear (4)
**18** Out of the ordinary (6)
**20** Good physical condition (11)

**Down**

**2** Movements of air in the lungs (7)
**3** Plastic ball-support (3)
**4** Indicating a maximum amount (2,2)
**5** Inherent skills (7)
**6** Livestock food seed (3)
**10** Fidgety (7)
**12** Adversaries (7)
**15** Advanced products (4)
**17** Amazement (3)
**19** Confess to something: ___ up (3)

# PUZZLE 495

**Across**

**1** Organ donation ops (11)
**7** Hurry (6)
**8** Drains (4)
**9** Small change (5)
**11** Cutting tool (5)
**13** Opinion piece (5)
**14** A single leaf of a flower (5)
**16** Upper hand (4)
**18** Imply (6)
**20** Made a formal decision on a matter (11)

**Down**

**2** Newspaper purchasers (7)
**3** The online world (3)
**4** Small horse (4)
**5** Failure to attend (7)
**6** Gratuity (3)
**10** French castle (7)
**12** Flimsy (7)
**15** Denoting 'half' (4)
**17** Past tense of 'do' (3)
**19** Japanese pop star (3)

# PUZZLE 496

**Across**

**1** Strains (7)
**5** Crisp, long-leaved lettuce (3)
**7** More agile (7)
**8** Mother Teresa was one (3)
**9** Feeds (4)
**10** Christian service prayer (6)
**12** Hassle (6)
**13** Newspaper death notice (4)
**15** Before now (3)
**16** From an Eastern continent (7)
**17** Previous core PC software (init.) (3)
**18** Related to rule by multiple states (7)

**Down**

**1** Neck of a stringed instrument (11)
**2** Constraints (11)
**3** Slippery fish (4)
**4** Leisurely walk (6)
**5** Donor (11)
**6** Well-formed, as in language (11)
**11** Sake (6)
**14** Feral (4)

# PUZZLE 497

**Across**

**1** Magnifying device (9)
**8** Opening (5)
**9** Sturdy footwear (5)
**10** School papers (6)
**12** Indian flatbread (4)
**14** Thick and bushy hairstyle (4)
**15** Swiss city (6)
**17** Pick up (5)
**18** Penniless (5)
**20** Conveyed (9)

**Down**

**2** Tolkien forest giant (3)
**3** Word formed from a person's name (6)
**4** Taxis (4)
**5** Suggest (7)
**6** Verbatim (9)
**7** Reckons (9)
**11** Family moniker (7)
**13** Small stone (6)
**16** Someone opposed to a policy (4)
**19** Rock containing metal (3)

# PUZZLE 498

**Across**

**1** Trailer (7)
**5** A free win, in sport (3)
**7** Someone who responds to a stimulus (7)
**8** Knock quickly (3)
**9** Cause for regret (4)
**10** Signal light (6)
**12** Surpass (6)
**13** Dog-eared (4)
**15** School drawing subject (3)
**16** Decorative paper-folding (7)
**17** Former Pink Floyd member, Barrett (3)
**18** Elixir (4-3)

**Down**

**1** Devices with USB leads, perhaps (11)
**2** Stretchable (11)
**3** Letter after theta (4)
**4** Heated up (6)
**5** 44th US President (6,5)
**6** Raised to a power (11)
**11** Brave (6)
**14** Landing stage (4)

# PUZZLE 499

**Across**

**1** Statesmen (11)
**7** Expression of agreement (3)
**8** Highly transparent glass (7)
**9** Next in line (4)
**10** Tiled picture (6)
**13** Divine messengers (6)
**14** Flabbergast (4)
**16** Formalized ceremonies (7)
**18** Ventilate (3)
**19** Of Antarctica or of Africa, eg (11)

**Down**

**1** Relating to mental illness (11)
**2** Enduring (7)
**3** Clock's 'tick' counterpart (4)
**4** Tea variety (6)
**5** Computer key (3)
**6** Power over your own actions (4-7)
**11** Draw in (7)
**12** Substance with pH greater than 7 (6)
**15** Part of an archipelago (4)
**17** Two hours before midday (3)

# PUZZLE 500

**Across**

**1** Fear of crowds (11)
**7** Police officer (3)
**8** Requires (7)
**9** Submissive (4)
**10** Possible effect of a long flight (3,3)
**13** Respond (6)
**14** Showing no emotion (4)
**16** Moment (7)
**18** Electrically charged particle (3)
**19** Advises against (11)

**Down**

**1** Not solo (11)
**2** Persecute (7)
**3** Bends through the air (4)
**4** Tool for putting in nails (6)
**5** Honey-making insect (3)
**6** Grants (11)
**11** Departing (7)
**12** Smoothly, in music (6)
**15** Agitate (4)
**17** Sibling (3)

# PUZZLE 501

**Across**
**1** Published (6)
**4** Partition (4)
**8** Anticipates (7)
**9** Globe (3)
**10** Gull relative (4)
**11** Profession (6)
**13** Spiritual convictions (6)
**14** Codeword for 'E' (4)
**16** The self (3)
**17** Specifies (7)
**18** Not great (2-2)
**19** Reliable (6)

**Down**
**1** Usernames, eg (11)
**2** Activity overseers (11)
**3** Print a circuit board (4)
**5** Teenagers (11)
**6** With great effort (11)
**7** Academy award (5)
**12** Ghost (5)
**15** At a distance (4)

# PUZZLE 502

**Across**
**1** Surrounding (7)
**5** Her (3)
**7** Interstitials (3)
**8** Melancholy (7)
**9** Sixteenths of a pound (6)
**10** Stair (4)
**12** Remove from office (4)
**13** Cell components (6)
**15** Japanese feudal warrior (7)
**16** American explorer, Bancroft (3)
**17** Intense desire (3)
**18** Not allow to be seen (7)

**Down**
**1** In the same way (11)
**2** Executive workers (11)
**3** Levelled (6)
**4** They're on every foot (4)
**5** Sparkle (11)
**6** Extraordinary (11)
**11** Big-toe swelling (6)
**14** *Monty Python* actor, Idle (4)

# PUZZLE 503

**Across**

1 Four-way junction in the road (10)
7 Occupy, as in attention (6)
8 Promises (4)
9 Tree branches (5)
11 Colorado ski resort (5)
13 Spry (5)
14 Allow to enter (5)
16 Broad smile (4)
18 Technique (6)
20 Hanoi resident, eg (10)

**Down**

2 Phoning (7)
3 Forerunner of reggae (3)
4 Ridge of jagged rock or coral (4)
5 Notified (7)
6 Plant (3)
10 Weighing tool (7)
12 Text revisers (7)
15 Sign of good or evil (4)
17 A spin of a combustion engine (3)
19 Twain's Sawyer (3)

# PUZZLE 504

**Across**

7 Make uniform (11)
8 Taught (7)
9 Nickname for Leonard (3)
10 Jewish scholar (5)
12 Grumble (5)
13 Motor vehicle (3)
14 Not good at mixing (7)
16 Agreements (11)

**Down**

1 Love of the mysterious and exotic (11)
2 Apple variety (4)
3 Equivalently (11)
4 Men about to be married (11)
5 'I'll make it happen' (4,2)
6 Insignificant (11)
11 Breaks open (6)
15 Small hotels (4)

# PUZZLE 505

**Across**

**7** Believer in social equality (11)
**8** Chorus (7)
**9** Bitumen (3)
**10** Cancel (5)
**12** Nine-voice group (5)
**13** Jump on one foot (3)
**14** Begin again (7)
**16** Not confirmed (11)

**Down**

**1** Shameful (11)
**2** Fifty per cent (4)
**3** Dislike of everyone (11)
**4** Deliberate miss that threatens trouble (7,4)
**5** Cut into with teeth (6)
**6** Lack of graciousness (11)
**11** Resist (6)
**15** Performs a part (4)

# PUZZLE 506

**Across**

**1** Book collection overseer (9)
**8** Strict; meticulous (5)
**9** Disgrace (5)
**10** Polluted (6)
**12** Rash symptom (4)
**14** Happy (4)
**15** Gilt (6)
**17** Absolute (5)
**18** Doubter (5)
**20** Book producer (9)

**Down**

**2** Georgina, familiarly (3)
**3** Sharp reply (6)
**4** Corrosion (4)
**5** Expected (7)
**6** Type of lapdog (9)
**7** Workings (9)
**11** Area of level high ground (7)
**13** Speaks the part of (6)
**16** Type of language exam (4)
**19** Originally called (3)

# PUZZLE 507

**Across**

**1** One who studies living things (9)
**8** Sphere of activity (5)
**9** Nectarine (5)
**10** Fable (6)
**12** Lightweight boxing move (4)
**14** Horn sound (4)
**15** Opposite of alkaline (6)
**17** Sped (5)
**18** Became ice (5)
**20** Orders to leave (9)

**Down**

**2** Eisenhower (3)
**3** Discovers (6)
**4** Holes between objects (4)
**5** Flooded (7)
**6** Let down (4,5)
**7** Written or printed symbol (9)
**11** Trattoria dumplings (7)
**13** Shows scorn (6)
**16** Dutch cheese (4)
**19** Single unit (3)

# PUZZLE 508

**Across**

**7** Relating to ownership (11)
**8** World's highest mountain (7)
**9** Foot extremity (3)
**10** Start again (5)
**12** Absolute low (5)
**13** Correlative to 'neither' (3)
**14** Brass instrument (7)
**16** Thorough investigation (11)

**Down**

**1** Visual aspects (11)
**2** Exited slumber (4)
**3** Direction (11)
**4** Box-like (11)
**5** Intoxicated (slang) (6)
**6** Creating words on a mechanical machine (11)
**11** Peels (6)
**15** Stiffly formal (4)

# PUZZLE 509

**Across**
1 Not precisely given (11)
7 Kills (US slang) (4)
8 More advanced in age (6)
9 Prize disc (5)
10 Remains of a fire (5)
13 Dehydrates (5)
15 Holy chalice (5)
17 Surviving (6)
18 Ardent (4)
19 Deposit (4,7)

**Down**
2 Of the centre of an atom (7)
3 Musical section (7)
4 Barrel-like container (4)
5 Dublin residents (5)
6 Presumes (5)
11 Caustic remark (7)
12 Deletion (7)
13 Fear greatly (5)
14 Following on behind (2,3)
16 Italian volcano (4)

# PUZZLE 510

**Across**
1 Conviction (6)
4 Mockery (4)
6 Ruler (6)
7 Impudence (4)
8 Breadcrumbed seafood dish (6)
11 Object word (4)
12 In a short while, poetically (4)
13 Glorifies (6)
16 Raise (4)
17 All of your assets (6)
18 Self-images (4)
19 Jerks (6)

**Down**
1 Draft laws (5)
2 Woolly, camel-like animal (5)
3 Secretive behaviour (11)
4 Woman in the Book of Daniel (7)
5 Offensive (7)
9 Guile (7)
10 Hour divisions (7)
14 Debts (5)
15 Sows (5)

# PUZZLE 511

**Across**

**1** Initiate proceedings (4,3)
**5** Former jazz guitarist, Montgomery (3)
**7** Chance (11)
**8** Second-largest Scottish loch (4)
**10** Without being asked (2,4)
**12** Cared for (6)
**13** Social, black-and-white whale (4)
**15** Creative (11)
**17** Oxygen or nitrogen, eg (3)
**18** Sly creatures (7)

**Down**

**1** Ignorant person (4-7)
**2** Cover over (3)
**3** Boat poles with flat blades (4)
**4** Well spoken (6)
**5** Speak softly (7)
**6** Very tall buildings (11)
**9** Strapped shoes (7)
**11** Critique (6)
**14** Long story (4)
**16** Freezer deposits (3)

# PUZZLE 512

**Across**

**1** Suddenly (3,2,4)
**8** Shadow (5)
**9** Implements (5)
**10** Endured (6)
**12** Flightless bird (4)
**14** Green tree foliage (4)
**15** Jumping chess piece (6)
**17** Erased (5)
**18** Female sovereign (5)
**20** List of someone's previous locations (9)

**Down**

**2** Scientist's workplace (3)
**3** Astonishes (6)
**4** Solemn promise (4)
**5** Shutting (7)
**6** Completely developed (4-5)
**7** Helping (9)
**11** Hair detergent (7)
**13** Incomparable (6)
**16** Not in operation (4)
**19** Feed on (3)

# PUZZLE 513

**Across**
1 Forecasts (11)
7 National tree of India (6)
8 Block (4)
9 Inventory (5)
11 Loose (5)
13 Inched (5)
14 Short, pastoral poem (5)
16 Berserk (4)
18 They might be acute or obtuse (6)
20 Organized (11)

**Down**
2 Responded (7)
3 Period of 24 hours (3)
4 Circular-based geometric solid (4)
5 Ill person (7)
6 Inverting logic function (3)
10 Proofreader (7)
12 School (7)
15 Ancient Persian priests (4)
17 Chinese Chairman (3)
19 Tibetan gazelle (3)

# PUZZLE 514

**Across**
1 High-powered lamp (11)
6 Sardonic (6)
7 Greatest in amount (4)
8 Commence (5)
11 Moral principle (5)
12 Superior to (5)
13 Sought answers (5)
17 Philippine monetary unit (4)
18 Irish, eg (6)
19 Ridiculously (11)

**Down**
1 Sets out on a yacht (5)
2 Fragrance (5)
3 Write computer code (4)
4 Convicts (7)
5 Antagonistic (7)
9 Vivid pictorial impression (7)
10 Square pasta parcels (7)
14 Terminates (5)
15 Publicly denounce (5)
16 Gelatinous, seaweed-derived culture (4)

# PUZZLE 515

**Across**
**7** Working (11)
**8** Game official (7)
**9** Bustle (3)
**10** Tenet (5)
**12** Haloes (5)
**13** Mineral spring (3)
**14** Disordered (7)
**16** Hard to control or manage (11)

**Down**
**1** Camaraderie (11)
**2** Lacking the ability to hear (4)
**3** Relating to government by men (11)
**4** Medieval trivium and quadrivium studies (7,4)
**5** Not sporting (6)
**6** A leech or mosquito, eg (11)
**11** Financial endowments (6)
**15** Bass trumpet (4)

# PUZZLE 516

**Across**
**1** Or else (9)
**7** Grasp (5)
**8** Russian pancakes (5)
**10** Mother of Horus (4)
**11** Temporarily stopped (6)
**14** Trial (3-3)
**15** Ogres (4)
**17** Question (5)
**19** Strength (5)
**20** Belief in the Latter-Day Saints (9)

**Down**
**2** Cambridge college founded by Henry VIII (7)
**3** Thread holes (4)
**4** Computer-based video recorder (6)
**5** Slide across snow (3)
**6** Aided (8)
**9** Commercial enterprise (8)
**12** Spreads out in a straggling fashion (7)
**13** Practice (6)
**16** Atop (4)
**18** 'One', in Spanish (3)

# PUZZLE 517

**Across**
1 With good productivity (11)
7 Maned cat (4)
8 Soft colour shade (6)
9 Attempts to hole a golf ball (5)
10 Meat skewers (5)
13 Eats (5)
15 Endangered atmosphere layer (5)
17 Assigned a path (6)
18 Surrounded by (4)
19 Temporary storage area (7,4)

**Down**
2 Dud (7)
3 Caught fire (7)
4 Kids' spotting game (1,3)
5 All together, in music (5)
6 Utters a short, sharp cry (5)
11 Flair (7)
12 Mental strain (7)
13 Onward in time, formally (5)
14 The same as (5)
16 Japanese noodles (4)

# PUZZLE 518

**Across**
1 People (11)
7 Jail (6)
8 Haughty, spoiled woman (4)
9 Tropical tuber (4)
10 Quit (6)
13 Reverse a vehicle (4,2)
16 Fairy-tale villain (4)
17 They're used to unlock doors (4)
18 Robber; bandit (6)
19 With pros and cons (6-5)

**Down**
2 Paradise (7)
3 Available for immediate purchase (2,5)
4 Interior (5)
5 Defence excuse (5)
6 Cartoon sheep (5)
11 Blemished (7)
12 Trash (7)
13 Cooked in an oven (5)
14 South American beaver-like rodent (5)
15 Prostrate (5)

# PUZZLE 519

**Across**
- **1** Translator (11)
- **7** Stocky (6)
- **8** Necklace component (4)
- **9** Sleeved outer garments (5)
- **11** Digression (5)
- **13** Mentally prepare; excite (5)
- **14** Small shrew? (5)
- **16** Sixth letter of the Greek alphabet (4)
- **18** Employing (6)
- **20** Soft, rich milk product (5,6)

**Down**
- **2** Whimsies (7)
- **3** Tree in the genus *Ulmus* (3)
- **4** Suffers as a result of something (4)
- **5** Mission (7)
- **6** Scheduled arrival (init.) (3)
- **10** Fugue companion, often (7)
- **12** Requires (7)
- **15** Elegant (4)
- **17** Two are needed for stereo (3)
- **19** Lament (3)

# PUZZLE 520

**Across**
- **1** Solace (11)
- **7** Those shunned by society (6)
- **8** Pealed (4)
- **9** Arabian river valley (4)
- **10** Gift (6)
- **13** Track (6)
- **16** Unexciting (4)
- **17** Omani monetary unit (4)
- **18** Conjecture (6)
- **19** Branch of philosophy (11)

**Down**
- **2** Culinary herb related to mint (7)
- **3** Distinctive (7)
- **4** Romantic Hungarian pianist (5)
- **5** Picture (5)
- **6** Period of darkness (5)
- **11** Mail (7)
- **12** Made up of digits (7)
- **13** Discussion place (5)
- **14** Fewest (5)
- **15** Timepiece (5)

# PUZZLE 521

**Across**

**1** Mixtures (9)
**8** Conclude (5)
**9** Material gain (5)
**10** Aided (6)
**12** Central European river (4)
**14** Head-louse eggs (4)
**15** Results in (6)
**17** What the sun does during the day (5)
**18** Radial wheel rod (5)
**20** Needed (9)

**Down**

**2** Not on (3)
**3** Broke down syntactically (6)
**4** Unattractive (4)
**5** Makes up one's mind (7)
**6** Deceitful (9)
**7** Pushes into a lower position (9)
**11** Trellis (7)
**13** Succeeds at an exam (6)
**16** List of choices (4)
**19** Many a time, in poetry (3)

# PUZZLE 522

**Across**

**1** Strong desire to know (9)
**7** Very pale, as with fright (5)
**8** Flaw (5)
**10** No longer alive (4)
**11** Type of TV (6)
**14** Relating to the underworld (6)
**15** Make ready (4)
**17** First-class, informally (5)
**19** Looks at (5)
**20** Boundless (9)

**Down**

**2** Not listened to (7)
**3** Atoms with net electric charge (4)
**4** Without risk (6)
**5** Nineteenth Greek letter (3)
**6** Deprivation (8)
**9** Silent monk (8)
**12** Partitions (7)
**13** The largest island in a US state of the same name (6)
**16** Malevolence (4)
**18** Decorative pond fish (3)

# PUZZLE 523

**Across**
**1** Green concern (11)
**7** Speech defect affecting 's' (4)
**8** Stole from (6)
**9** Establish your position (3,2)
**10** Farmyard mammary gland (5)
**13** Newly made (5)
**15** Loft (5)
**17** Bigger (6)
**18** Professional charges (4)
**19** Possible outcome (11)

**Down**
**2** More clamorous (7)
**3** Weakens; damages (7)
**4** Lady's finger plant (4)
**5** Flowed back out (5)
**6** Henry VIII, eg (5)
**11** Obedient (7)
**12** Distinguished (7)
**13** Incorrect; untrue (5)
**14** Ghostly (5)
**16** Close Hindi relative (4)

# PUZZLE 524

**Across**
**1** Radio code word for 'Q' (6)
**4** What a vacuum does (4)
**6** Mythological female warrior (6)
**7** Aftersun treatment (4)
**8** An item of post (6)
**11** Pitch (4)
**12** Ancient neck ornament (4)
**13** Cherry red (6)
**16** Short skirt (4)
**17** Blue shade (6)
**18** Hitch (4)
**19** Get comfy against something (6)

**Down**
**1** Small game bird (5)
**2** Speak highly of (5)
**3** Abbreviation (11)
**4** Disperse (7)
**5** Both + and × (7)
**9** Sentiment (7)
**10** Nailing (7)
**14** Foolish person (5)
**15** Abscond with a lover (5)

# PUZZLE 525

**Across**

**1** Spell-casting word (11)
**7** Plain, narrow bed (3)
**8** Medical indicator (7)
**9** Dystopian sci-fi film, *The* ___ (6)
**10** Software identifier (4)
**13** Woman (4)
**14** Musical motifs (6)
**16** Even more minuscule (7)
**18** Dedicated sonnet (3)
**19** Circulates (11)

**Down**

**1** Gathered over time (11)
**2** Turned (7)
**3** Vast (6)
**4** Speechless (4)
**5** It's required to play baseball (3)
**6** Metes out (11)
**11** Decayed plant material (7)
**12** Winged childlike being (6)
**15** Row of seats (4)
**17** Canon SLR camera system (init.) (3)

# PUZZLE 526

**Across**

**1** Say bad things about (5,4,2)
**7** Stature; fame (US slang) (3)
**8** Tool used to tighten bolts (7)
**9** Female relative (4)
**10** England, in bygone days (6)
**13** Female sibling (6)
**14** Functions (4)
**16** All together (2,5)
**18** Wildebeest (3)
**19** Sent from one place to another (11)

**Down**

**1** 'Excel', eg (11)
**2** Grows (7)
**3** Caress with the lips (4)
**4** Practicable (6)
**5** Boy's name; also a girl's name (3)
**6** Execution party (6,5)
**11** Visible (2,5)
**12** Terminates (6)
**15** Large, hairy creature (4)
**17** Abba hit, *Mamma* ___ (3)

# PUZZLE 527

**Across**

**1** Liking better (10)
**7** Measure (6)
**8** Take part in an election (4)
**9** Sneering (5)
**11** Charged atom or molecule (5)
**13** Chinese or Thai, eg (5)
**14** Donkeys (5)
**16** Kind (4)
**18** Reanimated body (6)
**20** Transcriptions (10)

**Down**

**2** Prompts (7)
**3** Highly contagious viral infection (3)
**4** Old Testament book (4)
**5** Comes up with (7)
**6** Acquired (3)
**10** Severe (7)
**12** Gap (7)
**15** Government adviser (4)
**17** Rowing requirement (3)
**19** Josh Groban song (3)

# PUZZLE 528

**Across**

**1** Be destroyed by fire (2,2,2,5)
**7** Prohibited (6)
**8** 19th-century German engine designer (4)
**9** Brick oven (4)
**10** Furnish (6)
**13** Star system (6)
**16** Reductions in service (4)
**17** Crowds of troublemakers (4)
**18** Emergency (6)
**19** Modifying the position of (11)

**Down**

**2** Egg-shaped wind instrument (7)
**3** Predatory South American fish (7)
**4** Intersection points (5)
**5** Ready to be poured (2,3)
**6** Very dark wood (5)
**11** Filling (7)
**12** Riga resident (7)
**13** Interactive entertainment player (5)
**14** The Scales (5)
**15** Adam's needle (5)

# PUZZLE 529

**Across**
- **1** To strengthen physically (5,2)
- **5** Part of a circle's circumference (3)
- **7** Did nothing (3)
- **8** Flower on a fruit tree (7)
- **9** Platform bed (4)
- **10** 'Understood' (6)
- **12** Linger about (6)
- **13** Relaxed: ___ back (4)
- **15** Inventor (7)
- **16** Infuriation (3)
- **17** Hand over money for something (3)
- **18** Storage cupboard (7)

**Down**
- **1** Sports headgear (8,3)
- **2** Unremittingly (11)
- **3** Unpaid sum (4)
- **4** Snaps (6)
- **5** Connection (11)
- **6** Binding order (11)
- **11** Cornish, Irish or Scottish Gaelic, eg (6)
- **14** Thoroughly defeat (4)

# PUZZLE 530

**Across**
- **1** Shortens (11)
- **7** Alligator's cousin (4)
- **8** Change title (6)
- **9** Long, low sofa (5)
- **10** Like a reptile's skin (5)
- **13** Makes up (5)
- **15** Tropical trees (5)
- **17** String-shaped piece of pasta (6)
- **18** Party to (2,2)
- **19** Teaching (11)

**Down**
- **2** Tortilla dish (7)
- **3** Obtain the return of (7)
- **4** To a great amount (4)
- **5** Ornamental headgear (5)
- **6** Sordid (5)
- **11** Horse-drawn racing carriage (7)
- **12** Poke fun at (7)
- **13** Truffles, eg (5)
- **14** Genealogy (5)
- **16** Male admirer (4)

# PUZZLE 531

**Across**

**1** Potential (11)
**7** Is of the same opinion (6)
**8** Scarlet, puce and crimson (4)
**9** Explosive weapons (5)
**11** Visages (5)
**13** Religious verse (5)
**14** Land masses surrounded by water (5)
**16** A barren plateau in Asia (4)
**18** Get back together (6)
**20** Admit (11)

**Down**

**2** Areas (7)
**3** Appeal formally (3)
**4** Lack of difficulty (4)
**5** Ultimatums, perhaps (7)
**6** YouTube clip (3)
**10** Ten to the ninth power (7)
**12** Time when the sun sets (7)
**15** Summit of a hill (4)
**17** Mythical monster (3)
**19** Ordinary man? (3)

# PUZZLE 532

**Across**

**1** Arranging (11)
**7** Cow's meat (4)
**8** Spanish dish cooked in a shallow pan (6)
**9** Bond, eg (5)
**10** Extent (5)
**13** Stage (5)
**15** What Britain is a land of, according to Elgar (5)
**17** Each (6)
**18** Bird worshipped by ancient Egyptians (4)
**19** Extremely happy (4,3,4)

**Down**

**2** Ocular cleansing lotion (7)
**3** Balancing amounts (7)
**4** Sprites (4)
**5** Ice house (5)
**6** Tomb (5)
**11** Important bone mineral (7)
**12** Porch (7)
**13** Keyboard instrument (5)
**14** Originate (5)
**16** Interlaced structure (4)

# PUZZLE 533

**Across**

**1** Attempt to conceal wrongdoing (5-2)
**5** This girl (3)
**7** Possibly electric fish (3)
**8** Liberty (7)
**9** Flaw in a plan (4)
**10** Strand (6)
**12** Frothy (6)
**13** Units of electrical resistance (4)
**15** Left out (7)
**16** Opposite of 'hi' (3)
**17** Produce an egg, if you're a hen (3)
**18** Concise (7)

**Down**

**1** Very close together (5,2,4)
**2** With free will (11)
**3** Umpires (4)
**4** Modular house (6)
**5** Rabies water-fear symptom (11)
**6** Evocative (11)
**11** Inert (6)
**14** Distant ancestor? (4)

# PUZZLE 534

**Across**

**3** Substantial (5)
**6** Choir voice above alto (7)
**7** Follow someone's movements (5)
**8** What one? (5)
**9** Extinct kiwi relative (3)
**11** Powdery ice (5)
**13** Award (5)
**15** Timid (3)
**18** Trickery (5)
**19** Lazy start to the day (3-2)
**20** Suffered distress (7)
**21** Fasteners (5)

**Down**

**1** Female parent (6)
**2** Handle; deal with (7)
**3** Sausage sandwich (3,3)
**4** Attainment (4)
**5** Symbol of slavery (4)
**10** Got somewhere (7)
**12** Stuff (6)
**14** Essential (6)
**16** Allied countries (4)
**17** Meats and cheeses retailer (4)

# PUZZLE 535

**Across**

**1** Belief in nothing beyond what is material (11)
**7** Pompous (11)
**8** Unstable and aggressive people (11)
**13** Rebukes (11)
**18** Separated (11)
**20** Clichés about people (11)

**Down**

**2** Lena Dunham TV series (5)
**3** Relating to the eye (5)
**4** Unit of weight (3)
**5** Type of delicate pottery (5)
**6** Antarctic Pole (5)
**9** 'Great food!' (3)
**10** Female fowl (3)
**11** Household companion (3)
**12** As well (3)
**14** Distributed cards (5)
**15** External (5)
**16** Wryly amusing contradictions (5)
**17** Nephew's sister (5)
**19** Yin and yang philosophy (3)

# PUZZLE 536

**Across**

**1** Letter addressees (10)
**7** Corn-cutting tool (6)
**8** Program instructions (4)
**9** Nip (5)
**11** Water tubes (5)
**13** Spy (5)
**14** Man-eating giants (5)
**16** Part of a cowboy boot (4)
**18** Fixes computer software (6)
**20** Biased information (10)

**Down**

**2** Changing text (7)
**3** Sort (3)
**4** Decorated with a sugary coating (4)
**5** Cutting slightly (7)
**6** Feeling down (3)
**10** Spirited, as a musical direction (3,4)
**12** Appeared (7)
**15** Gist (4)
**17** Celebrity photographer (3)
**19** Farmyard cry (3)

# PUZZLE 537

**Across**

**1** Brief section of text (9)
**8** Chap, informally (5)
**9** Better-than-average golf score (5)
**10** Imitated (6)
**12** Type of fruit tree (4)
**14** Casually (4)
**15** Name plaques (6)
**17** Faux pas (5)
**18** Cite (5)
**20** Supposedly (9)

**Down**

**2** It's used for boring small holes (3)
**3** Blown away (6)
**4** Marsh-loving plant (4)
**5** Colouring matter (7)
**6** Donations (9)
**7** Downcast (9)
**11** Beneficial (7)
**13** Coterie (6)
**16** Measure, with 'out' (4)
**19** Broad-faced nocturnal bird (3)

# PUZZLE 538

**Across**

**1** Help pay for (9)
**7** Surplus (5)
**8** Hex (5)
**10** Send forth (4)
**11** Tour leaders (6)
**14** Relating to apes or monkeys (6)
**15** 4,840 square yards (4)
**17** Reddish-brown (5)
**19** Evade (5)
**20** Left-winger (9)

**Down**

**2** Radioactive element (7)
**3** Espies (4)
**4** Athletic throwing event (6)
**5** American-English 'Z' (3)
**6** Evaluates (8)
**9** Paid attention to a sound (8)
**12** Decrypts (7)
**13** Italian sausage variety (6)
**16** Role model (4)
**18** Master (3)

# PUZZLE 539

**Across**
**1** Depicting (10)
**7** Edits (6)
**8** Repeated jazz intro (4)
**9** Normal (5)
**11** Tale (5)
**13** Camera aperture setting (1-4)
**14** Point of contention (5)
**16** Vocational college (4)
**18** Private, as in information (6)
**20** Over a great distance (3,3,4)

**Down**
**2** Chemical diffusion process (7)
**3** Darken the skin (3)
**4** This as well (4)
**5** Polite attendance requests (7)
**6** Outstanding object (3)
**10** One more (7)
**12** Smoothed (7)
**15** Demeanour (4)
**17** Dobby, in *Harry Potter* (3)
**19** Observed (3)

# PUZZLE 540

**Across**
**1** Listings (11)
**7** Not open (4)
**8** Toasted Italian sandwiches (6)
**9** Wide (5)
**10** Fool's Day month (5)
**13** Remains (5)
**15** Periods of 60 minutes (5)
**17** Strongly encouraging (6)
**18** Ancient Roman calendar day (4)
**19** Extremely colourful (11)

**Down**
**2** Receive from your parents (7)
**3** Tidal river mouth (7)
**4** Waiter's bonuses (4)
**5** More glacial (5)
**6** Finesse (5)
**11** Supply (7)
**12** Certain Middle Eastern resident (7)
**13** Drink with a sucking sound (5)
**14** Irate (5)
**16** Shivering fit (4)

# PUZZLE 541

**Across**
1 Aptness (11)
7 Words of farewell (6)
8 Burden (4)
9 Retains (5)
11 Allotted quantity (5)
13 Michaelmas daisy (5)
14 Postpone (5)
16 British actress, Thompson (4)
18 Consign (6)
20 Informal; relaxed (4,3,4)

**Down**
2 Take off clothes (7)
3 Make a knot (3)
4 Lowest part of something (4)
5 Iceberg, perhaps (7)
6 Cheap ornaments (3)
10 Introduction (7)
12 Flatterers (7)
15 Sweep the eyes over (4)
17 Deface (3)
19 *The Simpsons* bar owner (3)

# PUZZLE 542

**Across**
1 Normal (7)
5 Thus (3)
7 Hiring process (11)
8 Beats on a serve (4)
10 Third sign of the zodiac (6)
12 Additions (6)
13 Very eager to hear (4)
15 Disturbed (11)
17 'I didn't know that!' (3)
18 Armed conflict (7)

**Down**
1 Intimidating (11)
2 Photograph (3)
3 Military takeover (4)
4 Rubbish (6)
5 Searching (7)
6 Highly advanced (7-4)
9 Give a right to (7)
11 Make less wide (6)
14 Prickly seed case (4)
16 Hot or iced drink (3)

# PUZZLE 543

**Across**

**1** Involving machinery (10)
**6** Strain (6)
**7** Not closed (4)
**10** Removed dirt (7)
**12** Furrow (3)
**13** Former Burmese capital (3)
**14** Map line of equal elevation (7)
**15** Pelted along (4)
**18** Gloomy (6)
**19** Again and again (10)

**Down**

**1** Instrumentalists (9)
**2** Correspond (9)
**3** Classic poison element (7)
**4** Loving murmur (3)
**5** Fib (3)
**8** Behaved (9)
**9** Inherently (9)
**11** Tooth doctor (7)
**16** Golfer's goal? (3)
**17** Briefly immerse (3)

# PUZZLE 544

**Across**

**1** Guesses (11)
**6** Glacial geological period (3,3)
**7** Writing table (4)
**8** Sharp slap (5)
**11** Provisional certificate of money (5)
**12** Reversed (5)
**13** Bedeck (5)
**17** Prayer ending (4)
**18** Wardrobe support (6)
**19** Indecisiveness (11)

**Down**

**1** Bad deeds (5)
**2** Letter after eta (5)
**3** Copied (4)
**4** Brought on (7)
**5** Viler (7)
**9** Least amount possible (7)
**10** Dry red Italian wine (7)
**14** Church keyboard (5)
**15** Doctor's assistant (5)
**16** Command to halt a horse (4)

# PUZZLE 545

**Across**
- **1** Money-based political system (10)
- **7** Voyaged (6)
- **8** Poultry (4)
- **9** Gulf War missiles (5)
- **11** Climb (5)
- **13** Airy spirit (5)
- **14** Breakfast tea component (5)
- **16** Sword used when fencing (4)
- **18** Occultist (6)
- **20** Sort out in advance (10)

**Down**
- **2** Chaos (7)
- **3** Unwell (3)
- **4** Contributes (4)
- **5** Contaminates (7)
- **6** Vicious animal's throat (3)
- **10** Reduce (7)
- **12** Re-opening, as in a saved computer document (7)
- **15** Islamic chieftain (4)
- **17** Small fruit seed (3)
- **19** Adriatic, eg (3)

# PUZZLE 546

**Across**
- **1** Local groups (11)
- **7** Short (6)
- **8** A title of high nobility (4)
- **9** Arms and legs (5)
- **11** Adds water to the brim (5)
- **13** Lopsided (5)
- **14** Intense suffering (5)
- **16** Landlocked African country (4)
- **18** Damage (6)
- **20** System of analysis (11)

**Down**
- **2** Roots (7)
- **3** Floor protector (3)
- **4** Want (4)
- **5** Straightening out (7)
- **6** Largest of all deer (3)
- **10** Flaw (7)
- **12** Giving temporarily (7)
- **15** Situated at the back (4)
- **17** Literary welcome or farewell (3)
- **19** Comrade (3)

# PUZZLE 547

**Across**
- **1** Changes one thing for another (11)
- **6** Unwind (6)
- **7** School snacks (4)
- **8** Juddered (5)
- **11** Banded ornamental stone (5)
- **12** Oneness (5)
- **13** Workroom (5)
- **17** Uncover (4)
- **18** From a distant place (6)
- **19** Meeting break (11)

**Down**
- **1** Spirits (5)
- **2** Pack donkey (5)
- **3** Woes (4)
- **4** Highly strung (7)
- **5** Agitated (7)
- **9** British Parliamentary proceedings (7)
- **10** Active (2,3,2)
- **14** Free from knots (5)
- **15** Marina vessel (5)
- **16** Scary feeling (4)

# PUZZLE 548

**Across**
- **1** Printed work (11)
- **6** Papal ambassador (6)
- **7** Not new (4)
- **8** Device for measuring time (5)
- **11** Leave the path (5)
- **12** Very unpleasant smell (5)
- **13** Love (5)
- **17** Glandular fever (4)
- **18** Social setting (6)
- **19** Narrow-mindedness (11)

**Down**
- **1** Overwhelming fear (5)
- **2** Type of stringed instrument (5)
- **3** Chef (4)
- **4** Relied upon (7)
- **5** Outside; unenclosed (4,3)
- **9** Anticlimax (3-4)
- **10** With movement, musically (3,4)
- **14** Pungent vegetable (5)
- **15** Discharge slowly (5)
- **16** Captain Hook's right-hand man (4)

# PUZZLE 549

**Across**

**1** Lack of straightforwardness (11)
**7** Lower down (6)
**8** Round sticks (4)
**9** Stiff (5)
**11** Wooden panelling (5)
**13** Once more (5)
**14** Chemical analysis (5)
**16** Adjoin (4)
**18** Foreign childcarer (2,4)
**20** Happenings (11)

**Down**

**2** Requiring (7)
**3** Cheeky sprite (3)
**4** Merit (4)
**5** Goals (7)
**6** Not new (3)
**10** Inane (7)
**12** Ending (7)
**15** Make into a bundle (4)
**17** Keep out (3)
**19** Greek letter before chi (3)

# PUZZLE 550

**Across**

**1** A wonderful thing (10)
**7** Facts (6)
**8** Implement that's used to smooth clothes (4)
**9** Butcher's leftovers (5)
**11** Married women (5)
**13** Narrow street (5)
**14** Lit-up (5)
**16** Transport vehicle (4)
**18** Dozen (6)
**20** New wave (5-5)

**Down**

**2** Likely to cause damage (7)
**3** Crank (3)
**4** Carpeting plant (4)
**5** Hammering, perhaps (7)
**6** Asteroid near-miss (init.) (3)
**10** Continent that straddles the Pacific and Atlantic oceans (7)
**12** Developed (7)
**15** Piece of numerical information (abbr.) (4)
**17** 'I've got it!' (3)
**19** *Evita* heroine (3)

# PUZZLE 551

**Across**
- **1** Dependent (11)
- **7** Divisions (11)
- **8** Measurement in farads (11)
- **13** Feasible (11)
- **18** Experts (11)
- **20** Publicizing (11)

**Down**
- **2** Last Greek letter (5)
- **3** Former Princess of Wales (5)
- **4** Add, with 'up' (3)
- **5** Musical drama (5)
- **6** Caper (5)
- **9** Legume seed (3)
- **10** It might be Oriental or Persian (3)
- **11** Involuntary muscular contraction (3)
- **12** Bag (3)
- **14** Quick (5)
- **15** Recurring series (5)
- **16** Assumed name (5)
- **17** Classical language (5)
- **19** Statute (3)

# PUZZLE 552

**Across**
- **1** Fabled (9)
- **7** Fake (5)
- **8** Parody (5)
- **10** With a sulphurous smell (4)
- **11** Indigenous groups (6)
- **14** Examined (6)
- **15** South Asian dress (4)
- **17** US airline (5)
- **19** No longer asleep (5)
- **20** United (9)

**Down**
- **2** Hires (7)
- **3** Very straightforward (4)
- **4** Wish (6)
- **5** Greek letter preceding sigma (3)
- **6** Took exception (8)
- **9** Trends (8)
- **12** Shelf support (7)
- **13** Leave suddenly (6)
- **16** Large, wide-mouthed jug (4)
- **18** Actor DiCaprio, informally (3)

# PUZZLE 553

**Across**

**1** Crossing hot ashes without shoes (4-7)
**7** Pre-Christmas period (6)
**8** Makes a knight (4)
**9** Jettisons (5)
**11** Female fox (5)
**13** Rose from sitting (5)
**14** Gawks at (5)
**16** Shells, eg (4)
**18** Extreme experience (6)
**20** Scientific research (11)

**Down**

**2** Open to question (2,5)
**3** Adam's mate (3)
**4** Creative skills (4)
**5** Joking (7)
**6** Bird's beak (3)
**10** Move to a better job (7)
**12** Chic (7)
**15** Centres of interest (4)
**17** Beat-matching segue (3)
**19** Ex-Korean president, Kim ___-jung (3)

# PUZZLE 554

**Across**

**1** Restore (11)
**6** Skulked (6)
**7** Besides that (4)
**8** Artistic skill (5)
**11** Fix a computer program (5)
**12** Suitably (5)
**13** Ait (5)
**17** Musical interface standard (init.) (4)
**18** Socialize with those of higher status (6)
**19** Hazardously (11)

**Down**

**1** Object from an earlier time (5)
**2** About (5)
**3** Extinct flightless bird (4)
**4** Sways back and forth (7)
**5** Barely known (7)
**9** Reproduction (7)
**10** Videoing (7)
**14** Joins (5)
**15** Domestic cat (5)
**16** Singer once married to Sonny Bono (4)

# PUZZLE 555

**Across**
**1** Small discussion group (7)
**5** Bodybuilding muscle (3)
**7** Usual (7)
**8** Alcoholic spirit (3)
**9** Not include (4)
**10** Dissimilar (6)
**12** Laceless shoe (4-2)
**13** Egalitarian online reference (4)
**15** Sheep (3)
**16** Orchestral drum set (7)
**17** Someone disabled by alcohol (3)
**18** Among (7)

**Down**
**1** Solemnity (11)
**2** Glorious (11)
**3** Invalid (4)
**4** Eager (6)
**5** Take part (11)
**6** Contest (11)
**11** Spa bath (3,3)
**14** Filth (4)

# PUZZLE 556

**Across**
**1** Not aware (11)
**6** Gift (6)
**7** Dolphin trick (4)
**8** Foyer (5)
**11** Benefactor (5)
**12** Noughts (5)
**13** Stalks (5)
**17** Bunkum; silly talk (4)
**18** Second-largest continent (6)
**19** Apt (11)

**Down**
**1** Up to (5)
**2** Personality, colloquially (5)
**3** Satisfy (4)
**4** Leading (2,5)
**5** Unvarying (7)
**9** Partly cover (7)
**10** Male sibling (7)
**14** Lloyd Webber musical (5)
**15** Apportion (5)
**16** Moist (4)

# PUZZLE 557

**Across**
1 Preliminary version (9)
8 Annoyed; tired (3,2)
9 Long, flat-bottomed boat (5)
10 Result (6)
12 Expression of disgust (4)
14 Decorative cloth band (4)
15 Fingerless glove (6)
17 Flow control (5)
18 Actor, Atkinson (5)
20 Funding (9)

**Down**
2 Primary light colour (3)
3 Subjects (6)
4 Basins (4)
5 Chase (7)
6 Abhorrent (9)
7 Tally (9)
11 Short spiral pasta (7)
13 From oranges or lemons (6)
16 Million, as a prefix (4)
19 Looking tired or pale (3)

# PUZZLE 558

**Across**
3 Dwelled (5)
6 Distinguished orchestra leaders (7)
7 Regions (5)
8 Remove all coverings (5)
9 Weapon (3)
11 Go and fetch (5)
13 Every day (5)
15 Subside downwards (3)
18 Map book (5)
19 Repeat mark (5)
20 Denied food (7)
21 One after fifth (5)

**Down**
1 Cause; reason (6)
2 Apportions (7)
3 Long-bodied reptile (6)
4 Plant creeper (4)
5 Prescribed amount (4)
10 Becomes expert in (7)
12 Waterproof overshoe (6)
14 Departs (6)
16 Paeans (4)
17 Underworld river (4)

# PUZZLE 559

**Across**

**1** Priced at (7)
**5** Biological bag-like structure (3)
**7** Drink like a dog (3)
**8** Act in accordance with expectations (7)
**9** Arf (4)
**10** Atom centres (6)
**12** Creature (6)
**13** Large creative work (4)
**15** First (7)
**16** Previous capital of Brazil (3)
**17** Mouth covering (3)
**18** Painters and sculptors (7)

**Down**

**1** Honouring (11)
**2** Overseeing (11)
**3** Crawl (4)
**4** Incredible intellect (6)
**5** Wet blankets (11)
**6** Orders the production of (11)
**11** Pretentious (2-2-2)
**14** Level; smooth (4)

# PUZZLE 560

**Across**

**1** Barge in (9)
**8** Unaffiliated record label (5)
**9** Shaggy (5)
**10** Live in (6)
**12** Prefix meaning 'one thousand' (4)
**14** Wound by scratching and tearing (4)
**15** Extent (6)
**17** Ramp (5)
**18** Middle rainbow colour (5)
**20** Gets rid of (9)

**Down**

**2** Kelly, Australian outlaw (3)
**3** Free from an obligation (6)
**4** They might be spare, in a meal (4)
**5** Pressing (7)
**6** Inconsistent (3-2-4)
**7** Wooden-barred musical instrument (9)
**11** Unit of electric charge (7)
**13** Melds together (6)
**16** Cure (4)
**19** It's surrounded by lashes (3)

# PUZZLE 561

**Across**
1 Original example (9)
8 Underground (5)
9 Barely perceptible (5)
10 Pencil remover (6)
12 Settee (4)
14 Time units of a billion years (4)
15 Absorbent paper (6)
17 Blackboard writing stick (5)
18 Iranian language (5)
20 Warped (9)

**Down**
2 Despicable person (3)
3 Addicted (6)
4 Tussock (4)
5 Intoxicates (7)
6 The process of coming into prominence (9)
7 Tactical (9)
11 Bangladeshi language (7)
13 Not have the same traits (6)
16 Sketch (4)
19 Shellfish eggs (3)

# PUZZLE 562

**Across**
1 Changed the position of (10)
7 Made tea (6)
8 Title (4)
9 Brass instruments, eg (5)
11 Mob (5)
13 Acquiesce (5)
14 Disparages (5)
16 Cache (4)
18 Achieve (6)
20 Science of the mind (10)

**Down**
2 Meriting (7)
3 Unrefined (3)
4 Helps (4)
5 All-purpose (7)
6 Not very intelligent (3)
10 Gradually fade out (3,4)
12 Admonition (7)
15 Mess (4)
17 Light knock (3)
19 Israeli city, ___ Aviv (3)

# PUZZLE 563

**Across**
**1** Meddle (9)
**8** Expire, like a subscription (5)
**9** Ballroom dance (5)
**10** Wearing smart clothes, perhaps (6)
**12** Celestial bodies (4)
**14** Bizarre; ridiculous (4)
**15** Hesitates (6)
**17** Value (5)
**18** Agitate (5)
**20** Blocked with mucus (9)

**Down**
**2** Doze (3)
**3** An hour before midnight (6)
**4** Palaver (4)
**5** Comments (7)
**6** Cease business (5,4)
**7** Wrong move (5,4)
**11** Conflagration (7)
**13** Eucharist services (6)
**16** Muffled engine sound (4)
**19** Fed (3)

# PUZZLE 564

**Across**
**1** Old fortified building (6)
**4** Oceanic swell (4)
**6** Leaning typeface (6)
**7** Makes a mistake (4)
**8** Department (6)
**11** Inkling (4)
**12** Sleeve end (4)
**13** Possibility of danger (6)
**16** Aspersion (4)
**17** Authoritarian government (6)
**18** Exercise locations (4)
**19** Respectable (6)

**Down**
**1** Scale (5)
**2** Used to connect floors (5)
**3** Ran into (11)
**4** Conjunction expressing a choice (7)
**5** Roofed portico (7)
**9** Ordinarily (7)
**10** Endeavours (7)
**14** A select group (5)
**15** Larceny (5)

# PUZZLE 565

**Across**
**1** Beforehand (2,7)
**8** Impulses (5)
**9** Foggy (5)
**10** Connected with vision (6)
**12** Two together (4)
**14** Uncouth (4)
**15** Type of fuel (6)
**17** Analyse, as in a sentence (5)
**18** Litigating (5)
**20** Double (9)

**Down**
**2** Old horse (3)
**3** Disappointment (6)
**4** Intentions (4)
**5** Practices (7)
**6** Signature (9)
**7** A set of foundation stories (9)
**11** Be put through (7)
**13** Glittery Christmas material (6)
**16** Exclamation of frustration (4)
**19** Rankle (3)

# PUZZLE 566

**Across**
**1** Horse competition event (4,7)
**6** Fantasy of perfection (6)
**7** Colour similar to turquoise (4)
**8** Useful (5)
**11** Go around the edge of (5)
**12** Belief system (5)
**13** Confuse (5)
**17** Illustrious warrior (4)
**18** Brushes up (6)
**19** At ease (11)

**Down**
**1** Coarse (5)
**2** Circus performer (5)
**3** Vivacity (4)
**4** Pursued (7)
**5** Gearstick position (7)
**9** 1920s decorative style (3,4)
**10** Fall asleep (4,3)
**14** Nerd (5)
**15** Follow as a result (5)
**16** Website member (4)

# PUZZLE 567

**Across**
1 At first (10)
7 Beams (6)
8 Flop on the big-screen (4)
9 Battery terminal (5)
11 Large case (5)
13 Common furniture timber source (5)
14 Biblical gift (5)
16 Mature female reproductive cell (4)
18 Release from a catch (6)
20 For general use (3-7)

**Down**
2 Courting (7)
3 Maiden (3)
4 Upfront facial feature (4)
5 Freedom (7)
6 'Delicious!' (3)
10 Using base ten (7)
12 Unrelaxed (7)
15 Code word for 'Z' (4)
17 By way of (3)
19 Joint between the thigh and pelvis (3)

# PUZZLE 568

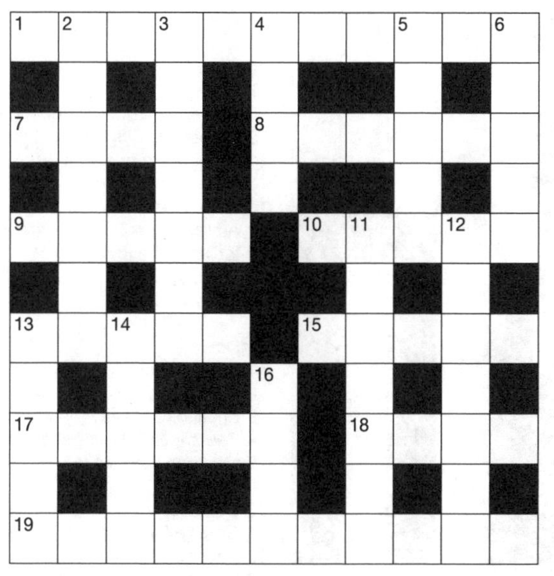

**Across**
1 Setting up (11)
7 Snow runners (4)
8 Japanese emperor (6)
9 *The Little Mermaid* princess (5)
10 Secret agents (5)
13 Preliminary rounds (5)
15 Words that say what is happening (5)
17 Wily (6)
18 Nobleman between viscount and marquess (4)
19 Nature; character (11)

**Down**
2 Durable timber source (3,4)
3 Quickest (7)
4 Pastes (4)
5 Baghdad resident (5)
6 Crass (5)
11 Keep from occurring (7)
12 Commerce restriction (7)
13 Despised (5)
14 The Ram (5)
16 Cheats (4)

# PUZZLE 569

**Across**

**1** Bringing back (11)
**7** Large, luxury car (4)
**8** A monkey's favourite fruit? (6)
**9** Acts like a baby? (5)
**10** Very large sea that spans large parts of the world (5)
**13** Belonging to which person? (5)
**15** Raised platform (5)
**17** Chauffeur (6)
**18** Throws through the air (4)
**19** Nostalgic (11)

**Down**

**2** Tomb inscription (7)
**3** Narrow strips of pasta (7)
**4** Small labels (4)
**5** Absurd (5)
**6** Wheat, eg (5)
**11** From Barcelona, eg (7)
**12** A branch of maths (7)
**13** Walks through water (5)
**14** Group of stars known as 'The Hunter' (5)
**16** Lip of a cup (4)

# PUZZLE 570

**Across**

**3** Not fair (5)
**6** Ape (7)
**7** Depart (5)
**8** Roman guardian of doors (5)
**9** On behalf of (3)
**11** Asked, as a question (5)
**13** Geeks (5)
**15** Short time (abbr.) (3)
**18** Artillery burst (5)
**19** Indian language (5)
**20** Slipping (7)
**21** Show (5)

**Down**

**1** Edible tuber (6)
**2** Pathogens (7)
**3** Small bird of prey (6)
**4** December 25th, for short (4)
**5** Membership fees (4)
**10** Judges (7)
**12** Death (6)
**14** Godlike (6)
**16** Boutique (4)
**17** Cancel, on a computer (4)

# PUZZLE 571

**Across**

**1** Get to work (7,4)
**7** Long-necked waterbird (4)
**8** Noisier (6)
**9** Precious stone (5)
**10** Bender (5)
**13** Satisfies (5)
**15** Ancient Egyptian symbols of life (5)
**17** Absorb food (6)
**18** Masterfully (4)
**19** Presuppositions (11)

**Down**

**2** Not any place (7)
**3** Transform (7)
**4** Large, showy flower (4)
**5** More senior (5)
**6** Viking (5)
**11** Inhabitant of northern India territory (7)
**12** Organizational level (7)
**13** Means of mass communication (5)
**14** Borders (5)
**16** Red light instruction (4)

# PUZZLE 572

**Across**

**1** Fawning (11)
**7** Receiver (7)
**8** Any whatever (3)
**9** Industrial fair (4)
**11** Excellent (6)
**13** Planetarium (6)
**14** Printing error? (4)
**16** Mud-coloured (3)
**17** Tossed (7)
**19** Exemplified (11)

**Down**

**1** Someone with an interest in a business (11)
**2** Slice with a knife (3)
**3** Body of still water, sometimes found in a garden (4)
**4** Manual counting tool (6)
**5** Dramatic genre (7)
**6** Callous (4-7)
**10** Long, tapering, edible root (7)
**12** Something of little value (6)
**15** Predatory freshwater fish (4)
**18** Flower container (3)

# PUZZLE 573

**Across**
- **1** Under soil (6)
- **4** Nip with a beak (4)
- **6** Loads (6)
- **7** Ancient writing symbol (4)
- **8** Digit (6)
- **11** South American native (4)
- **12** A lecherous gaze (4)
- **13** Construction sheets (6)
- **16** Material for burning (4)
- **17** Completely (2,4)
- **18** Enclosures for domestic animals (4)
- **19** Apart from (6)

**Down**
- **1** Concise (5)
- **2** Come to maturity (5)
- **3** Explanatory (11)
- **4** Iranian (7)
- **5** Contemptuous (7)
- **9** US rapper (3,4)
- **10** Distorts (7)
- **14** Escape (5)
- **15** Break in pieces (5)

# PUZZLE 574

**Across**
- **1** Opposition (10)
- **7** Narrow, steep valley (6)
- **8** The London Underground (4)
- **9** Dance moves (5)
- **11** Everest, eg (5)
- **13** Synthetic clothing material (5)
- **14** Tally (3,2)
- **16** Egg-shaped (4)
- **18** Biblical shrub (6)
- **20** Find by chance (4,6)

**Down**
- **2** Precisely (7)
- **3** Climbing vine (3)
- **4** Adjust the pitch of (4)
- **5** Obstacle that must be cleared when serving? (3,4)
- **6** Decline (3)
- **10** Puzzle (7)
- **12** Brain cells (7)
- **15** Second-largest moon of Saturn (4)
- **17** 1980s computer, ___ 20 (3)
- **19** Respectful address (3)

# PUZZLE 575

**Across**

**3** Fasten (5)
**6** Via unknown means (7)
**7** Inner psyche (5)
**8** Secret supply (5)
**9** Weird (3)
**11** Jazz variant (5)
**13** Narrow water inlet (5)
**15** Signal 'yes' (3)
**18** Woodwind instrument (5)
**19** Type of medical dialysis (5)
**20** Far out (7)
**21** Start (5)

**Down**

**1** Liquid container (6)
**2** Edition (7)
**3** Prizes (6)
**4** Be unsuccessful (4)
**5** Revealing photo? (1-3)
**10** Bucks (7)
**12** Powder from flowers (6)
**14** A very short moment (2,4)
**16** Dull; lacking brightness (4)
**17** Cosy (4)

# PUZZLE 576

**Across**

**1** Continually self-referencing (9)
**7** Spicy cuisine (5)
**8** Relating to charged particles (5)
**10** Semi-precious agate (4)
**11** Brawn (6)
**14** Long-handled spoons (6)
**15** Photo (4)
**17** Dance nightclub (5)
**19** Towers (5)
**20** The state of being unknown (9)

**Down**

**2** Liked (7)
**3** Elbow bone (4)
**4** Incite (4,2)
**5** Railway transport vehicle (3)
**6** Moved through a document (8)
**9** Least expensive (8)
**12** Bend out of shape (7)
**13** Epic (6)
**16** Make fuzzy (4)
**18** Replace during a game (3)

# PUZZLE 577

**Across**
**1** Outdoor meal (6)
**4** Mail (4)
**6** Loll (6)
**7** Kills (4)
**8** Type of gundog (6)
**11** Plant with large, showy flowers (4)
**12** Defrost (4)
**13** Conjured up (6)
**16** Deceiver (4)
**17** Evening meal (6)
**18** Items laid by birds (4)
**19** Completely without (6)

**Down**
**1** Tugs (5)
**2** Enumerate (5)
**3** Alert and coherent (5-6)
**4** Stipulation (7)
**5** Be enough (7)
**9** Resounding (7)
**10** Successfully opposes (7)
**14** Japanese bamboo-sword fencing (5)
**15** Took a chance (5)

# PUZZLE 578

**Across**
**1** Contrary (11)
**7** Showreel (4)
**8** Boneless meat (6)
**9** Craze (5)
**10** Make mischief (3,2)
**13** First NATO phonetic letter (5)
**15** Besmirch (5)
**17** By mouth (6)
**18** Way out (4)
**19** In advance (5,2,4)

**Down**
**2** Protective garment (7)
**3** Unwise (7)
**4** Data (4)
**5** Bay or cove (5)
**6** Arise from bed (3,2)
**11** Remark (7)
**12** Nuclear-reactor fuel (7)
**13** Odour (5)
**14** Flat geometric surface (5)
**16** Device for maintaining orientation (4)

# PUZZLE 579

**Across**

**3** Long, hard seat (5)
**6** Merit (7)
**7** People (5)
**8** Kitchen shield (5)
**9** Covenant's chest (3)
**11** Reasoning (5)
**13** One having lunch, perhaps (5)
**15** Grammar article (3)
**18** Be attracted to (5)
**19** Suitor (5)
**20** From Ankara, perhaps (7)
**21** Ten Commandments scribe (5)

**Down**

**1** Avoid leaving (4,2)
**2** Down payment (7)
**3** Prior to (6)
**4** World's longest river (4)
**5** Booing sound (4)
**10** Bar-based singing activity (7)
**12** Maps (6)
**14** Abundance (6)
**16** Having doggy-paddled (4)
**17** Cuts, as in grass (4)

# PUZZLE 580

**Across**

**1** Prestidigitation (11)
**7** Owner (6)
**8** Tease (4)
**9** Sofa (5)
**11** Extracts ore (5)
**13** Words from a song (5)
**14** White-feathered wading bird (5)
**16** Hike (4)
**18** Not familiar (6)
**20** Tools (11)

**Down**

**2** Thrift (7)
**3** Halt (3)
**4** Challenge to do something (4)
**5** Charting (7)
**6** Kind (3)
**10** Game with two wickets (7)
**12** Primary constituent of matter (7)
**15** Spiritual teacher (4)
**17** Exercise on a treadmill (3)
**19** Operate (3)

# PUZZLE 581

**Across**
**1** Rations (10)
**7** Method (6)
**8** 'Sorry!' (4)
**9** Ice-skate support (5)
**11** Amusing (5)
**13** Member of a travelling people (5)
**14** Bird homes (5)
**16** Small, jumping insect (4)
**18** Portable computer (6)
**20** Reword (10)

**Down**
**2** Faithfulness (7)
**3** Not at home (3)
**4** Weapons (4)
**5** Ending (7)
**6** Wear down (3)
**10** Misery (7)
**12** Countries (7)
**15** Flashing light on a radar (4)
**17** Fleshy mouth opening (3)
**19** By way of (3)

# PUZZLE 582

**Across**
**1** In error (10)
**7** Enumerates (6)
**8** Stare open-mouthed (4)
**9** Men (5)
**11** Post (5)
**13** Phobias (5)
**14** Official order (5)
**16** Tide movements out to sea (4)
**18** Consign (6)
**20** Generally speaking (2,3,5)

**Down**
**2** Seclude (7)
**3** Metal container (3)
**4** Loving lip touch (4)
**5** Logically inverted (7)
**6** Natter (3)
**10** Europe and Asia combined (7)
**12** Hitting with the foot (7)
**15** Sour substance (4)
**17** Float gently up and down (3)
**19** Acceptance of fault, ___ culpa (3)

# PUZZLE 583

**Across**
- **1** Citrus fruit preserve (9)
- **8** Evaluated (5)
- **9** Indian minced-meat ball (5)
- **10** Counsel (6)
- **12** Egyptian cross (4)
- **14** Specific day (4)
- **15** Burped, as in a baby (6)
- **17** Lady (5)
- **18** Italian seaport (5)
- **20** Introduce; establish (9)

**Down**
- **2** Formicarium resident (3)
- **3** Unassuming (6)
- **4** Gospel author (4)
- **5** Stated the meaning of (7)
- **6** Mechanical failure (9)
- **7** Principal church (9)
- **11** Required dietary nutrient (7)
- **13** Very small (6)
- **16** String tangle (4)
- **19** Parasitic insect egg (3)

# PUZZLE 584

**Across**
- **1** Conjecture (11)
- **7** Vivacity (4)
- **8** Preserve a body from decay (6)
- **9** Accounts inspection (5)
- **10** Concepts (5)
- **13** Rule as monarch (5)
- **15** Tongue of fire (5)
- **17** Woman graduate (6)
- **18** Organized criminals (4)
- **19** The study of numbers (11)

**Down**
- **2** Fragrance (7)
- **3** Dropping in temperature (7)
- **4** Didn't tell the truth (4)
- **5** Angry (5)
- **6** Titles (5)
- **11** Greatly please (7)
- **12** Factual yearbook (7)
- **13** Give new weapons to (5)
- **14** Arctic native (5)
- **16** Soothing ointment (4)

# PUZZLE 585

**Across**
**1** Setting off (10)
**7** Cigarette addict (6)
**8** Needle-leaved evergreen tree (4)
**9** Flicks (5)
**11** Well-known (5)
**13** Mocks (5)
**14** Young bird (5)
**16** Aid a crime (4)
**18** Allows entry (6)
**20** Written good-luck wish (3,3,4)

**Down**
**2** Join together (7)
**3** Bother (3)
**4** Subtle or invisible emanation (4)
**5** Charge with misconduct (7)
**6** Pistol (3)
**10** Nuptial (7)
**12** Makes enthusiastic (7)
**15** Deep wound (4)
**17** Type of snake (3)
**19** Rabble (3)

# PUZZLE 586

**Across**
**1** Flunked (6)
**4** A thin layer of dirt (4)
**6** Work-experience trainee (6)
**7** Close (4)
**8** Notify (6)
**11** Computer operating system (4)
**12** Catapult (4)
**13** Not any person (6)
**16** Hood (4)
**17** Large soup dish (6)
**18** Affirmative votes (4)
**19** Elevates (6)

**Down**
**1** Buckwheat pancakes (5)
**2** Theme (5)
**3** Divisor (11)
**4** Trouble (7)
**5** Learned (7)
**9** Badly behaved (7)
**10** Does as requested (7)
**14** Auguries (5)
**15** Jerks (5)

# PUZZLE 587

**Across**

**1** Deliberately arousing (11)
**7** Hit a golf ball on the green (6)
**8** Recommend strongly (4)
**9** Sends a parcel (5)
**11** Impudence (5)
**13** Without doubt (2,3)
**14** Adjust (5)
**16** Field (4)
**18** Wound (6)
**20** Not being quite right (11)

**Down**

**2** Approximately (7)
**3** Person who treats sick animals (3)
**4** Encryption system (4)
**5** Came into contact with (7)
**6** Laze about (slang) (3)
**10** Body of troops (7)
**12** Ends a period of validity (7)
**15** Silvery white metal (4)
**17** Ballot vote for new candidates (abbr.) (3)
**19** *Game of Thrones* character, Snow (3)

# PUZZLE 588

**Across**

**1** Accusation (6)
**4** Spurt (4)
**6** Assistance (6)
**7** Night-time birds (4)
**8** Boundary (6)
**11** Hammer target (4)
**12** Heat-retaining, as clothes (4)
**13** Group of states under one power (6)
**16** Trigonometry function (4)
**17** Less at ease (6)
**18** Successor to Edmund Ironside (4)
**19** Ideas (6)

**Down**

**1** Chocolate substitute pod (5)
**2** More competent (5)
**3** Application of rules (11)
**4** Adult (5-2)
**5** Wackier (7)
**9** Sustained show of appreciation (7)
**10** Most moist (7)
**14** Upper part of the pelvis (5)
**15** Merits (5)

# PUZZLE 589

**Across**

**1** Move around freely (4,3,2)
**7** Spiritual emblem (5)
**8** Viral disease that can cause paralysis (5)
**10** Having little or no rain (4)
**11** Round shape (6)
**14** Absolute truth (6)
**15** Signs a contract (4)
**17** Pictorial word puzzle (5)
**19** Contemptible person (5)
**20** Nations (9)

**Down**

**2** Acquires (7)
**3** Furry, red Muppet monster (4)
**4** Serviette (6)
**5** Hairstyling substance (3)
**6** A new face (8)
**9** Exceed a limit (8)
**12** Perform a magic trick (7)
**13** Teaching unit (6)
**16** Musical legato mark (4)
**18** Pal (3)

# PUZZLE 590

**Across**

**1** Not wanted (11)
**7** Braking parachute (6)
**8** Advisor (4)
**9** Devoutness (5)
**11** Entertain (5)
**13** Gawked at (5)
**14** Make one's own (5)
**16** A line of soldiers (4)
**18** Deed (6)
**20** Approximately (11)

**Down**

**2** Caring for (7)
**3** It may be boiled or scrambled (3)
**4** Individual account entry (4)
**5** Fearful (7)
**6** Youth (3)
**10** Hiker (7)
**12** Backing (7)
**15** 'That's funny' (2,2)
**17** Material thrown from a volcano (3)
**19** Possible die decision (3)

# PUZZLE 591

**Across**

**3** Ungainly (5)
**6** Marriage dissolution (7)
**7** Collection of songs (5)
**8** Infectious agent (5)
**9** Nourished (3)
**11** Pale purple shade (5)
**13** Lightheaded (5)
**15** Angling essential (3)
**18** Small garden ornament (5)
**19** Scarcer (5)
**20** Bear the weight of (7)
**21** Push (5)

**Down**

**1** Bathing top and bottoms (6)
**2** Fashionable (7)
**3** Intermeshed (6)
**4** Spiders' homes (4)
**5** Edible roots (4)
**10** Gravitas (7)
**12** Unrefined (6)
**14** Horror movie staple (6)
**16** Experts (4)
**17** Half a sextet (4)

# PUZZLE 592

**Across**

**3** Messes (5)
**6** Flowering plant grown as fodder (7)
**7** Incite; goad (5)
**8** Dirty mark (5)
**9** Chop away at (3)
**11** Leave somewhere (2,3)
**13** Intoxicated (5)
**15** For example (3)
**18** Grumpy expression (5)
**19** Sharp end (5)
**20** Non-believer (7)
**21** Vehicle that travels on rails (5)

**Down**

**1** Extremely inebriated (slang) (6)
**2** Different (7)
**3** Posted (6)
**4** Reproduce (4)
**5** Pepper's mate (4)
**10** Ruined (7)
**12** Patterned Scottish cloth (6)
**14** Freshest (6)
**16** Expectorate (4)
**17** Capital of Peru (4)

# PUZZLE 593

**Across**

**1** List someone's faults (9)
**7** Tosses (5)
**8** Original New Zealander (5)
**10** Make changes (4)
**11** Self-service meal (6)
**14** Two-way switch (6)
**15** Damage, as in a muscle or ligament (4)
**17** Sink opening (5)
**19** Jabs (5)
**20** Went down (9)

**Down**

**2** Bringing up (7)
**3** Exam (4)
**4** University site (6)
**5** Animal park (3)
**6** Impacted (8)
**9** Bank earnings (8)
**12** Small, brown skin mark (7)
**13** Medical centre (6)
**16** Whirled (4)
**18** Bitter (3)

# PUZZLE 594

**Across**

**1** Trivial (11)
**7** Roll of thunder (4)
**8** Scottish highland language (6)
**9** Hirsute (5)
**10** Disperse a liquid mist (5)
**13** Musical combination (5)
**15** Pimples (5)
**17** River crossing (6)
**18** Enormous (4)
**19** Calculation (11)

**Down**

**2** Free from restraint (7)
**3** Ruler of multiple countries (7)
**4** Obscures (4)
**5** Pulley guide (5)
**6** Fortunate (5)
**11** Seer (7)
**12** Briskly, tempo-wise (7)
**13** Involving a third dimension (5)
**14** Poppy-derived narcotic (5)
**16** Outlet (4)

# PUZZLE 595

**Across**
- **1** Linked to the universe (6)
- **4** Small restaurant (4)
- **6** Take a weapon away from (6)
- **7** Former Oasis member, Gallagher (4)
- **8** Mostly useless information (6)
- **11** Dubious (4)
- **12** Assert (4)
- **13** Risky venture (6)
- **16** Adhesive (4)
- **17** Bothering (6)
- **18** Additional subscription fee (4)
- **19** Soft (6)

**Down**
- **1** Young army or police trainee (5)
- **2** Japanese rice dish (5)
- **3** Pressing for a particular outcome (11)
- **4** Verify (7)
- **5** Irritable (7)
- **9** Rotate (7)
- **10** Kind; sort (7)
- **14** Constructed (5)
- **15** Symbol of the US (5)

# PUZZLE 596

**Across**
- **1** Strictly; according to the facts (11)
- **6** Claim (6)
- **7** There are seven in a week (4)
- **8** Hand covering (5)
- **11** Connects (5)
- **12** Smug and ingratiating behaviour (5)
- **13** Off the cuff (2,3)
- **17** Vagrant (4)
- **18** Bob, bun or beehive (6)
- **19** Clever; brainy (11)

**Down**
- **1** Pluck a guitar string (5)
- **2** Large, stringed instrument (5)
- **3** Mountain goat (4)
- **4** Humanlike robot (7)
- **5** Berate (3,4)
- **9** Satirize (7)
- **10** Wordy (7)
- **14** Animal that's often ridden (5)
- **15** Appropriate (2-3)
- **16** Singer, Collins (4)

# PUZZLE 597

**Across**

**1** Inept person (11)
**6** Foreigners (6)
**7** Small notch (4)
**8** Bottomless pit (5)
**11** Having a high opinion of yourself (5)
**12** Settle a debt (5)
**13** Curiously (5)
**17** Deep gulp (4)
**18** Many-tiered temple (6)
**19** Facial looks (11)

**Down**

**1** Australian marsupial (5)
**2** Unite (5)
**3** Come last, perhaps (4)
**4** Century (7)
**5** Regular receipt of money (7)
**9** Hive-building material (7)
**10** Behave arrogantly (7)
**14** Florence religious sight (5)
**15** Groups of twelve months (5)
**16** Chooses, with 'for' (4)

# PUZZLE 598

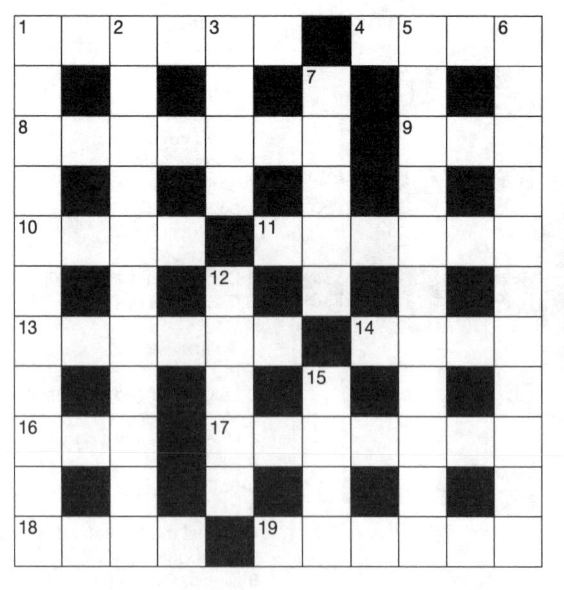

**Across**

**1** Small, useful tool (6)
**4** Action word (4)
**8** Nose opening (7)
**9** Low bank of coral (3)
**10** Very infrequent (4)
**11** Stead (6)
**13** Tags (6)
**14** A person's head (4)
**16** Pimple (3)
**17** Eroding (7)
**18** Cola, eg, in the US (4)
**19** Dog's house (6)

**Down**

**1** Makes less specific (11)
**2** Gave out (11)
**3** Hearing organs (4)
**5** Outcry (11)
**6** North-eastern part of the Indian Ocean (3,2,6)
**7** Provided, as in with food or drink (5)
**12** Imperfections (5)
**15** Walk through water (4)

# PUZZLE 599

**Across**
1 Model used for testing (4-2)
4 Concluding passage (4)
6 Creamy ice cream (6)
7 Tall, rounded vases (4)
8 Nest-invading bird (6)
11 Frozen rain (4)
12 Old (4)
13 Call into question (6)
16 Reduce in size (4)
17 Frozen water drops (6)
18 Female birds (4)
19 Pleasantly (6)

**Down**
1 Supernatural powers (5)
2 Baby's potential affliction (5)
3 Proffered plan (11)
4 Pay money (5,2)
5 Swaying to music (7)
9 Improve (7)
10 Waste-filtering organs (7)
14 Parental sibling (5)
15 Very poor (5)

# PUZZLE 600

**Across**
3 Chart (5)
6 Stores with a wide range of goods (7)
7 Violent disturbances (5)
8 Cog projection (5)
9 Cry like a cat (3)
11 Pointy; not blunt (5)
13 Yellow quartz (5)
15 Result of addition (3)
18 Speak without a script (2-3)
19 US film actress, Christina (5)
20 Giving out light (7)
21 Molars, eg (5)

**Down**
1 Legato, musically (6)
2 Duty rolls (7)
3 Attic room (6)
4 State openly (4)
5 Finely chopped meat and veg dish (4)
10 Phrasing (7)
12 Penalize (6)
14 Makes flush (6)
16 'Curses!' (4)
17 Continuous dull pain (4)

# SOLUTIONS

## 1

| S | W | E | E | P | S | T | A | K | E | S |
|---|---|---|---|---|---|---|---|---|---|---|
| I |  | V |  |  | I |  | N |  | T |  |
| G | U | I | D | E | D |  | C | H | E | F |
| N |  | T |  |  | E |  | I |  | R |  |
| S | P | A | C | E |  | B | E | I | N | G |
|  | L |  | L |  |  |  | N |  | A |  |
| R | A | D | A | R |  | S | T | I | L | L |
|  | T |  | I |  | I |  |  | D |  | E |
| H | E | L | M |  | M | I | X | I | N | G |
|  | A |  | E |  | A |  |  | O |  | A |
| F | U | N | D | A | M | E | N | T | A | L |

## 2

| D | E | S | P | E | R | A | T | E | L | Y |
|---|---|---|---|---|---|---|---|---|---|---|
|  | L |  | E |  | H |  | R |  | I |  |
| R | E | L | A | T | E |  | E | V | E | R |
|  | C |  |  |  | A |  | S |  |  |  |
| S | T | E | E | L |  | I | T | C | H | Y |
|  | E |  | N |  |  |  | L |  | A |  |
| I | D | E | A | S |  | T | E | M | P | O |
|  |  |  | B |  | M |  |  |  | P |  |
| F | U | R | L |  | A | D | O | N | I | S |
|  | N |  | E |  | Y |  | F |  | E |  |
| C | O | L | D | C | O | M | F | O | R | T |

## 3

| G | I | V | E | B | I | R | T | H | T | O |
|---|---|---|---|---|---|---|---|---|---|---|
|  | G |  | A |  | V |  | H |  | I |  |
| C | L | E | R | G | Y | W | O | M | A | N |
|  | O |  | T |  |  |  | R |  | R |  |
| N | O | W | H | E | R | E | N | E | A | R |
|  |  | I |  | M |  | N |  | O |  |  |
| C | O | N | S | U | L | T | A | N | T | S |
|  | V |  | T |  |  |  | L |  | R |  |
| B | A | N | A | N | A | S | P | L | I | T |
|  | T |  | I |  | R |  | H |  | A |  |
| R | E | G | R | E | T | T | A | B | L | Y |

## 4

| S | A | C | H | E | R | T | O | R | T | E |
|---|---|---|---|---|---|---|---|---|---|---|
|  | L |  | E |  | U |  |  | I |  | V |
| F | L | E | A |  | G | U | I | N | E | A |
|  | E |  | V |  | S |  |  | S |  | D |
| O | G | L | E | S |  | O | B | E | S | E |
|  | R |  | N |  |  |  | L |  | U |  |
| N | O | I | S | E |  | Y | E | L | P | S |
| U |  | S |  |  | O |  | S |  | R |  |
| D | O | L | L | A | R |  | S | E | E | P |
| G |  | E |  |  | A |  | E |  | M |  |
| E | S | T | A | B | L | I | S | H | E | S |

## 5

| A | S | O | P | P | O | S | E | D | T | O |
|---|---|---|---|---|---|---|---|---|---|---|
| G |  | V |  | A |  | C |  | R |  | B |
| O | P | A | Q | U | E | R |  | A | T | S |
| R |  |  |  | L |  | E |  | C |  | E |
| A | W | R | Y |  | L | A | T | H | E | R |
| P |  | O |  | U |  | M |  | M |  | V |
| H | A | B | I | T | S |  | S | A | G | A |
| O |  | O |  | O |  | A |  |  |  | T |
| B | I | T |  | P | U | N | J | A | B | I |
| I |  | I |  | I |  | N |  | L |  | O |
| A | C | C | L | A | M | A | T | I | O | N |

## 6

| P | E | R | S | P | E | C | T | I | V | E |
|---|---|---|---|---|---|---|---|---|---|---|
| L |  | E |  |  | K |  | H |  | O |  |
| E | N | L | A | C | E |  | R | U | L | E |
| A |  | I |  |  | D |  | U |  | T |  |
| S | A | C | K | S |  | A | S | S | A | M |
|  | R |  | N |  |  |  | T |  | G |  |
| O | T | T | E | R |  | A | S | P | E | N |
|  | I |  | A |  | A |  |  | A |  | O |
| A | C | I | D |  | M | U | E | S | L | I |
|  | L |  | E |  | E |  |  | T |  | S |
| L | E | A | D | I | N | G | L | A | D | Y |

## 7

| C | O | N | J | U | N | C | T | I | O | N |
|---|---|---|---|---|---|---|---|---|---|---|
| O |  | E |  | N |  | A |  | N |  | E |
| G | U | E | S | S | E | S |  | T | A | U |
| N |  |  |  | U |  | E |  | O |  | R |
| O | N | W | A | R | D |  | J | U | D | O |
| S |  | A |  | E |  | D |  | C |  | L |
| C | U | R | E |  | T | E | C | H | N | O |
| E |  | S |  | N |  | F |  |  |  | G |
| N | T | H |  | O | R | I | G | A | M | I |
| T |  | I |  | N |  | N |  | G |  | S |
| I | M | P | R | O | V | E | M | E | N | T |

## 8

| A | B | R | A | C | A | D | A | B | R | A |
|---|---|---|---|---|---|---|---|---|---|---|
|  | E |  | G |  | U |  | B |  | O |  |
| B | A | R | A | C | K | O | B | A | M | A |
|  | R |  | I |  |  |  | E |  | A |  |
| I | D | E | N | T | I | F | Y | I | N | G |
|  |  | L |  | O |  | L |  | N |  |  |
| U | N | F | O | R | T | U | N | A | T | E |
|  | A |  | W |  |  |  | I |  | I |  |
| S | I | G | N | I | F | I | C | A | N | T |
|  | V |  | E |  | A |  | E |  | G |  |
| S | E | C | R | E | T | A | R | I | E | S |

9

10

11

12

| A | G | E | O | F | R | E | A | S | O | N |
|---|---|---|---|---|---|---|---|---|---|---|
|  | U |  | B |  | A |  | D |  | C |  |
| A | S | C | E | R | T | A | I | N | E | D |
|  | T |  | Y |  |  |  | E |  | A |  |
| C | O | N | S | T | I | T | U | E | N | T |
|  |  | I |  | H |  | A |  | A |  |  |
| C | O | M | M | E | N | T | A | T | O | R |
|  | Z |  | O |  |  |  | R |  | N |  |
| S | O | C | I | O | L | O | G | I | S | T |
|  | N |  | S |  | E |  | U |  | E |  |
| S | E | T | T | L | E | M | E | N | T | S |

13

14

| D | U | P | L | I | C | A | T | E | S |  |
|---|---|---|---|---|---|---|---|---|---|---|
| I |  | I |  | S |  |  | A |  | K |  |
| S | U | N | D | R | Y |  | G | N | A | T |
| C |  | E |  | A |  |  |  | E |  | E |
| H | E | A | V | E | H | O |  | V | I | D |
| A |  | P |  | L |  | F |  | E |  | I |
| R | I | P |  | I | N | F | E | R | N | O |
| G |  | L |  |  |  | E |  | M |  | U |
| E | D | E | N |  | B | R | A | I | N | S |
|  | O |  | I |  |  | E |  | N |  | L |
|  | S | P | L | E | N | D | I | D | L | Y |

15

16

## 17

| B | A | D | T | E | M | P | E | R | E | D |
|---|---|---|---|---|---|---|---|---|---|---|
|  | R |  | O |  | A |  |  | I |  | O |
| S | T | E | R | E | O |  | O | V | E | R |
|  | D |  | T |  | R |  |  | A |  | I |
| M | E | N | U |  | I | T | A | L | I | C |
|  | C |  | R |  |  |  | M |  | N |  |
| V | O | T | E | R | S |  | E | A | T | S |
| I |  | R |  |  | T |  | R |  | E |  |
| L | O | A | F |  | O | R | I | E | N | T |
| L |  | M |  |  | I |  | C |  | S |  |
| A | P | P | R | E | C | I | A | T | E | D |

## 18

| S | A | C | H | E | T |  | A | P | S | E |
|---|---|---|---|---|---|---|---|---|---|---|
| U |  | O |  | D |  | A |  | R |  | X |
| B | I | N | D | I | N | G |  | O | R | C |
| M |  | V |  | T |  | O |  | N |  | E |
| E | P | E | E |  | I | N | C | O | M | E |
| R |  | N |  | H |  | Y |  | U |  | D |
| S | P | I | N | A | L |  | A | N | T | I |
| I |  | E |  | L |  | C |  | C |  | N |
| B | A | N |  | V | A | L | U | I | N | G |
| L |  | C |  | E |  | A |  | N |  | L |
| E | Y | E | S |  | S | M | O | G | G | Y |

## 19

| I | M | I | T | A | T | E |  | G | A | B |
|---|---|---|---|---|---|---|---|---|---|---|
| N |  | D |  | B |  | X |  | O |  | O |
| I | K | E |  | S | O | A | P | B | O | X |
| T |  | N |  | U |  | M |  | A |  | I |
| I | N | T | E | R | N |  | P | L | A | N |
| A |  | I |  | D |  | P |  | L |  | G |
| T | A | C | T |  | R | I | S | I | N | G |
| I |  | A |  | G |  | C |  | S |  | L |
| V | I | L | L | A | I | N |  | T | O | O |
| E |  | L |  | R |  | I |  | I |  | V |
| S | O | Y |  | B | I | C | Y | C | L | E |

## 20

| C | U | R | I | N | G |  | T | O | M | E |
|---|---|---|---|---|---|---|---|---|---|---|
| O |  | E |  | E |  | S |  | F |  | M |
| N | O | S | I | E | S | T |  | F | O | P |
| S |  | E |  | D |  | O |  | H |  | T |
| E | L | M | S |  | T | R | E | A | T | Y |
| N |  | B |  | B |  | E |  | N |  | H |
| S | A | L | A | R | Y |  | E | D | G | E |
| U |  | A |  | I |  | A |  | E |  | A |
| S | I | N |  | D | I | V | I | D | E | D |
| E |  | C |  | E |  | E |  | L |  | E |
| S | L | E | D |  | P | R | A | Y | E | D |

## 21

| A | T | T | R | I | B | U | T | I | N | G |
|---|---|---|---|---|---|---|---|---|---|---|
|  | A |  | E |  | U |  |  | O |  | E |
| A | N | S | W | E | R |  | A | N | O | N |
|  | G |  | R |  | S |  |  | I |  | E |
| P | E | S | O |  | T | R | A | C | E | S |
|  | N |  | T |  |  |  | P |  | X |  |
| I | T | S | E | L | F |  | R | O | O | K |
| R |  | H |  |  | A |  | I |  | T |  |
| A | R | E | A |  | R | E | C | O | I | L |
| Q |  | L |  |  | C |  | O |  | C |  |
| I | N | F | L | U | E | N | T | I | A | L |

## 22

| P | A | S | T | E | L |  | C | U | R | T |
|---|---|---|---|---|---|---|---|---|---|---|
| L |  | A |  |  | E |  | O |  | E |  |
| O | W | N | I | N | G |  | L | O | T | S |
| T |  | E |  |  | A |  | L |  | R |  |
| S | C | R | A | W | L |  | E | D | A | M |
|  | A |  | N |  | T |  | C |  | C |  |
| C | R | U | X |  | E | N | T | I | T | Y |
|  | E |  | I |  | N |  |  | C |  | I |
| D | E | C | O |  | D | E | V | I | C | E |
|  | R |  | U |  | E |  |  | N |  | L |
| I | S | I | S |  | R | I | N | G | E | D |

## 23

| C | O | C | H | L | E | A |  | A | L | F |
|---|---|---|---|---|---|---|---|---|---|---|
| L |  | O |  | A |  | D |  | P |  | O |
| E | L | M |  | W | R | A | P | P | E | R |
| A |  | E |  | Y |  | M |  | A |  | G |
| R | O | T | T | E | N |  | U | R | G | E |
| T |  | O |  | R |  | C |  | A |  | T |
| H | A | T | E |  | R | H | Y | T | H | M |
| E |  | E |  | B |  | A |  | C |  | E |
| W | A | R | L | O | C | K |  | H | E | N |
| A |  | M |  | M |  | R |  | I |  | O |
| Y | E | S |  | B | L | A | N | K | E | T |

## 24

|  | B | R | E | A | K | F | A | S | T |  |
|---|---|---|---|---|---|---|---|---|---|---|
| A |  | I |  | B |  | L |  | A |  | S |
| C | O | B | R | A |  | A | D | M | I | T |
| I |  |  |  | C |  | N |  | U |  | R |
| D | R | O | G | U | E |  | U | R | D | U |
| H |  | R |  | S |  | E |  | A |  | C |
| O | D | E | R |  | A | S | S | I | S | T |
| U |  | G |  | M |  | K |  |  |  | U |
| S | P | A | D | E |  | I | N | F | E | R |
| E |  | N |  | A |  | M |  | E |  | E |
|  | P | O | S | T | P | O | N | E | D |  |

## 25

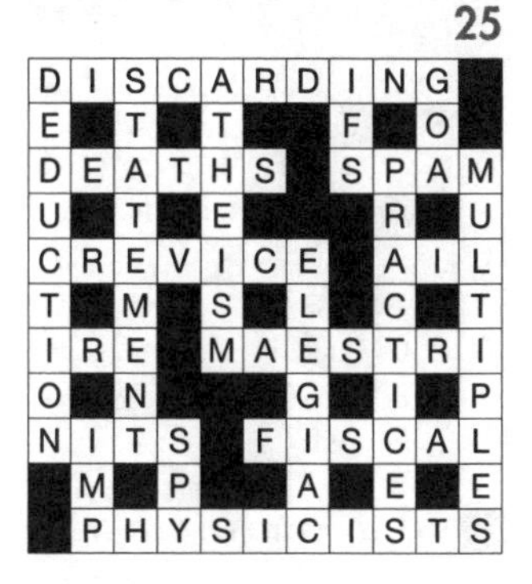

| D | I | S | C | A | R | D | I | N | G |  |
|---|---|---|---|---|---|---|---|---|---|---|
| E |  | T |  | T |  |  | F |  | O |  |
| D | E | A | T | H | S |  | S | P | A | M |
| U |  | T |  | E |  |  |  | R |  | U |
| C | R | E | V | I | C | E |  | A | I | L |
| T |  | M |  | S |  | L |  | C |  | T |
| I | R | E |  | M | A | E | S | T | R | I |
| O |  | N |  |  |  | G |  | I |  | P |
| N | I | T | S |  | F | I | S | C | A | L |
|  | M |  | P |  |  | A |  | E |  | E |
|  | P | H | Y | S | I | C | I | S | T | S |

## 26

| G | R | A | N | D | M | O | T | H | E | R |
|---|---|---|---|---|---|---|---|---|---|---|
|  | E |  | U |  | A |  | R |  | W |  |
| E | D | I | T | O | R |  | E | Y | E | D |
|  | D |  |  |  | K |  | A |  |  |  |
| R | E | E | F | S |  | A | C | T | E | D |
|  | N |  | O |  |  |  | L |  | F |  |
| U | S | E | R | S |  | B | E | E | F | Y |
|  |  |  | G |  | S |  |  |  | E |  |
| E | T | N | A |  | P | O | L | I | C | E |
|  | A |  | V |  | E |  | E |  | T |  |
| F | R | I | E | N | D | L | I | E | S | T |

## 27

| W | E | L | L | G | R | O | O | M | E | D |
|---|---|---|---|---|---|---|---|---|---|---|
|  | M |  | U |  | I |  |  | O |  | O |
| S | P | U | N |  | S | O | L | V | E | D |
|  | O |  | A |  | K |  |  | E |  | G |
| T | R | U | T | H |  | A | D | D | L | E |
|  | I |  | I |  |  |  | E |  | O |  |
| B | A | T | C | H |  | O | P | I | U | M |
| U |  | W |  |  | A |  | R |  | D |  |
| R | A | I | S | E | S |  | I | C | E | D |
| K |  | N |  |  | K |  | V |  | S |  |
| A | S | S | E | S | S | M | E | N | T | S |

## 28

| O | B | L | I | G | A | T | I | O | N | S |
|---|---|---|---|---|---|---|---|---|---|---|
|  | L |  | M |  | B |  |  | U |  | I |
| B | A | L | M |  | B | E | A | T | E | N |
|  | T |  | E |  | A |  |  | D |  | G |
| P | A | I | N | S |  | R | O | O | M | S |
|  | N |  | S |  |  |  | C |  | E |  |
| S | T | E | E | P |  | G | A | S | S | Y |
| W |  | V |  |  | E |  | R |  | S |  |
| E | Y | E | F | U | L |  | I | R | I | S |
| E |  | R |  |  | M |  | N |  | A |  |
| P | S | Y | C | H | O | P | A | T | H | S |

## 29

| S | U | S | C | E | P | T | I | B | L | E |
|---|---|---|---|---|---|---|---|---|---|---|
| E |  | T |  |  | E |  | N |  | E |  |
| P | A | Y | I | N | G |  | O | W | N | S |
| I |  | L |  |  | S |  | R |  | I |  |
| A | C | I | D | S |  | I | D | L | E | S |
|  | A |  | E |  |  |  | E |  | N |  |
| B | R | E | A | K |  | C | R | E | T | E |
|  | I |  | D |  | O |  |  | N |  | R |
| E | B | B | S |  | V | O | O | D | O | O |
|  | O |  | E |  | E |  |  | E |  | D |
| C | U | T | T | I | N | G | E | D | G | E |

## 30

| I | M | P | O | R | T | A | N | T | L | Y |
|---|---|---|---|---|---|---|---|---|---|---|
|  | E |  | W |  | O |  | E |  | Y |  |
| E | X | T | E | N | D |  | W | E | N | T |
|  | I |  |  |  | O |  | B |  |  |  |
| S | C | O | P | E |  | B | O | O | K | S |
|  | A |  | R |  |  |  | R |  | N |  |
| U | N | I | O | N |  | A | N | I | O | N |
|  |  |  | N |  | T |  |  |  | C |  |
| U | P | T | O |  | I | N | J | O | K | E |
|  | I |  | U |  | E |  | E |  | E |  |
| S | T | U | N | G | R | E | N | A | D | E |

## 31

| C | O | N | T | R | I | B | U | T | E | D |
|---|---|---|---|---|---|---|---|---|---|---|
| A |  | O |  | O |  | E |  | E |  | I |
| L | O | T |  | L | E | A | D | E | R | S |
| C |  | I |  | E |  | T |  |  |  | T |
| U | P | O | N |  | M | I | L | I | E | U |
| L |  | N |  | E |  | T |  | T |  | R |
| A | B | S | E | N | T |  | L | A | M | B |
| T |  |  |  | O |  | H |  | L |  | A |
| I | N | C | L | U | D | E |  | I | N | N |
| O |  | A |  | G |  | L |  | A |  | C |
| N | O | N | C | H | A | L | A | N | C | E |

## 32

| S | C | H | O | L | A | R | S | H | I | P |
|---|---|---|---|---|---|---|---|---|---|---|
| T |  | I |  | E |  | E |  | A |  | R |
| E | A | S | I | E | S | T |  | N | E | O |
| W |  |  |  | K |  | A |  | D |  | G |
| A | R | T | S |  | K | I | L | L | E | R |
| R |  | E |  | K |  | L |  | E |  | E |
| D | R | A | W | U | P |  | U | S | E | S |
| S |  | C |  | N |  | H |  |  |  | S |
| H | U | H |  | G | N | O | C | C | H | I |
| I |  | E |  | F |  | E |  | A |  | V |
| P | E | R | S | U | A | D | A | B | L | E |

## 33

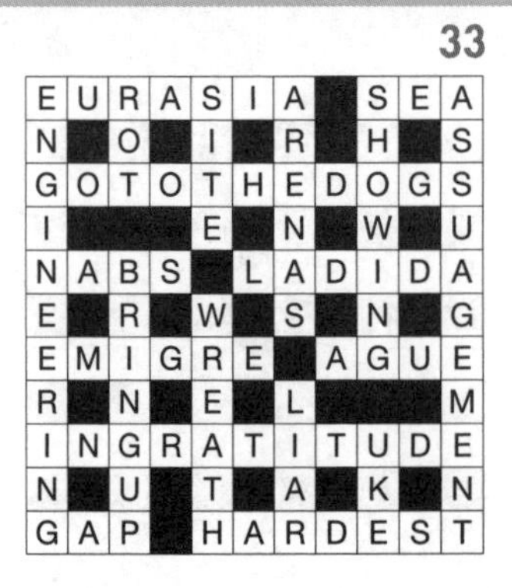

| | | | | | | | | | | |
|---|---|---|---|---|---|---|---|---|---|---|
| E | U | R | A | S | I | A | | S | E | A |
| N | | O | | I | | R | | H | | S |
| G | O | T | O | T | H | E | D | O | G | S |
| I | | | | E | | N | | W | | U |
| N | A | B | S | | L | A | D | I | D | A |
| E | | R | | W | | S | | N | | G |
| E | M | I | G | R | E | | A | G | U | E |
| R | | N | | E | | L | | | | M |
| I | N | G | R | A | T | I | T | U | D | E |
| N | | U | | T | | A | | K | | N |
| G | A | P | | H | A | R | D | E | S | T |

## 34

| | | | | | | | | | | |
|---|---|---|---|---|---|---|---|---|---|---|
| | O | V | E | R | D | R | A | F | T | |
| F | | I | | A | | I | | A | | P |
| U | N | C | U | T | | L | A | S | E | R |
| L | | | | I | | E | | H | | O |
| L | E | S | S | O | N | | W | I | S | P |
| S | | T | | S | | C | | O | | O |
| C | L | U | B | | P | L | A | N | E | S |
| A | | B | | A | | O | | | | A |
| L | I | B | E | L | | S | N | A | I | L |
| E | | L | | S | | E | | I | | S |
| | S | E | C | O | N | D | A | R | Y | |

## 35

| | | | | | | | | | | |
|---|---|---|---|---|---|---|---|---|---|---|
| | P | H | Y | S | I | C | I | S | T | |
| M | | I | | O | | O | | P | | A |
| I | N | T | E | R | | L | O | O | K | S |
| S | | | | D | | D | | I | | S |
| D | A | H | L | I | A | | F | L | E | E |
| I | | I | | D | | C | | E | | M |
| R | A | G | E | | C | H | E | R | U | B |
| E | | H | | E | | A | | | | L |
| C | R | E | A | M | | P | R | I | M | E |
| T | | S | | I | | E | | O | | D |
| | S | T | A | R | T | L | I | N | G | |

## 36

| | | | | | | | | | | |
|---|---|---|---|---|---|---|---|---|---|---|
| P | R | A | C | T | I | C | A | L | L | Y |
| | I | | O | | N | | | E | | E |
| U | S | E | R | | C | A | N | A | D | A |
| | O | | R | | H | | | S | | R |
| S | T | O | U | T | | A | C | T | O | N |
| | T | | P | | | | L | | U | |
| C | O | S | T | S | | R | O | O | T | S |
| H | | Q | | | G | | C | | W | |
| O | C | U | L | A | R | | K | N | O | B |
| S | | I | | | I | | I | | R | |
| E | M | B | O | L | D | E | N | I | N | G |

## 37

| | | | | | | | | | | |
|---|---|---|---|---|---|---|---|---|---|---|
| A | S | S | O | R | T | M | E | N | T | S |
| B | | P | | O | | E | | O | | Y |
| A | G | O | | A | N | A | G | R | A | M |
| N | | N | | N | | N | | | | P |
| D | A | S | H | | W | I | D | E | S | T |
| O | | O | | P | | E | | Y | | O |
| N | A | R | R | O | W | | T | E | R | M |
| S | | | | L | | A | | B | | A |
| H | O | L | D | I | N | G | | A | P | T |
| I | | A | | S | | E | | L | | I |
| P | S | Y | C | H | E | D | E | L | I | C |

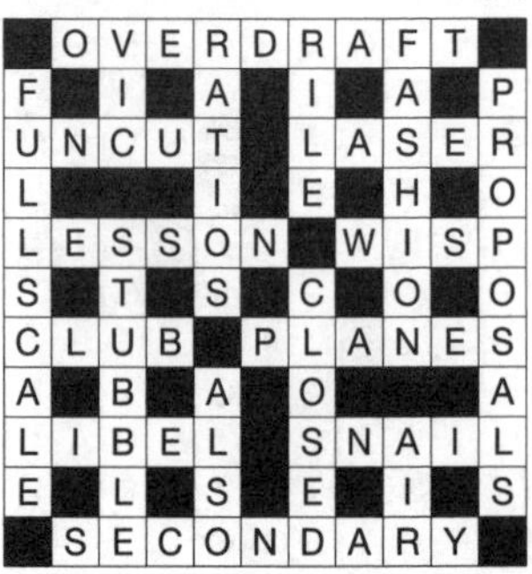

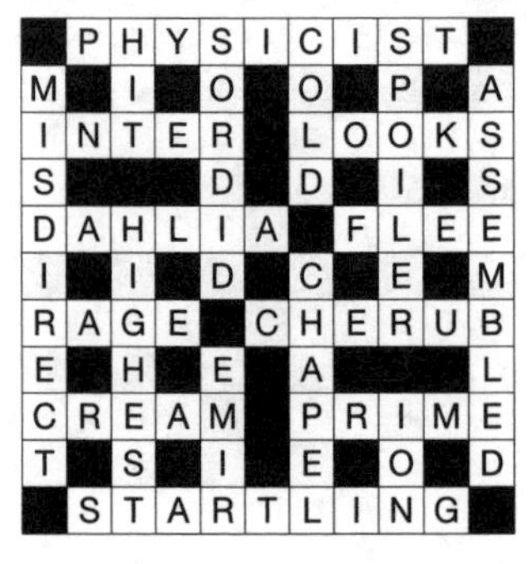

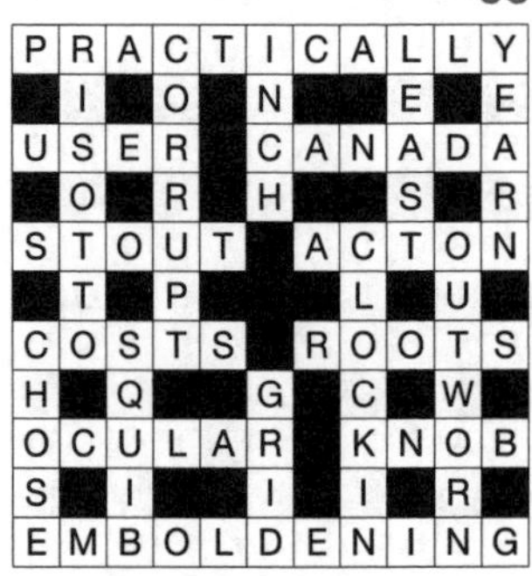

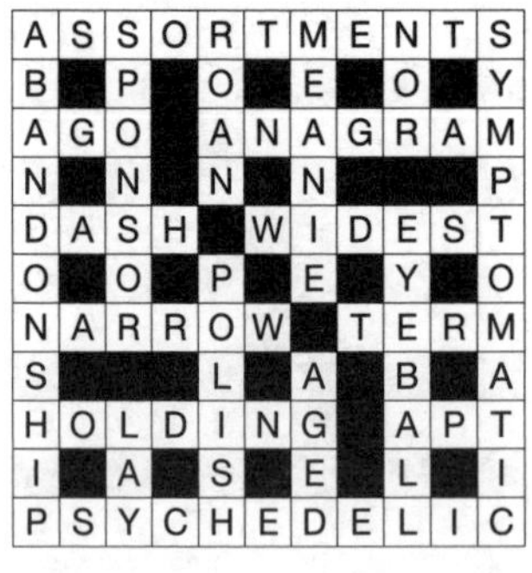

## 38

| | | | | | | | | | | |
|---|---|---|---|---|---|---|---|---|---|---|
| H | I | G | H | L | I | G | H | T | E | R |
| Y | | R | | A | | O | | U | | E |
| D | U | E | | C | H | A | N | G | E | S |
| R | | A | | T | | T | | | | E |
| O | B | T | A | I | N | | P | L | E | A |
| P | | E | | C | | T | | O | | R |
| H | E | R | S | | I | R | O | N | I | C |
| O | | | | T | | A | | G | | H |
| B | U | R | N | I | N | G | | E | K | E |
| I | | A | | E | | I | | S | | R |
| A | D | J | U | D | I | C | A | T | E | S |

## 39

| | | | | | | | | | | |
|---|---|---|---|---|---|---|---|---|---|---|
| | D | I | V | E | R | S | I | T | Y | |
| S | | L | | W | | T | | O | | |
| V | A | L | U | E | | A | T | T | I | C |
| E | | N | | S | | I | | | | A |
| N | O | E | L | | P | R | I | M | E | S |
| G | | S | | B | | S | | I | | S |
| A | S | S | U | R | E | | I | D | L | E |
| L | | | | E | | V | | G | | T |
| I | M | A | G | E | | I | N | E | P | T |
| | | N | | Z | | E | | T | | E |
| | O | T | H | E | R | W | I | S | E | |

## 40

| | | | | | | | | | | |
|---|---|---|---|---|---|---|---|---|---|---|
| S | W | E | A | R | A | N | O | A | T | H |
| Y | | L | | O | | E | | S | | E |
| M | O | E | | P | H | A | L | A | N | X |
| P | | M | | Y | | R | | | | A |
| A | H | E | M | | M | E | N | D | E | D |
| T | | N | | F | | R | | I | | E |
| H | O | T | A | I | R | | E | P | I | C |
| E | | | | E | | O | | L | | I |
| T | A | N | G | R | A | M | | O | H | M |
| I | | U | | C | | I | | M | | A |
| C | O | N | C | E | R | T | H | A | L | L |

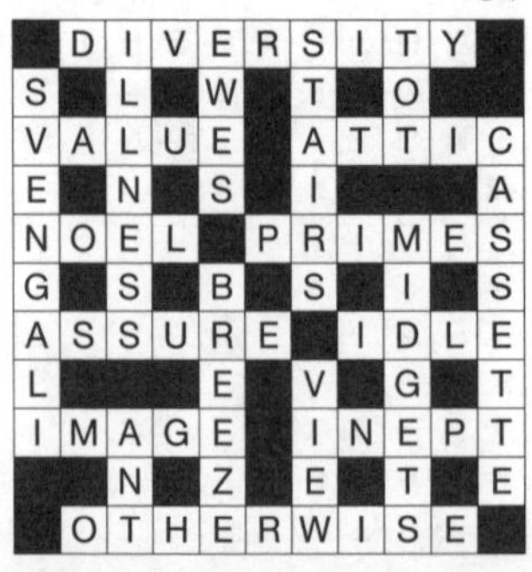

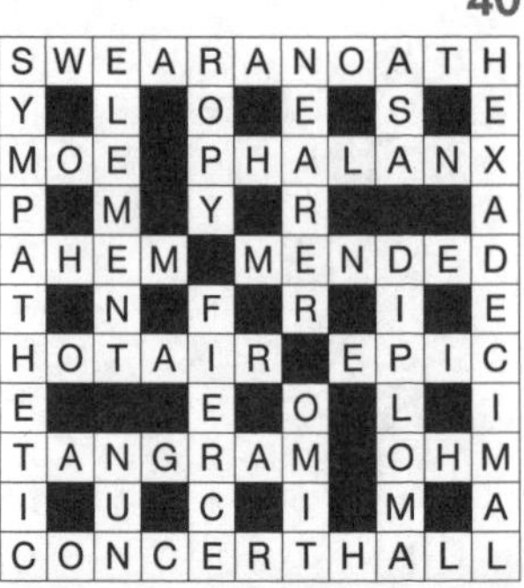

## 41

| B | U | S | S | T | O | P |  | J | O | E |
|---|---|---|---|---|---|---|---|---|---|---|
| U |  | U |  | I |  | L |  | U |  | X |
| T | O | G |  | D | R | E | S | S | U | P |
| T |  | G |  | Y |  | D |  | T |  | E |
| E | W | E | R |  | U | G | L | I | E | R |
| R |  | S |  | D |  | E |  | F |  | I |
| K | I | T | T | E | N |  | V | I | L | E |
| N |  | I |  | C |  | L |  | A |  | N |
| I | S | O | L | A | T | E |  | B | I | C |
| F |  | N |  | M |  | E |  | L |  | E |
| E | O | S |  | P | O | R | T | E | R | S |

## 42

| A | R | C | H | I | P | E | L | A | G | O |
|---|---|---|---|---|---|---|---|---|---|---|
| T |  | H |  | N |  | V |  | H |  | V |
| M | O | A |  | C | L | I | M | A | T | E |
| O |  | T |  | U |  | L |  |  |  | R |
| S | T | E | E | R | S |  | F | L | A | W |
| P |  | A |  | S |  | S |  | I |  | H |
| H | A | U | L |  | R | O | T | A | T | E |
| E |  |  |  | M |  | M |  | I |  | L |
| R | E | P | L | I | C | A |  | S | U | M |
| I |  | E |  | N |  | L |  | O |  | E |
| C | O | N | D | I | T | I | O | N | E | D |

## 43

|  | R | E | S | T | R | I | C | T | S |  |
|---|---|---|---|---|---|---|---|---|---|---|
| T |  | G |  | E |  | F |  | A |  | A |
| E | D | G | E | S |  | F | I | N | E | S |
| L |  |  |  | T |  | Y |  | K |  | T |
| E | L | E | V | E | N |  | S | T | A | R |
| S |  | N |  | D |  | W |  | O |  | O |
| C | O | L | T |  | H | A | P | P | E | N |
| O |  | A |  | T |  | S |  |  |  | A |
| P | O | R | C | H |  | H | A | I | K | U |
| E |  | G |  | E |  | E |  | A |  | T |
|  | R | E | V | E | R | S | I | N | G |  |

## 44

| P | H | O | T | O | G | R | A | P | H | S |
|---|---|---|---|---|---|---|---|---|---|---|
|  | E |  | A |  | O |  |  | L |  | T |
| T | A | L | C |  | D | A | M | A | G | E |
|  | V |  | K |  | S |  |  | I |  | P |
| D | I | A | L | S |  | W | I | N | G | S |
|  | E |  | E |  |  |  | N |  | R |  |
| C | R | U | D | E |  | P | E | C | A | N |
| I |  | N |  |  | Y |  | R |  | N |  |
| R | E | F | I | N | E |  | T | H | I | N |
| C |  | I |  |  | T |  | I |  | T |  |
| A | N | T | I | C | I | P | A | T | E | D |

## 45

|  | J |  | S |  |  | A | P | P | L | E |
|---|---|---|---|---|---|---|---|---|---|---|
| L | O | T | I | O | N | S |  | A |  | C |
|  | Y |  | L |  |  | W | I | D | T | H |
| A | F | F | I | X |  | E |  | S |  | O |
|  | U |  | C |  | I | L | L |  |  |  |
| A | L | L | O | W |  | L | I | N | E | S |
|  |  |  | N | I | B |  | B |  | D |  |
| S |  | K |  | L |  | D | R | U | I | D |
| C | A | N | A | L |  |  | A |  | T |  |
| U |  | I |  | D | E | G | R | E | E | S |
| M | E | T | R | O |  |  | Y |  | D |  |

## 46

| D | O | W | N | G | R | A | D | I | N | G |
|---|---|---|---|---|---|---|---|---|---|---|
|  | U |  | I |  | U |  | E |  | O |  |
| S | T | A | T | U | S |  | P | A | W | S |
|  | C |  |  |  | E |  | R |  |  |  |
| G | R | O | U | P |  | T | E | E | T | H |
|  | O |  | P |  |  |  | S |  | R |  |
| S | P | O | T | S |  | U | S | U | A | L |
|  |  |  | I |  | W |  |  |  | N |  |
| G | O | N | G |  | A | R | R | E | S | T |
|  | D |  | H |  | I |  | O |  | I |  |
| C | E | R | T | I | F | I | C | A | T | E |

## 47

|  | S | U | G | A | R | C | U | B | E |  |
|---|---|---|---|---|---|---|---|---|---|---|
| A |  | N |  | I |  | A |  | I |  |  |
| G | R | I | N | D |  | S | T | O | R | M |
| R |  | F |  | S |  | I |  |  |  | O |
| E | G | O | S |  | U | N | S | E | E | N |
| E |  | R |  | A |  | G |  | N |  | A |
| I | M | M | U | N | E |  | A | F | A | R |
| N |  |  |  | C |  | O |  | O |  | C |
| G | N | A | S | H |  | B | I | R | T | H |
|  |  | S |  | O |  | O |  | C |  | Y |
|  | S | H | O | R | T | E | N | E | D |  |

## 48

| I | N | V | I | T | A | T | I | O | N |  |
|---|---|---|---|---|---|---|---|---|---|---|
|  | A |  | N |  | C |  | D |  | E |  |
| S | U | N | S | E | T |  | Y | A | W | N |
|  | G |  |  |  | S |  | L |  |  |  |
| C | H | E | C | K |  | B | L | O | W | N |
|  | T |  | A |  |  |  | I |  | A |  |
| H | Y | D | R | A |  | S | C | E | N | E |
|  |  |  | A |  | A |  |  |  | T |  |
| G | E | R | M |  | R | A | B | B | I | T |
|  | V |  | E |  | C |  | A |  | N |  |
|  | A | L | L | T | H | E | R | A | G | E |

## 49

## 50

## 51

## 52

## 53

## 54

## 55

## 56

T G PUTTY
QUARTER O O
X A EMERY
LEANS T D O
D D ATE
COYPU YANKS
ANY R E
U F C OTHER
SPELL H P
E A APPLIES
DARED Y R

57

58

59

60

61

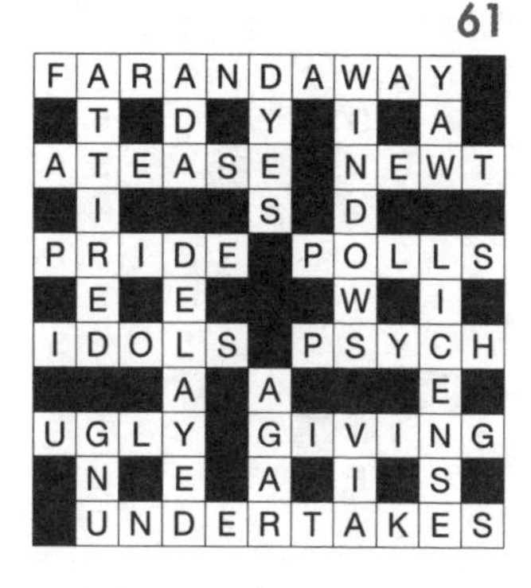

62

| E | M | O | T | I | O | N | A | L | L | Y |
|---|---|---|---|---|---|---|---|---|---|---|
|  | A |  | I |  | N |  | N |  | O |  |
| S | M | A | T | T | E | R | I | N | G | S |
|  | M |  | L |  |  |  | M |  | I |  |
| S | A | F | E | T | Y | M | A | T | C | H |
|  |  | R |  | E |  | A |  | I |  |  |
| E | G | O | M | A | N | I | A | C | A | L |
|  | R |  | E |  |  |  | L |  | N |  |
| P | O | S | S | E | S | S | I | O | N | S |
|  | W |  | O |  | A |  | E |  | U |  |
| U | N | K | N | O | W | I | N | G | L | Y |

63

65

66

67

68

69

70

| E | N | C | O | U | R | A | G | I | N | G |
|---|---|---|---|---|---|---|---|---|---|---|
| | A | | D | | E | | O | | U | |
| H | I | D | D | E | N | | V | I | B | E |
| | L | | | | D | | E | | | |
| N | I | C | K | S | | B | R | I | E | F |
| | N | | I | | | | N | | J | |
| A | G | A | T | E | | A | S | H | E | S |
| | | | C | | C | | | | C | |
| B | L | A | H | | Z | Y | G | O | T | E |
| | E | | E | | A | | A | | E | |
| C | O | U | N | T | R | Y | S | I | D | E |

71

72

## 73

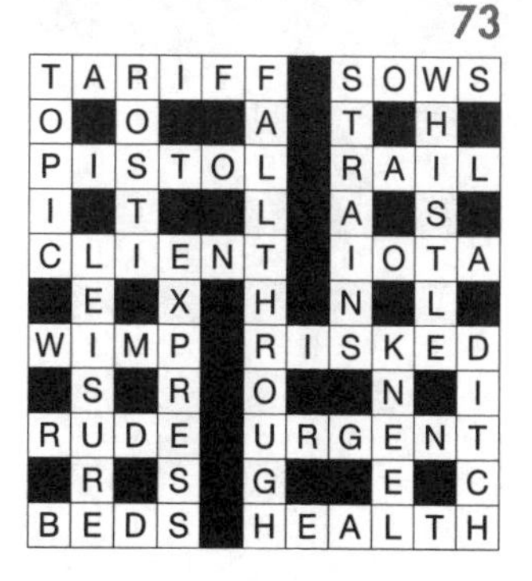

| | | | | | | | | | | |
|---|---|---|---|---|---|---|---|---|---|---|
| T | A | R | I | F | F | | S | O | W | S |
| O | | O | | | A | | T | | H | |
| P | I | S | T | O | L | | R | A | I | L |
| I | | T | | | L | | A | | S | |
| C | L | I | E | N | T | | I | O | T | A |
| | E | | X | | H | | N | | L | |
| W | I | M | P | | R | I | S | K | E | D |
| | S | | R | | O | | | N | | I |
| R | U | D | E | | U | R | G | E | N | T |
| | R | | S | | G | | | E | | C |
| B | E | D | S | | H | E | A | L | T | H |

## 74

| | | | | | | | | | | |
|---|---|---|---|---|---|---|---|---|---|---|
| I | N | V | E | S | T | M | E | N | T | S |
| | E | | S | | I | | Q | | E | |
| D | A | N | C | E | D | | U | L | N | A |
| | R | | | | E | | A | | | |
| L | E | A | R | N | | C | L | O | T | H |
| | S | | E | | | | L | | H | |
| S | T | A | T | E | | C | Y | N | I | C |
| | | | A | | D | | | | R | |
| S | E | M | I | | R | E | V | I | S | E |
| | R | | N | | A | | O | | T | |
| P | A | S | S | A | G | E | W | A | Y | S |

## 75

| | | | | | | | | | | |
|---|---|---|---|---|---|---|---|---|---|---|
| C | O | N | T | R | A | C | T | I | N | G |
| H | | O | | | D | | R | | U | |
| I | N | T | E | N | D | | A | R | C | S |
| N | | E | | | S | | I | | L | |
| A | U | D | I | T | | A | N | G | E | R |
| | N | | N | | | | E | | U | |
| S | C | U | D | S | | P | R | I | S | M |
| | L | | U | | W | | | N | | O |
| M | E | W | L | | A | R | G | A | L | I |
| | A | | G | | T | | | P | | R |
| G | R | E | E | N | T | U | R | T | L | E |

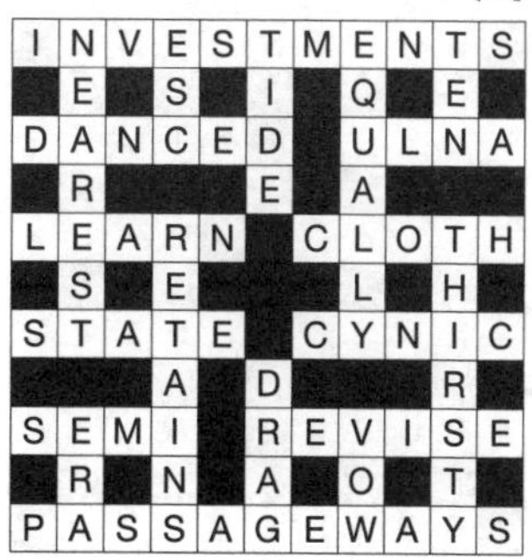

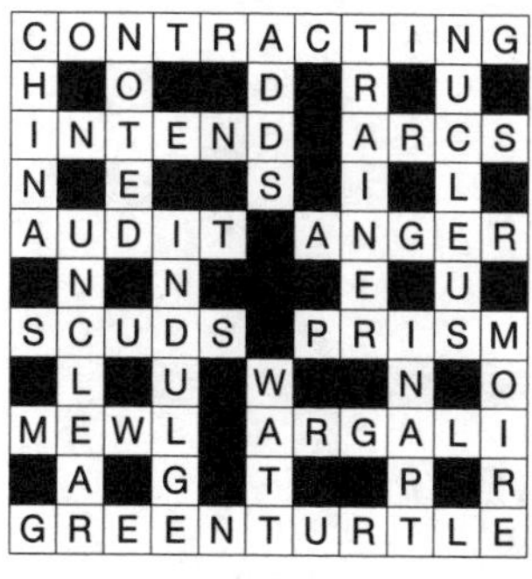

## 76

| | | | | | | | | | | |
|---|---|---|---|---|---|---|---|---|---|---|
| R | E | S | T | O | R | A | T | I | O | N |
| | C | | Y | | E | | | R | | E |
| C | O | U | P | O | N | | L | I | R | A |
| | L | | I | | E | | | S | | R |
| T | O | R | C | | W | I | S | H | E | S |
| | G | | A | | | | O | | P | |
| C | Y | C | L | E | S | | U | N | I | X |
| R | | A | | | M | | R | | S | |
| A | I | D | E | | E | X | C | I | T | E |
| V | | E | | | L | | E | | L | |
| E | S | T | A | B | L | I | S | H | E | D |

## 77

| | | | | | | | | | | |
|---|---|---|---|---|---|---|---|---|---|---|
| | F | U | L | L | B | L | O | W | N | |
| P | | R | | A | | E | | I | | S |
| R | A | N | K | S | | A | N | N | O | Y |
| E | | | | T | | D | | N | | M |
| S | U | B | S | E | T | | W | E | E | P |
| C | | U | | D | | F | | R | | H |
| R | A | R | E | | F | I | A | S | C | O |
| I | | R | | S | | S | | | | N |
| B | R | I | C | K | | H | I | N | D | I |
| E | | T | | I | | E | | O | | C |
| | P | O | M | P | O | S | I | T | Y | |

## 78

| | | | | | | | | | | |
|---|---|---|---|---|---|---|---|---|---|---|
| | A | P | O | L | O | G | I | Z | E | |
| F | | O | | A | | I | | E | | |
| R | E | S | I | N | | V | E | N | O | M |
| E | | T | | D | | E | | | | A |
| E | L | A | N | | M | U | F | F | I | N |
| W | | G | | F | | P | | O | | A |
| I | B | E | R | I | A | | B | R | A | G |
| L | | | | N | | Y | | G | | I |
| L | L | A | M | A | | O | R | I | O | N |
| | | Y | | L | | D | | V | | G |
| | P | E | R | S | U | A | D | E | S | |

## 79

| | | | | | | | | | | |
|---|---|---|---|---|---|---|---|---|---|---|
| | I | N | T | E | G | R | A | T | E | |
| C | | E | | A | | I | | E | | |
| O | M | E | N | S | | B | E | L | O | W |
| N | | D | | T | | B | | | | H |
| F | A | L | L | | B | O | N | S | A | I |
| I | | E | | G | | N | | O | | T |
| R | U | S | H | E | D | | A | C | N | E |
| M | | | | L | | I | | I | | N |
| S | A | M | B | A | | N | I | E | C | E |
| | | A | | T | | O | | T | | R |
| | A | T | T | O | R | N | E | Y | S | |

## 80

| | | | | | | | | | | |
|---|---|---|---|---|---|---|---|---|---|---|
| S | A | N | D | W | I | C | H | E | S | |
| | G | | U | | B | | O | | I | |
| L | E | A | G | U | E | | R | O | C | K |
| | L | | | | X | | R | | | |
| W | E | A | R | S | | S | I | Z | E | S |
| | S | | E | | | | F | | X | |
| O | S | C | A | R | | C | Y | S | T | S |
| | | | S | | P | | | | R | |
| A | M | M | O | | A | R | C | H | E | R |
| | U | | N | | I | | O | | M | |
| | D | I | S | T | R | E | S | S | E | S |

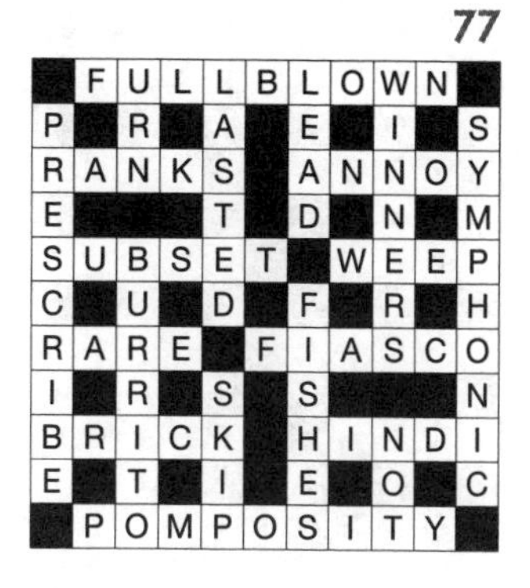

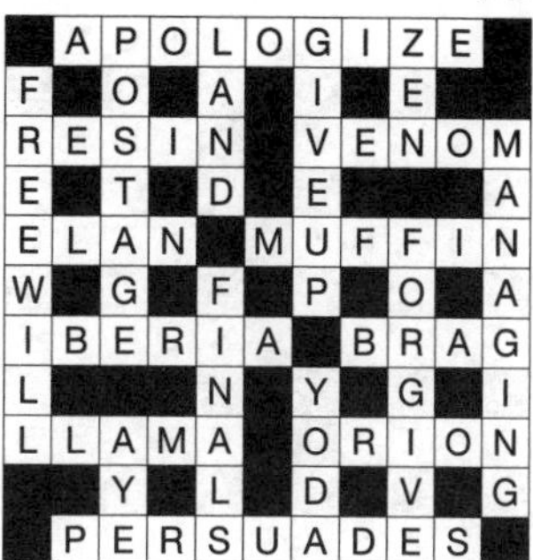

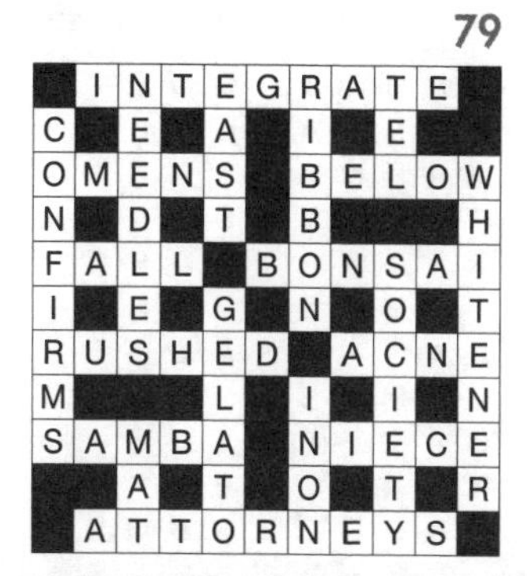

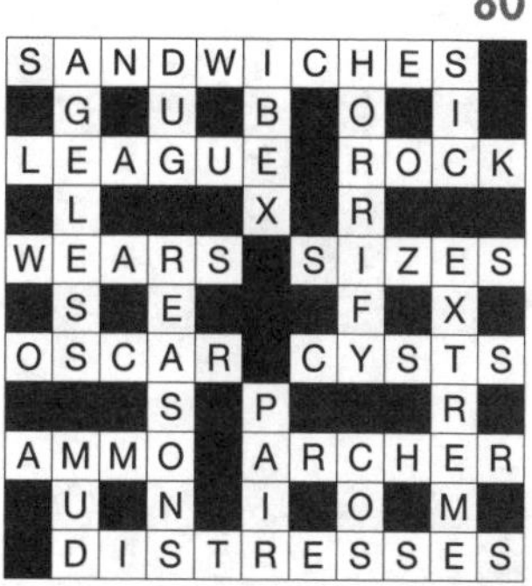

81

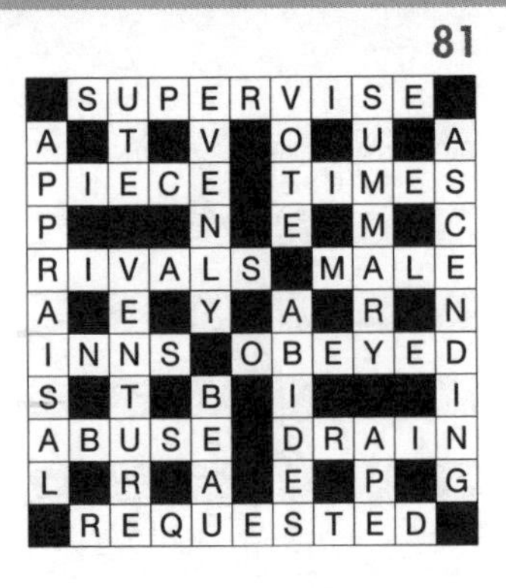


82

83

84

85

86

87

88

## 89

## 90

## 91

## 92

| | E | M | P | I | R | I | C | A | L | |
|---|---|---|---|---|---|---|---|---|---|---|
| E | | A | | D | | D | | N | | E |
| N | O | R | S | E | | L | O | O | P | S |
| C | | | | A | | Y | | D | | S |
| O | V | E | R | L | Y | | P | Y | R | E |
| U | | P | | S | | N | | N | | N |
| R | A | I | D | | R | A | R | E | S | T |
| A | | T | | D | | P | | | | I |
| G | O | O | S | E | | K | R | O | N | A |
| E | | M | | L | | I | | A | | L |
| | D | E | S | I | G | N | E | R | S | |

## 93

## 94

| | I | M | P | E | R | F | E | C | T | |
|---|---|---|---|---|---|---|---|---|---|---|
| E | | A | | V | | A | | O | | |
| V | A | G | U | E | | M | I | X | U | P |
| A | | I | | S | | O | | | | E |
| L | O | C | O | | S | U | M | M | E | R |
| U | | A | | L | | S | | A | | V |
| A | S | L | E | E | P | | B | R | I | E |
| T | | | | G | | T | | T | | R |
| E | X | T | R | A | | R | A | I | D | S |
| | | I | | T | | E | | A | | E |
| | U | N | L | O | C | K | I | N | G | |

## 95

| | D | I | A | L | E | C | T | A | L | |
|---|---|---|---|---|---|---|---|---|---|---|
| O | | N | | U | | L | | L | | |
| V | I | S | I | T | | O | P | T | I | C |
| E | | U | | E | | T | | | | O |
| R | E | L | Y | | C | H | O | S | E | N |
| T | | T | | B | | E | | T | | D |
| I | S | S | U | E | D | | M | E | M | E |
| M | | | | A | | T | | P | | N |
| E | N | A | C | T | | H | O | P | E | S |
| | | D | | U | | O | | E | | E |
| | C | O | M | P | O | U | N | D | S | |

## 96

## 97

## 98

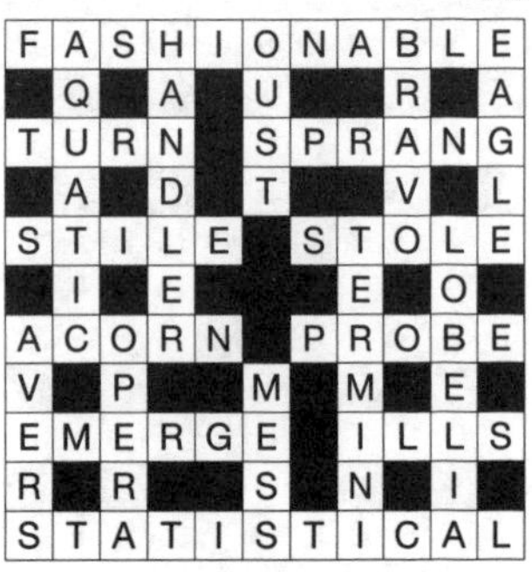


## 99

## 100

## 101

## 102

GATEKEEPER
T V M R H
STREAM AHOY
A Y Y
SCOWL PENNY
K A R E
PSALM ASSET
K T D
THAI ARCTIC
O N R H N
BEGINNINGS

## 103

## 104

## 105

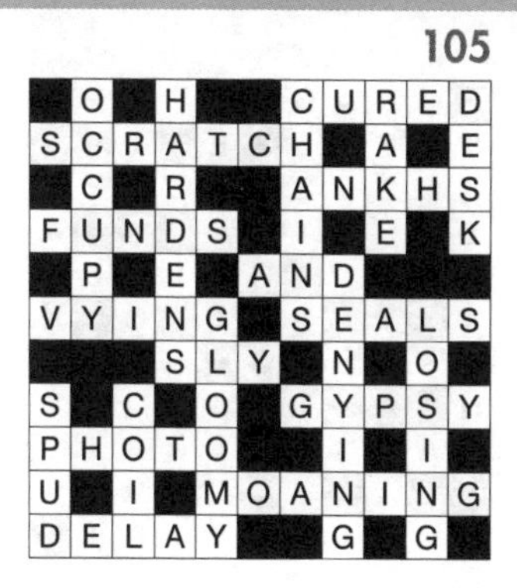

| | | | | | | | | | | |
|---|---|---|---|---|---|---|---|---|---|---|
| | O | | H | | | C | U | R | E | D |
| S | C | R | A | T | C | H | | A | | E |
| | C | | R | | | A | N | K | H | S |
| F | U | N | D | S | | I | | E | | K |
| | P | | E | | A | N | D | | | |
| V | Y | I | N | G | | S | E | A | L | S |
| | | | S | L | Y | | N | | O | |
| S | | C | | O | | G | Y | P | S | Y |
| P | H | O | T | O | | | I | | I | |
| U | | I | | M | O | A | N | I | N | G |
| D | E | L | A | Y | | | G | | G | |

## 106

| | | | | | | | | | | |
|---|---|---|---|---|---|---|---|---|---|---|
| O | F | F | E | N | S | I | V | E | L | Y |
| | R | | S | | U | | | E | | E |
| G | E | T | S | | D | H | A | R | M | A |
| | E | | E | | S | | | I | | R |
| E | B | O | N | Y | | I | T | E | M | S |
| | I | | C | | | | I | | I | |
| R | E | F | E | R | | A | M | O | N | G |
| U | | A | | | I | | P | | I | |
| L | A | D | D | E | R | | A | R | M | S |
| E | | E | | | O | | N | | A | |
| R | E | S | P | O | N | S | I | B | L | E |

## 107

| | | | | | | | | | | |
|---|---|---|---|---|---|---|---|---|---|---|
| C | O | N | D | E | N | S | I | N | G | |
| | D | | U | | I | | N | | I | |
| C | Y | M | B | A | L | | S | O | N | S |
| | S | | | | E | | I | | | |
| A | S | K | E | W | | A | G | I | L | E |
| | E | | C | | | | H | | E | |
| M | Y | T | H | S | | S | T | A | G | Y |
| | | | E | | S | | | | A | |
| M | A | U | L | | P | A | D | D | L | E |
| | L | | O | | O | | E | | L | |
| | L | E | N | G | T | H | W | A | Y | S |

## 108

| | | | | | | | | | | |
|---|---|---|---|---|---|---|---|---|---|---|
| A | M | B | A | S | S | A | D | O | R | |
| | E | | W | | O | | R | | A | |
| A | D | U | L | T | S | | Y | A | N | K |
| | I | | | | O | | D | | | |
| S | C | I | O | N | | H | O | L | L | Y |
| | A | | P | | | | C | | E | |
| S | L | O | T | S | | S | K | A | T | E |
| | | | I | | S | | | | G | |
| S | L | U | M | | P | I | G | E | O | N |
| | U | | U | | I | | A | | O | |
| | C | O | M | E | T | O | L | I | F | E |

## 109

| | | | | | | | | | | |
|---|---|---|---|---|---|---|---|---|---|---|
| T | I | D | I | E | S | | D | R | O | P |
| R | | R | | | T | | I | | U | |
| O | R | A | T | O | R | | O | N | T | O |
| O | | P | | | E | | R | | S | |
| P | A | E | L | L | A | | A | M | I | D |
| | N | | O | | M | | M | | D | |
| R | O | T | I | | L | O | A | D | E | D |
| | T | | T | | I | | | U | | I |
| S | H | O | E | | N | E | A | T | E | N |
| | E | | R | | E | | | C | | E |
| E | R | R | S | | D | A | S | H | E | D |

## 110

| | | | | | | | | | | |
|---|---|---|---|---|---|---|---|---|---|---|
| G | A | R | D | E | N | T | O | O | L | S |
| O | | E | | | E | | S | | U | |
| I | N | C | H | E | S | | T | O | G | A |
| N | | A | | | S | | R | | G | |
| G | U | P | P | Y | | V | I | T | A | L |
| | N | | R | | | | C | | G | |
| S | C | O | O | P | | S | H | E | E | T |
| | L | | V | | M | | | | L | R |
| T | A | X | I | | U | N | D | U | L | Y |
| | S | | S | | O | | | D | | S |
| A | P | P | O | I | N | T | M | E | N | T |

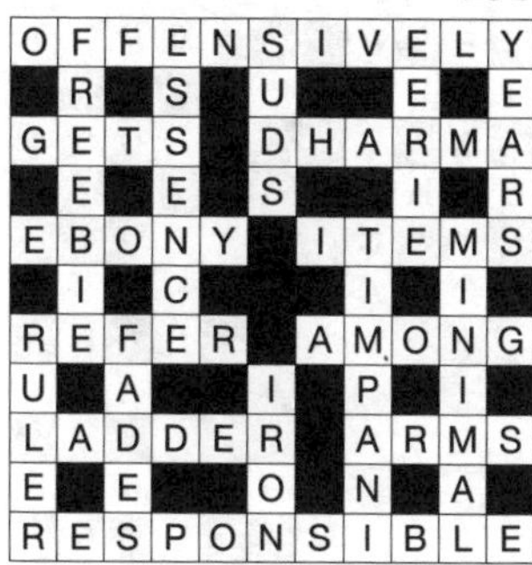

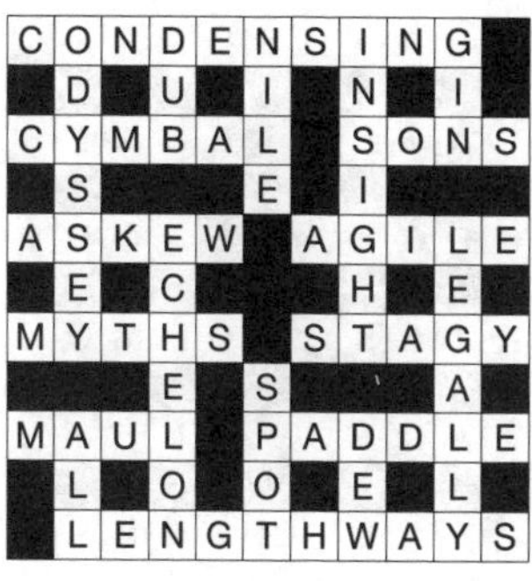

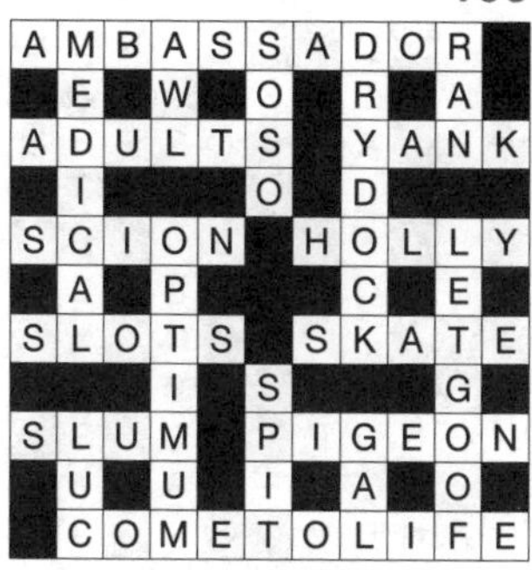

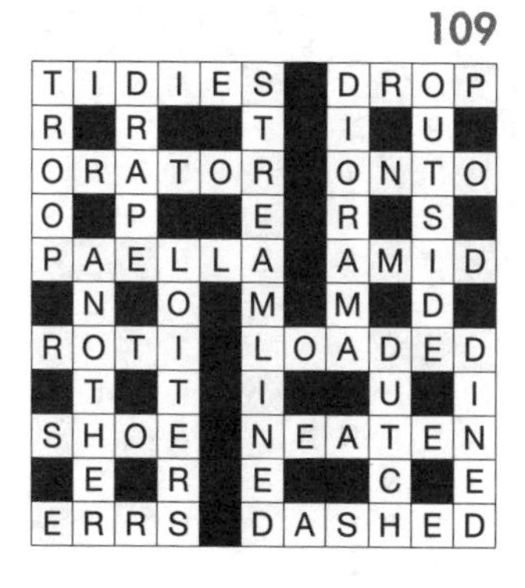

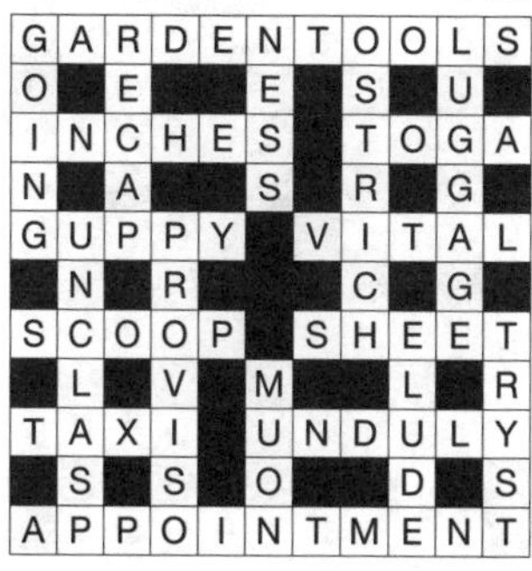

## 111

| | | | | | | | | | | |
|---|---|---|---|---|---|---|---|---|---|---|
| M | I | S | D | I | R | E | C | T | E | D |
| | N | | I | | E | | | A | | R |
| D | U | N | G | | A | Z | A | L | E | A |
| | T | | I | | L | | | L | | G |
| H | E | A | T | H | | A | B | Y | S | S |
| | R | | A | | | | E | | H | |
| W | O | U | L | D | | E | N | J | O | Y |
| O | | N | | | O | | G | | R | |
| R | A | I | S | I | N | | A | N | T | S |
| L | | T | | | U | | L | | E | |
| D | I | S | C | U | S | S | I | O | N | S |

## 112

| | | | | | | | | | | |
|---|---|---|---|---|---|---|---|---|---|---|
| | C | L | A | S | S | R | O | O | M | |
| B | | U | | A | | O | | R | | |
| L | O | C | K | S | | B | L | E | S | S |
| A | | K | | H | | B | | | | U |
| C | A | I | N | | T | E | R | S | E | R |
| K | | L | | S | | R | | P | | P |
| O | X | Y | G | E | N | | F | A | I | R |
| U | | | | A | | V | | C | | I |
| T | O | W | E | L | | E | D | I | T | S |
| | | O | | E | | I | | N | | E |
| | G | O | L | D | E | N | A | G | E | |

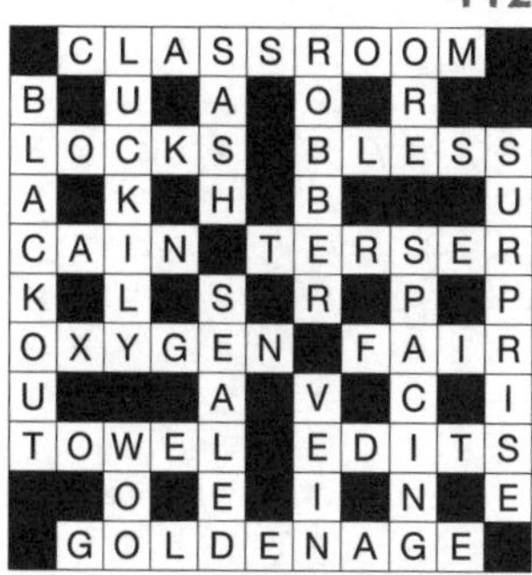

## 113

## 114

## 115

## 116

## 117

## 118

A A PASTS
TRIGGER O U
M I INDIE
WASTE C A S
D A ZEE
MALTA SYNOD
ELK E P
M L P CLUES
ARENA A N
I N CLOSEUP
MEDEA H P

## 119

## 120

## 121

## 122

## 123

## 124

## 125

## 126

| | A | P | P | R | O | V | I | N | G | |
|---|---|---|---|---|---|---|---|---|---|---|
| C | | R | | E | | A | | U | | P |
| L | A | Y | U | P | | M | O | T | O | R |
| E | | | | A | | P | | C | | E |
| A | F | F | A | I | R | | B | A | S | S |
| R | | O | | R | | S | | S | | E |
| A | I | R | Y | | L | I | N | E | A | R |
| N | | E | | G | | N | | | | V |
| C | I | V | I | L | | F | A | B | L | E |
| E | | E | | E | | U | | O | | D |
| | T | R | A | N | S | L | A | T | E | |

## 127

## 128

**129**

**130**

**131**

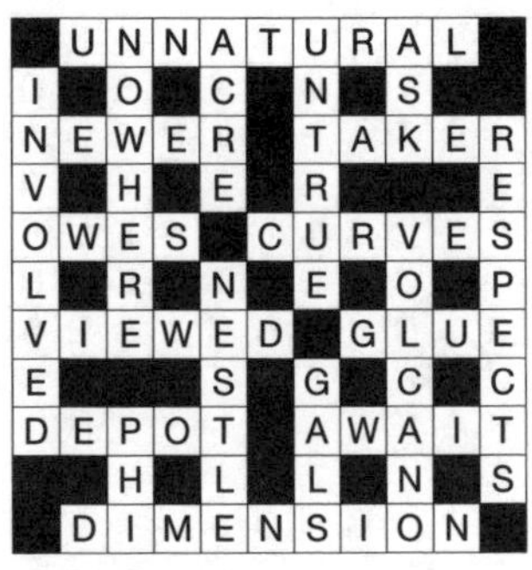


**132**

**133**

**134**

REPUBLISH
P B N A U S
RABBI RISKY
O T D P N
TABLES DEFT
O R S W N H
TOES WADDLE
Y A Y L S
PEKOE RICCI
E U A U U S
OPPRESSED

**135**

**136**

## 137

## 138

## 139

## 140

HACKER DORM
U O E R E
MIMOSA AILS
A I L S E
NUCLEI TRAP
N A Z I R
TUTU ARCANE
S G T G A
RUTH IMPAIR
A E O P L
PLOD NAMELY

## 141

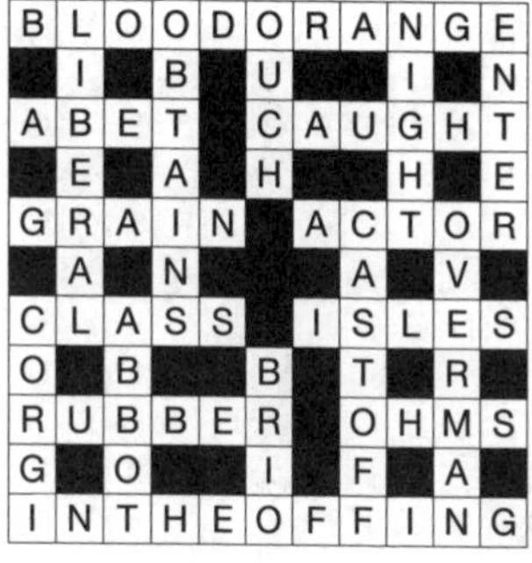


## 142

ASREGARDS
H O A R E D
AMBER ELATE
L N S D E
FISHED PEEP
T Y D C N S
RUNG HOLDUP
U O K W A
TENSE BASIC
H Y E O H E
EMPLOYEES

## 143

## 144

## 145

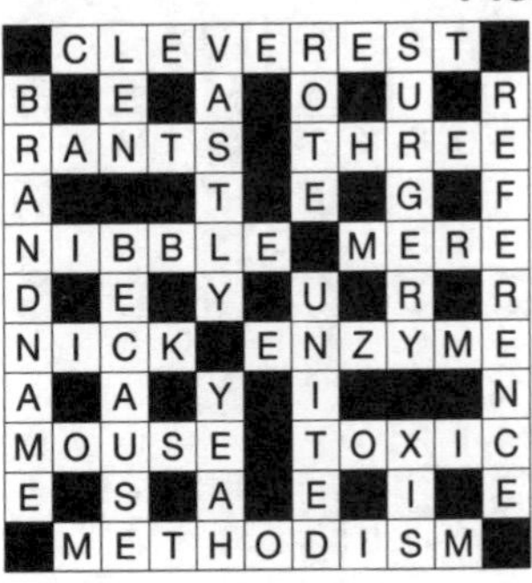

| | | | | | | | | | | |
|---|---|---|---|---|---|---|---|---|---|---|
| | C | L | E | V | E | R | E | S | T | |
| B | | E | | A | | O | | U | | R |
| R | A | N | T | S | | T | H | R | E | E |
| A | | | | T | | E | | G | | F |
| N | I | B | B | L | E | | M | E | R | E |
| D | | E | | Y | | U | | R | | R |
| N | I | C | K | | E | N | Z | Y | M | E |
| A | | A | | Y | | I | | | | N |
| M | O | U | S | E | | T | O | X | I | C |
| E | | S | | A | | E | | I | | E |
| | M | E | T | H | O | D | I | S | M | |

## 146

| | | | | | | | | | | |
|---|---|---|---|---|---|---|---|---|---|---|
| S | P | E | A | K | E | V | I | L | O | F |
| | R | | S | | R | | | I | | I |
| L | E | G | S | | G | A | D | G | E | T |
| | V | | U | | O | | | H | | I |
| P | A | D | R | E | | O | F | T | E | N |
| | I | | E | | | | I | | R | |
| C | L | O | S | E | | A | G | L | O | W |
| H | | F | | | B | | H | | S | |
| E | F | F | A | C | E | | T | R | I | M |
| S | | E | | | E | | E | | O | |
| S | T | R | U | C | T | U | R | I | N | G |

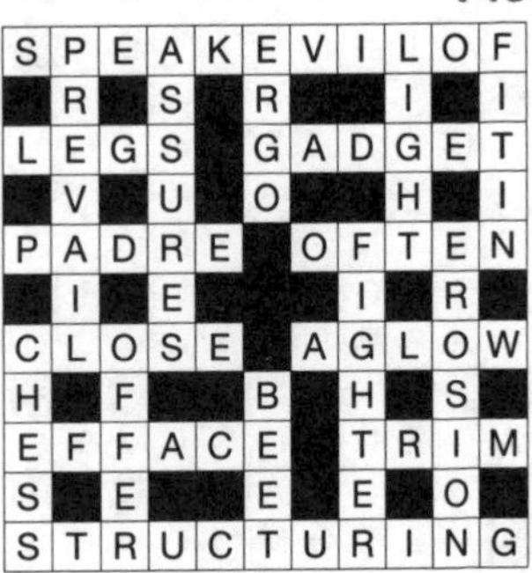

## 147

| | | | | | | | | | | |
|---|---|---|---|---|---|---|---|---|---|---|
| C | O | L | L | A | R | | C | O | S | H |
| A | | O | | | E | | O | | T | |
| M | O | R | T | A | L | | N | E | A | R |
| E | | D | | | U | | C | | R | |
| O | N | S | P | E | C | | O | U | T | S |
| | O | | L | | T | | C | | E | |
| T | U | N | A | | A | S | T | E | R | N |
| | R | | C | | N | | | V | | A |
| W | I | K | I | | T | S | H | I | R | T |
| | S | | N | | L | | | L | | T |
| C | H | U | G | | Y | E | A | S | T | Y |

## 148

| | | | | | | | | | | |
|---|---|---|---|---|---|---|---|---|---|---|
| S | H | A | V | I | N | G | F | O | A | M |
| | U | | I | | I | | | M | | E |
| T | R | I | O | | P | E | S | E | T | A |
| | R | | L | | S | | | G | | N |
| F | I | N | A | L | | A | P | A | R | T |
| | E | | T | | | | E | | I | |
| U | D | D | E | R | | D | R | O | P | S |
| P | | U | | | B | | F | | I | |
| E | N | C | O | R | E | | E | O | N | S |
| N | | K | | | A | | C | | T | |
| D | E | S | T | I | N | A | T | I | O | N |

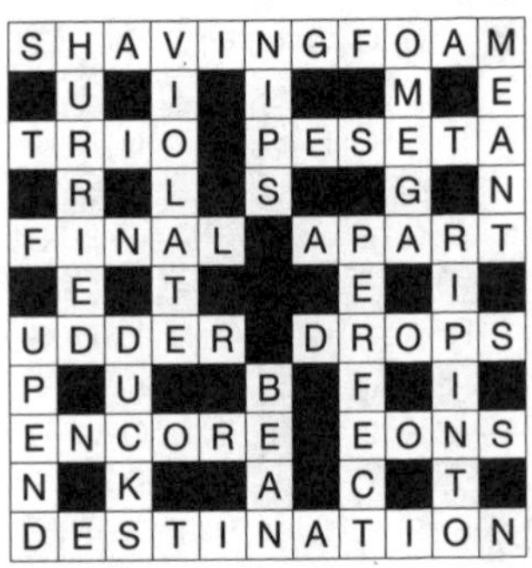

## 149

| | | | | | | | | | | |
|---|---|---|---|---|---|---|---|---|---|---|
| S | O | N | A | T | A | | V | A | S | E |
| C | | A | | | C | | A | | H | |
| R | E | S | U | M | E | | N | O | U | N |
| U | | T | | | O | | I | | T | |
| B | U | Y | O | F | F | | L | A | T | E |
| | T | | U | | S | | L | | L | |
| F | I | S | T | | P | R | A | Y | E | R |
| | L | | L | | A | | | A | | A |
| K | I | L | O | | D | U | L | C | E | T |
| | T | | U | | E | | | H | | E |
| D | Y | E | D | | S | E | A | T | E | D |

## 150

| | | | | | | | | | | |
|---|---|---|---|---|---|---|---|---|---|---|
| | U | N | H | E | A | L | T | H | Y | |
| A | | O | | A | | O | | A | | |
| C | A | T | E | R | | C | O | L | I | C |
| I | | H | | L | | K | | | | O |
| D | A | I | S | | P | E | R | S | O | N |
| J | | N | | E | | D | | E | | C |
| A | N | G | O | R | A | | O | V | A | L |
| Z | | | | R | | W | | E | | U |
| Z | E | B | R | A | | H | I | R | E | D |
| | | E | | N | | E | | A | | E |
| | E | V | I | D | E | N | T | L | Y | |

## 151

| | | | | | | | | | | |
|---|---|---|---|---|---|---|---|---|---|---|
| | F | O | R | T | N | I | G | H | T | |
| P | | U | | E | | N | | U | | A |
| A | F | T | E | R | | K | I | N | D | S |
| S | | | | R | | S | | T | | S |
| S | C | H | O | O | L | | R | I | M | E |
| W | | A | | R | | F | | N | | N |
| O | A | R | S | | H | E | I | G | H | T |
| R | | P | | F | | E | | | | I |
| D | U | O | M | O | | B | E | G | I | N |
| S | | O | | C | | L | | O | | G |
| | I | N | C | I | D | E | N | T | S | |

## 152

| | | | | | | | | | | |
|---|---|---|---|---|---|---|---|---|---|---|
| | C | | H | | | S | T | I | N | G |
| G | I | V | E | O | U | T | | C | | I |
| | N | | X | | | A | V | O | W | S |
| D | E | C | A | Y | | T | | N | | T |
| | M | | G | | Z | I | G | | | |
| H | A | V | O | C | | C | R | U | S | H |
| | | | N | E | D | | E | | T | |
| T | | J | | L | | S | C | O | U | T |
| H | A | U | N | T | | | I | | P | |
| E | | G | | I | N | H | A | B | I | T |
| M | U | S | I | C | | | N | | D | |

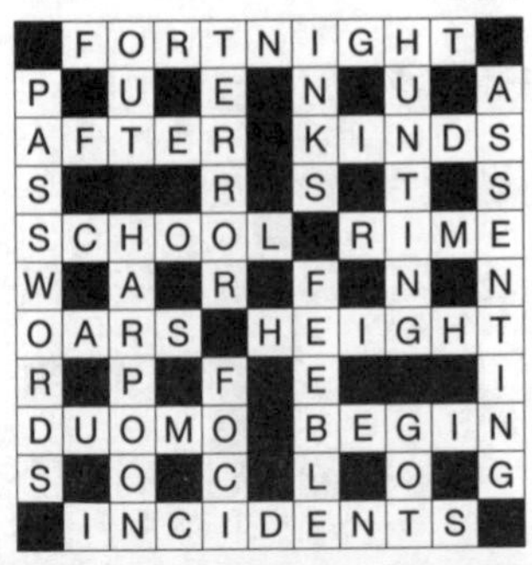

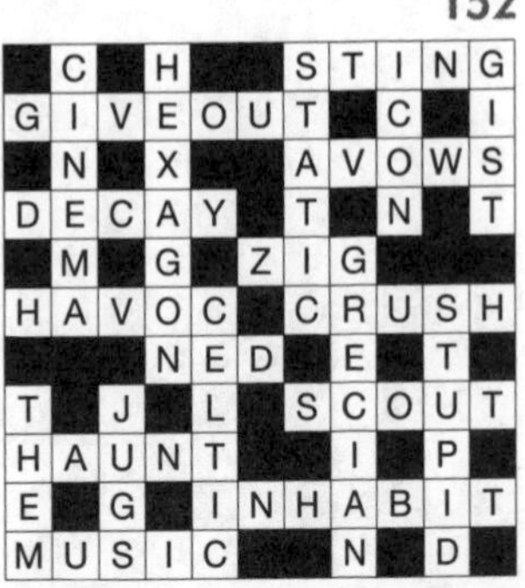

## 153

## 154

## 155

## 156

## 157

## 158

## 159

## 160

## 161

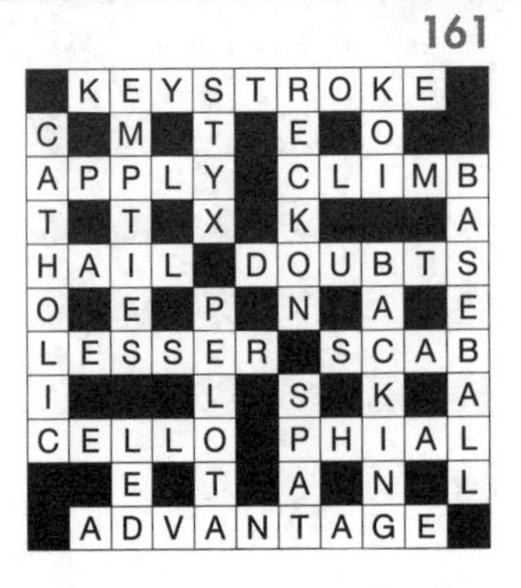

| | | | | | | | | | | |
|---|---|---|---|---|---|---|---|---|---|---|
| | K | E | Y | S | T | R | O | K | E | |
| C | | M | | T | | E | | O | | |
| A | P | P | L | Y | | C | L | I | M | B |
| T | | T | | X | | K | | | | A |
| H | A | I | L | | D | O | U | B | T | S |
| O | | E | | P | | N | | A | | E |
| L | E | S | S | E | R | | S | C | A | B |
| I | | | | L | | S | | K | | A |
| C | E | L | L | O | | P | H | I | A | L |
| | | E | | T | | A | | N | | L |
| | A | D | V | A | N | T | A | G | E | |

## 162

| | | | | | | | | | | |
|---|---|---|---|---|---|---|---|---|---|---|
| P | O | S | T | P | O | N | I | N | G | |
| | R | | O | | A | | G | | A | |
| O | B | J | E | C | T | | N | I | G | H |
| | I | | | | S | | O | | | |
| S | T | A | F | F | | B | R | A | V | E |
| | A | | A | | | | E | | I | |
| F | L | U | I | D | | A | S | K | E | D |
| | | | R | | T | | | | W | |
| C | L | U | E | | A | U | F | A | I | T |
| | E | | S | | M | | I | | N | |
| | G | E | T | U | P | A | N | D | G | O |

## 163

| | | | | | | | | | | |
|---|---|---|---|---|---|---|---|---|---|---|
| S | P | E | C | T | A | C | U | L | A | R |
| | R | | H | | I | | | I | | E |
| L | I | A | O | | M | O | C | K | U | P |
| | N | | I | | S | | | E | | L |
| S | T | I | C | K | | A | S | S | A | Y |
| | E | | E | | | | H | | R | |
| D | R | E | S | S | | T | O | G | A | S |
| R | | V | | | B | | W | | B | |
| A | N | I | M | A | L | | B | A | I | L |
| M | | C | | | U | | I | | A | |
| A | U | T | H | O | R | I | Z | I | N | G |

## 164

| | | | | | | | | | | |
|---|---|---|---|---|---|---|---|---|---|---|
| | K | N | O | W | L | E | D | G | E | |
| A | | I | | H | | A | | E | | C |
| P | I | X | I | E | | C | O | N | G | O |
| O | | | | E | | H | | E | | M |
| C | U | D | D | L | Y | | S | T | O | P |
| R | | E | | S | | B | | I | | L |
| Y | A | N | G | | G | O | T | C | H | A |
| P | | I | | S | | T | | | | I |
| H | A | Z | E | L | | T | R | A | I | N |
| A | | E | | U | | O | | D | | T |
| | A | N | D | R | O | M | E | D | A | |

## 165

| | | | | | | | | | | |
|---|---|---|---|---|---|---|---|---|---|---|
| B | U | L | L | T | E | R | R | I | E | R |
| | N | | I | | G | | | M | | E |
| T | E | A | M | | G | R | A | P | H | S |
| | Q | | I | | S | | | E | | E |
| S | U | I | T | S | | S | P | L | I | T |
| | A | | E | | | | I | | N | |
| B | L | A | D | E | | W | R | I | S | T |
| A | | W | | | H | | A | | H | |
| S | C | A | M | P | I | | N | O | O | N |
| I | | K | | | V | | H | | R | |
| L | I | E | U | T | E | N | A | N | T | S |

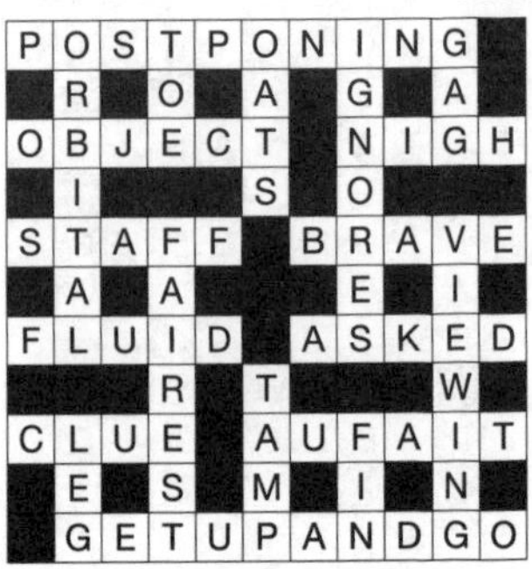

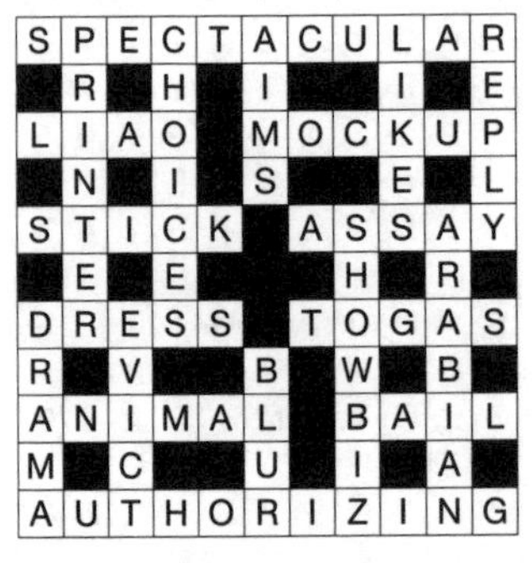

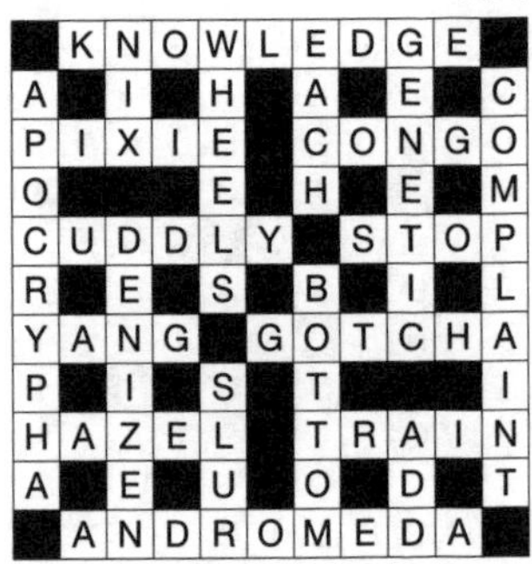

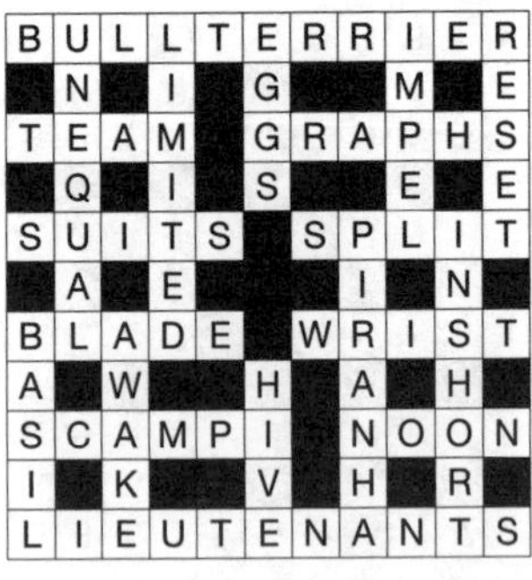

## 166

| | | | | | | | | | | |
|---|---|---|---|---|---|---|---|---|---|---|
| | S | T | A | N | D | A | R | D | S | |
| A | | H | | O | | S | | O | | |
| S | W | E | E | T | | H | U | T | C | H |
| S | | O | | E | | R | | | | A |
| E | A | R | S | | J | A | G | U | A | R |
| S | | E | | G | | M | | G | | D |
| S | Y | M | B | O | L | | S | L | I | D |
| E | | | | S | | C | | I | | I |
| D | E | B | T | S | | H | E | E | L | S |
| | | Y | | I | | A | | S | | K |
| | T | E | M | P | E | R | A | T | E | |

## 167

| | | | | | | | | | | |
|---|---|---|---|---|---|---|---|---|---|---|
| | D | R | E | S | S | D | O | W | N | |
| W | | O | | E | | U | | O | | A |
| O | L | D | E | R | | S | T | R | A | W |
| N | | | | V | | K | | K | | A |
| D | E | G | R | E | E | | V | E | E | R |
| E | | L | | D | | T | | R | | E |
| R | E | I | N | | P | O | I | S | O | N |
| F | | T | | T | | P | | | | E |
| U | N | T | I | E | | H | O | L | E | S |
| L | | E | | C | | A | | O | | S |
| | A | R | C | H | E | T | Y | P | E | |

## 168

| | | | | | | | | | | |
|---|---|---|---|---|---|---|---|---|---|---|
| | A | T | L | I | B | E | R | T | Y | |
| E | | W | | C | | C | | A | | |
| D | R | I | N | K | | H | O | O | K | S |
| U | | T | | Y | | O | | | | C |
| C | I | T | Y | | K | E | E | P | T | O |
| A | | E | | M | | S | | H | | T |
| T | H | R | O | A | T | | D | R | A | T |
| E | | | | N | | G | | A | | I |
| D | E | A | L | T | | R | I | S | E | S |
| | | R | | E | | I | | E | | H |
| | A | M | P | L | I | T | U | D | E | |

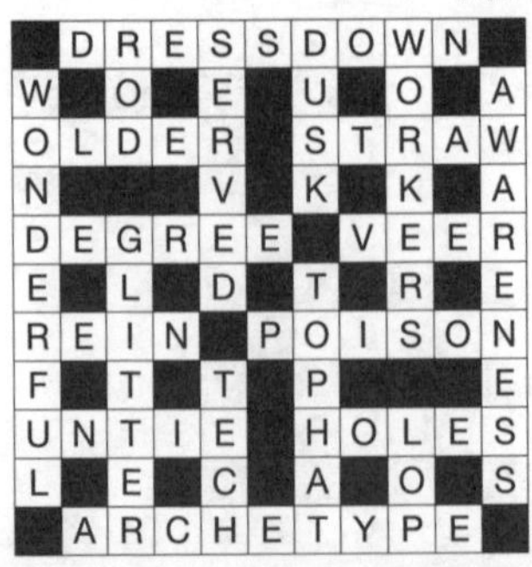

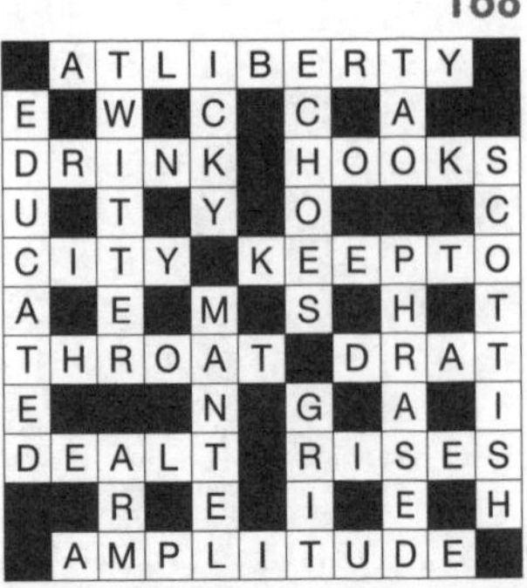

## 169

## 170

## 171

## 172

| | C | R | O | S | S | R | O | A | D | |
|---|---|---|---|---|---|---|---|---|---|---|
| R | | Y | | A | | I | | C | | C |
| E | N | E | M | Y | | C | A | T | C | H |
| M | | | | I | | H | | R | | E |
| E | X | T | E | N | T | | D | E | E | M |
| M | | U | | G | | T | | S | | I |
| B | O | R | N | | C | H | A | S | M | S |
| E | | K | | F | | R | | | | T |
| R | H | I | N | O | | A | U | G | U | R |
| S | | S | | U | | S | | E | | Y |
| | S | H | O | R | T | H | A | N | D | |

## 173

## 174

## 175

## 176

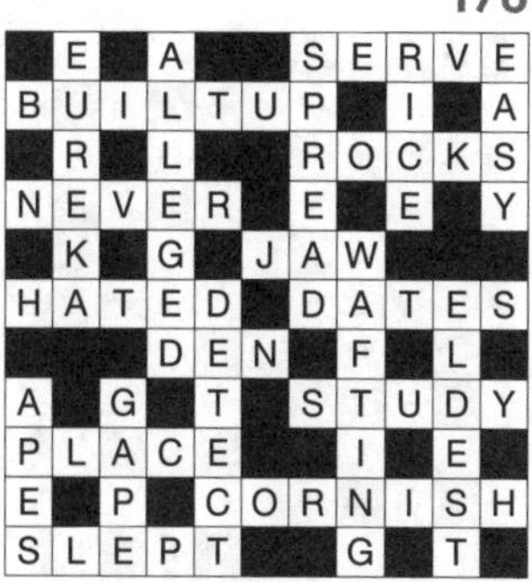

## 177

## 178

## 179

## 180

## 181

## 182

| | | | | | | | | | | |
|---|---|---|---|---|---|---|---|---|---|---|
| | P | | T | | | F | I | L | M | S |
| J | A | M | A | I | C | A | | A | | A |
| | L | | C | | | M | E | N | U | S |
| P | A | S | T | E | | I | | E | | S |
| | C | | I | | F | L | Y | | | |
| K | E | T | C | H | | Y | U | M | M | Y |
| | | | S | O | W | | L | | A | |
| L | | O | | R | | J | E | A | N | S |
| O | R | D | E | R | | | L | | U | |
| A | | E | | I | M | M | O | R | A | L |
| N | O | S | E | D | | | G | | L | |

## 183

## 184

185

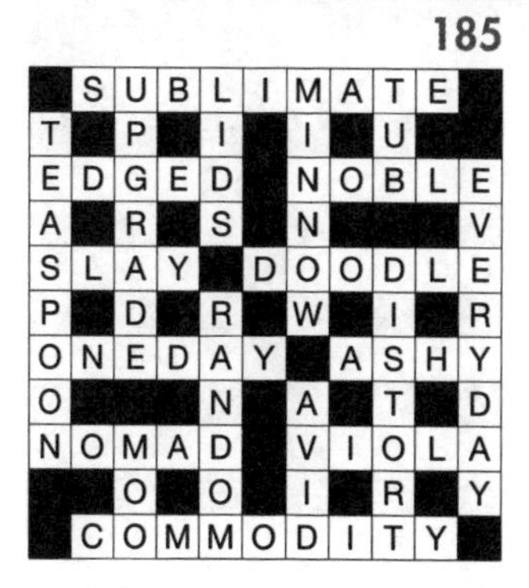

186

187

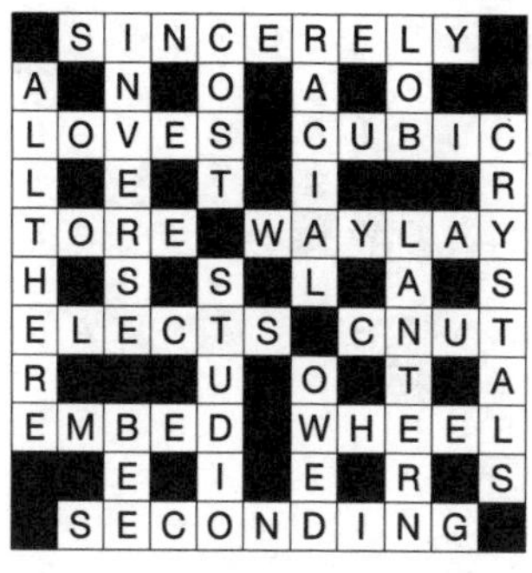

188

189

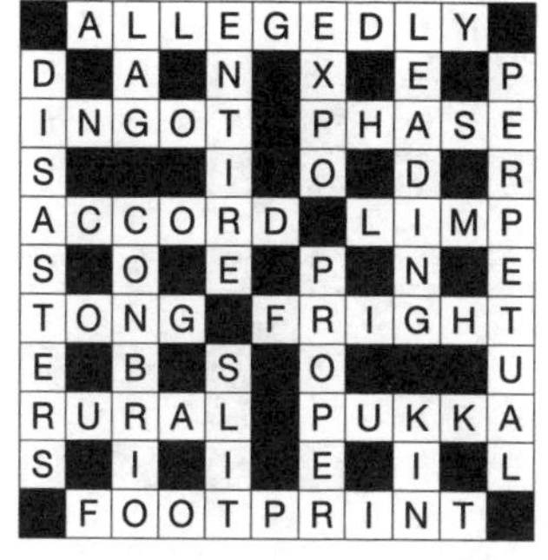

190

| | | | | | | | | | | |
|---|---|---|---|---|---|---|---|---|---|---|
| ■ | L | O | O | K | A | L | I | K | E | ■ |
| C | ■ | F | ■ | I | ■ | U | ■ | E | ■ | ■ |
| L | I | F | T | S | ■ | M | A | N | I | A |
| I | ■ | I | ■ | S | ■ | B | ■ | ■ | ■ | T |
| N | E | C | K | ■ | B | A | M | B | O | O |
| I | ■ | E | ■ | H | ■ | R | ■ | U | ■ | M |
| C | U | R | S | O | R | ■ | S | N | O | B |
| A | ■ | ■ | ■ | T | ■ | M | ■ | K | ■ | O |
| L | I | S | Z | T | ■ | A | L | B | U | M |
| ■ | ■ | E | ■ | U | ■ | M | ■ | E | ■ | B |
| ■ | K | E | Y | B | O | A | R | D | S | ■ |

191

192

## 193

## 194

## 195

| | | | | | | | | | | |
|---|---|---|---|---|---|---|---|---|---|---|
| S | Q | U | A | R | E | | D | E | C | K |
| O | | P | | | M | | A | | A | |
| L | A | P | T | O | P | | Y | A | R | N |
| E | | E | | | H | | T | | A | |
| S | T | R | A | T | A | | R | A | V | E |
| | R | | T | | S | | I | | A | |
| W | I | T | H | | I | M | P | E | N | D |
| | L | | L | | Z | | | X | | I |
| S | O | R | E | | I | N | T | A | C | T |
| | G | | T | | N | | | C | | T |
| L | Y | R | E | | G | E | N | T | L | Y |

## 196

## 197

## 198

| | | | | | | | | | | |
|---|---|---|---|---|---|---|---|---|---|---|
| U | N | R | E | P | E | N | T | A | N | T |
| | E | | M | | U | | | R | | H |
| D | U | M | P | | R | E | M | O | T | E |
| | T | | L | | O | | | M | | R |
| P | R | I | O | R | | S | P | A | D | E |
| | A | | Y | | | | O | | R | |
| C | L | A | S | H | | P | I | V | O | T |
| O | | W | | | K | | N | | P | |
| D | R | A | G | O | N | | T | O | O | L |
| E | | R | | | O | | E | | F | |
| S | P | E | N | D | T | H | R | I | F | T |

## 199

## 200

## 201

## 202

## 203

## 204

| | O | | S | | | S | O | R | T | S |
|---|---|---|---|---|---|---|---|---|---|---|
| T | R | O | U | B | L | E | | U | | I |
| | D | | C | | | R | E | I | G | N |
| P | E | R | C | H | | V | | N | | G |
| | A | | U | | V | E | G | | | |
| B | L | I | M | P | | R | O | A | S | T |
| | | | B | R | O | | S | | I | |
| B | | K | | O | | P | L | U | G | S |
| A | L | A | R | M | | | I | | N | |
| G | | N | | P | A | I | N | F | U | L |
| S | T | A | R | T | | | G | | P | |

## 205

## 206

| B | R | O | N | Z | E | M | E | D | A | L |
|---|---|---|---|---|---|---|---|---|---|---|
| | E | | E | | N | | | U | | U |
| T | W | I | T | | V | E | R | M | I | N |
| | R | | W | | Y | | | B | | G |
| W | I | D | O | W | | W | H | O | S | E |
| | T | | R | | | | A | | U | |
| W | E | E | K | S | | A | N | G | S | T |
| I | | L | | | R | | D | | A | |
| P | R | I | N | C | E | | B | A | N | S |
| E | | T | | | A | | A | | N | |
| S | P | E | C | T | R | O | G | R | A | M |

## 207

| | W | | M | | | S | H | O | C | K |
|---|---|---|---|---|---|---|---|---|---|---|
| R | E | M | O | V | A | L | | P | | I |
| | A | | N | | | I | N | U | I | T |
| C | L | A | I | M | | C | | S | | E |
| | T | | T | | P | E | R | | | |
| T | H | R | O | W | | S | O | L | V | E |
| | | | R | A | G | | T | | I | |
| S | | G | | R | | F | A | T | A | L |
| L | Y | R | I | C | | | T | | B | |
| O | | I | | R | E | V | E | A | L | S |
| P | O | P | P | Y | | | S | | E | |

## 208

## 209

| | A | M | B | U | L | A | N | C | E | |
|---|---|---|---|---|---|---|---|---|---|---|
| A | | I | | N | | U | | U | | I |
| C | O | A | S | T | | R | E | S | T | S |
| A | | | | I | | A | | T | | O |
| D | E | C | A | D | E | | C | A | L | L |
| E | | O | | Y | | D | | R | | A |
| M | E | M | O | | C | R | E | D | I | T |
| I | | P | | E | | I | | | | I |
| C | R | O | P | S | | V | I | D | E | O |
| S | | S | | P | | E | | A | | N |
| | R | E | C | Y | C | L | I | N | G | |

## 210

| | L | U | N | C | H | T | I | M | E | |
|---|---|---|---|---|---|---|---|---|---|---|
| A | | N | | O | | A | | I | | |
| B | A | S | I | N | | R | A | C | E | D |
| S | | O | | S | | G | | | | R |
| T | A | U | T | | S | E | E | T | H | E |
| R | | N | | S | | T | | R | | A |
| A | D | D | I | C | T | | H | A | N | D |
| C | | | | O | | T | | C | | I |
| T | I | M | E | R | | A | L | I | G | N |
| | | A | | C | | I | | N | | G |
| | M | Y | T | H | O | L | O | G | Y | |

## 211

| A | L | T | E | R | A | T | I | O | N | S |
|---|---|---|---|---|---|---|---|---|---|---|
| L | | H | | | T | | N | | O | |
| O | V | E | R | D | O | | F | A | T | S |
| N | | M | | | M | | L | | V | |
| G | R | E | B | E | | B | I | T | E | S |
| | U | | U | | | | C | | R | |
| U | N | I | F | Y | | S | T | A | Y | S |
| | D | | F | | S | | | M | | H |
| N | O | V | A | | T | O | M | A | T | O |
| | W | | L | | E | | | Z | | O |
| I | N | C | O | M | P | E | T | E | N | T |

## 212

| | H | E | R | B | I | C | I | D | E | |
|---|---|---|---|---|---|---|---|---|---|---|
| P | | D | | O | | A | | I | | |
| R | I | G | I | D | | V | I | P | E | R |
| O | | I | | E | | E | | | | E |
| B | L | E | D | | M | A | R | G | I | N |
| L | | S | | C | | T | | E | | E |
| E | N | T | A | I | L | | S | T | O | W |
| M | | | | T | | M | | L | | I |
| S | A | T | Y | R | | A | D | O | R | N |
| | | A | | I | | L | | S | | G |
| | S | P | E | C | U | L | A | T | E | |

## 213

| B | A | S | E | S | T | | G | I | G | S |
|---|---|---|---|---|---|---|---|---|---|---|
| I | | T | | | H | | O | | O | |
| G | R | U | D | G | E | | R | I | O | T |
| O | | N | | | O | | I | | D | |
| T | A | S | T | E | R | | L | O | B | S |
| | C | | Y | | E | | L | | Y | |
| C | H | I | P | | T | R | A | D | E | S |
| | I | | H | | I | | | E | | E |
| L | E | G | O | | C | H | E | E | S | E |
| | V | | O | | A | | | M | | K |
| T | E | E | N | | L | O | S | S | E | S |

## 214

| F | E | L | L | O | W | | B | A | R | B |
|---|---|---|---|---|---|---|---|---|---|---|
| E | | E | | | E | | R | | E | |
| D | U | M | P | E | D | | A | L | A | S |
| U | | O | | | D | | V | | L | |
| P | A | N | I | N | I | | A | X | I | S |
| | R | | N | | N | | D | | Z | |
| A | C | E | S | | G | L | O | W | E | D |
| | H | | T | | R | | | O | | O |
| C | I | A | O | | I | D | I | O | T | S |
| | V | | C | | N | | | E | | E |
| P | E | A | K | | G | U | A | R | D | S |

## 215

| D | O | M | A | I | N | | O | R | C | S |
|---|---|---|---|---|---|---|---|---|---|---|
| A | | E | | | I | | T | | L | |
| R | A | T | I | N | G | | T | H | E | Y |
| E | | A | | | H | | O | | A | |
| S | I | L | E | N | T | | M | A | R | E |
| | N | | C | | M | | A | | L | |
| O | F | F | S | | A | N | N | O | Y | S |
| | R | | T | | R | | | P | | I |
| S | O | F | A | | I | N | D | E | E | D |
| | N | | S | | S | | | N | | E |
| S | T | A | Y | | H | O | R | S | E | S |

## 216

| | S | H | O | U | L | D | E | R | S | |
|---|---|---|---|---|---|---|---|---|---|---|
| P | | A | | N | | I | | E | | C |
| R | A | N | G | E | | P | O | L | I | O |
| E | | | | V | | S | | A | | M |
| M | A | P | P | E | D | | S | T | E | M |
| A | | A | | N | | A | | E | | O |
| T | A | R | O | | O | D | D | S | O | N |
| U | | A | | C | | A | | | | L |
| R | O | D | E | O | | P | I | Z | Z | A |
| E | | O | | L | | T | | O | | W |
| | E | X | H | A | U | S | T | E | D | |

217

| | C | | S | | | B | A | C | K | S |
|---|---|---|---|---|---|---|---|---|---|---|
| H | O | W | E | V | E | R | | L | | A |
| | R | | A | | | U | N | I | T | Y |
| G | R | U | F | F | | T | | P | | S |
| | A | | O | | P | U | P | | | |
| E | L | B | O | W | | S | H | A | K | Y |
| | | | D | I | G | | A | | E | |
| T | | H | | S | | S | N | O | R | E |
| H | O | U | S | E | | | T | | N | |
| I | | N | | S | C | O | O | T | E | R |
| S | I | G | H | T | | | M | | L | |

218

| E | X | P | E | C | T | A | T | I | O | N |
|---|---|---|---|---|---|---|---|---|---|---|
| Q | | O | | | E | | R | | V | |
| U | N | W | I | S | E | | A | R | A | B |
| I | | E | | | S | | V | | T | |
| P | A | R | S | E | | R | A | P | I | D |
| | F | | C | | | | I | | O | |
| O | F | F | A | L | | B | L | E | N | D |
| | R | | N | | M | | | X | | A |
| M | O | R | N | | O | B | O | I | S | T |
| | N | | E | | O | | | T | | E |
| S | T | A | R | C | R | O | S | S | E | D |

219

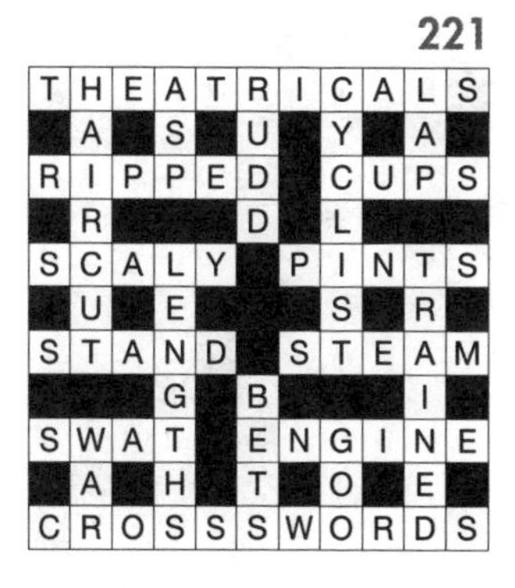

| | D | | S | | | I | M | P | L | Y |
|---|---|---|---|---|---|---|---|---|---|---|
| D | O | L | P | H | I | N | | O | | A |
| | O | | A | | | V | I | L | E | R |
| S | W | O | R | E | | O | | O | | D |
| | O | | R | | S | K | Y | | | |
| S | P | O | O | F | | E | I | G | H | T |
| | | | W | O | K | | D | | O | |
| B | | J | | R | | A | D | O | P | T |
| R | E | A | R | M | | | I | | I | |
| A | | V | | A | M | U | S | I | N | G |
| T | O | A | S | T | | | H | | G | |

220

| | A | S | T | R | O | N | O | M | Y | |
|---|---|---|---|---|---|---|---|---|---|---|
| U | | A | | E | | O | | E | | A |
| N | O | D | E | S | | G | A | R | B | S |
| W | | | | E | | O | | M | | S |
| E | N | M | I | T | Y | | D | A | L | E |
| L | | A | | S | | O | | I | | S |
| C | U | E | S | | G | R | A | D | E | S |
| O | | S | | D | | P | | | | I |
| M | O | T | T | O | | H | E | R | O | N |
| E | | R | | S | | A | | U | | G |
| | C | O | M | E | A | N | D | G | O | |

221

| T | H | E | A | T | R | I | C | A | L | S |
|---|---|---|---|---|---|---|---|---|---|---|
| | A | | S | | U | | Y | | A | |
| R | I | P | P | E | D | | C | U | P | S |
| | R | | | | D | | L | | | |
| S | C | A | L | Y | | P | I | N | T | S |
| | U | | E | | | | S | | R | |
| S | T | A | N | D | | S | T | E | A | M |
| | | | G | | B | | | | I | |
| S | W | A | T | | E | N | G | I | N | E |
| | A | | H | | T | | O | | E | |
| C | R | O | S | S | S | W | O | R | D | S |

222

| | T | O | L | E | R | A | N | C | E | |
|---|---|---|---|---|---|---|---|---|---|---|
| E | | A | | N | | W | | L | | G |
| C | A | K | E | S | | A | L | I | N | E |
| O | | | | U | | Y | | E | | T |
| N | O | T | A | R | Y | | A | N | E | W |
| O | | R | | E | | Z | | T | | I |
| M | A | I | N | | G | O | D | S | O | N |
| I | | U | | W | | M | | | | D |
| C | O | M | M | A | | B | U | R | R | O |
| S | | P | | I | | I | | I | | F |
| | C | H | A | L | L | E | N | G | E | |

223

| | B | | S | | | C | O | P | E | S |
|---|---|---|---|---|---|---|---|---|---|---|
| C | A | R | W | A | S | H | | A | | K |
| | R | | E | | | E | X | I | L | E |
| O | R | G | A | N | | E | | N | | W |
| | E | | T | | T | R | Y | | | |
| B | L | E | E | P | | S | E | N | D | S |
| | | | D | I | E | | A | | R | |
| T | | G | | Z | | G | R | I | E | F |
| W | A | L | T | Z | | | N | | A | |
| I | | O | | A | R | R | E | A | R | S |
| G | A | W | K | S | | | D | | Y | |

224

| | A | L | O | N | G | S | I | D | E | |
|---|---|---|---|---|---|---|---|---|---|---|
| P | | A | | O | | U | | I | | |
| R | A | R | E | R | | B | I | N | D | S |
| O | | G | | M | | T | | | | N |
| F | R | E | D | | B | L | O | T | T | O |
| I | | L | | P | | Y | | H | | B |
| L | A | Y | O | U | T | | T | O | M | B |
| E | | | | R | | S | | U | | E |
| S | I | F | T | S | | L | A | G | E | R |
| | | A | | U | | O | | H | | Y |
| | O | R | I | E | N | T | A | T | E | |

## 225

|  | C | A | P | R | I | C | O | R | N |  |
|---|---|---|---|---|---|---|---|---|---|---|
| A |  | N |  | A |  | O |  | A |  |  |
| T | E | X | T | S |  | M | O | D | E | M |
| T |  | I |  | P |  | I |  |  |  | I |
| R | U | E | D |  | S | C | O | F | F | S |
| A |  | T |  | E |  | S |  | L |  | L |
| C | R | Y | I | N | G |  | D | O | M | E |
| T |  |  |  | C |  | S |  | R |  | A |
| S | I | G | M | A |  | C | H | I | L | D |
|  |  | U |  | M |  | U |  | S |  | S |
|  | S | T | U | P | I | D | I | T | Y |  |

## 226

| C | A | R | B | O | N | P | A | P | E | R |
|---|---|---|---|---|---|---|---|---|---|---|
|  | N |  | E |  | O |  |  | R |  | O |
| C | O | R | N | E | R |  | D | A | U | B |
|  | M |  | E |  | T |  |  | W |  | O |
| H | A | L | F |  | H | O | R | N | E | T |
|  | L |  | I |  |  |  | E |  | A |  |
| S | Y | S | T | E | M |  | F | U | S | E |
| A |  | U |  |  | E |  | R |  | T |  |
| N | U | M | B |  | D | I | E | S | E | L |
| T |  | U |  |  | I |  | S |  | R |  |
| A | P | P | R | O | A | C | H | I | N | G |

## 227

|  | C | U | S | T | O | M | A | R | Y |  |
|---|---|---|---|---|---|---|---|---|---|---|
| S |  | N |  | O |  | U |  | A |  |  |
| W | A | K | E | S |  | S | U | P | E | R |
| E |  | N |  | S |  | E |  |  |  | E |
| A | V | O | W |  | N | U | R | S | E | S |
| R |  | W |  | T |  | M |  | T |  | O |
| I | G | N | O | R | E |  | B | A | W | L |
| N |  |  |  | U |  | H |  | T |  | V |
| G | O | W | N | S |  | A | C | U | T | E |
|  |  | O |  | T |  | H |  | T |  | S |
|  | N | E | W | S | P | A | P | E | R |  |

## 228

|  | B |  | S |  |  | R | E | F | I | T |
|---|---|---|---|---|---|---|---|---|---|---|
| F | U | C | H | S | I | A |  | L |  | U |
|  | T |  | A |  |  | N | A | I | L | S |
| S | T | U | D | S |  | G |  | T |  | K |
|  | E |  | O |  | B | E | D |  |  |  |
| B | R | O | W | N |  | D | R | A | W | N |
|  |  |  | S | O | P |  | Y |  | I |  |
| B |  | M |  | R |  | P | L | A | N | S |
| R | E | A | L | M |  |  | A |  | D |  |
| A |  | I |  | A | B | A | N | D | O | N |
| M | E | D | A | L |  |  | D |  | W |  |

## 229

|  | T | H | E | R | A | P | I | S | T |  |
|---|---|---|---|---|---|---|---|---|---|---|
| C |  | A |  | E |  | U |  | I |  | A |
| O | U | T | E | R |  | M | I | N | D | S |
| S |  |  |  | E |  | P |  | C |  | S |
| M | A | D | C | A | P |  | Z | E | R | O |
| O |  | I |  | D |  | A |  | R |  | R |
| L | A | C | Y |  | O | L | D | E | S | T |
| O |  | T |  | T |  | B |  |  |  | I |
| G | L | A | Z | E |  | U | R | B | A | N |
| Y |  | T |  | A |  | M |  | E |  | G |
|  | R | E | P | R | E | S | E | N | T |  |

## 230

|  | R | E | I | T | E | R | A | T | E |  |
|---|---|---|---|---|---|---|---|---|---|---|
| S |  | M |  | A |  | A |  | I |  |  |
| P | A | I | R | S |  | D | U | M | P | S |
| E |  | N |  | S |  | I |  |  |  | C |
| C | R | E | W |  | P | U | L | S | A | R |
| T |  | N |  | M |  | S |  | C |  | A |
| R | E | T | A | I | N |  | G | I | L | T |
| U |  |  |  | L |  | C |  | E |  | C |
| M | O | D | E | L |  | L | U | N | C | H |
|  |  | Y |  | E |  | O |  | C |  | Y |
|  | R | E | W | R | I | T | T | E | N |  |

## 231

| F | O | R | G | I | V | E | N | E | S | S |
|---|---|---|---|---|---|---|---|---|---|---|
|  | N |  | U |  | O |  |  | M |  | W |
| W | A | L | N | U | T |  | G | A | L | A |
|  | H |  | D |  | E |  |  | I |  | P |
| B | I | K | E |  | S | H | E | L | L | S |
|  | G |  | C |  |  |  | N |  | A |  |
| S | H | A | K | E | N |  | T | O | W | S |
| H |  | D |  |  | I |  | E |  | Y |  |
| R | E | A | D |  | N | E | R | V | E | S |
| U |  | P |  |  | T |  | E |  | R |  |
| B | I | T | E | T | H | E | D | U | S | T |

## 232

|  | T | H | O | U | S | A | N | D | S |  |
|---|---|---|---|---|---|---|---|---|---|---|
| S |  | I |  | P |  | B |  | E |  | C |
| L | U | M | P | S |  | L | A | S | S | O |
| I |  |  |  | E |  | Y |  | I |  | N |
| G | R | O | W | T | H |  | A | G | E | S |
| H |  | R |  | S |  | F |  | N |  | T |
| T | A | G | S |  | F | I | E | S | T | A |
| E |  | A |  | G |  | L |  |  |  | B |
| S | U | N | N | Y |  | L | A | B | E | L |
| T |  | I |  | R |  | U |  | U |  | E |
|  | A | C | C | O | M | P | A | N | Y |  |

## 233

## 234

## 235

## 236

## 237

## 238

PROMISING
S I E I I A
TUDOR FACED
R I T K V
ODDITY WIDE
N I S T N R
GOES REIGNS
E D W N E
STOMA NAVAL
T W N I E Y
INTENSITY

## 239

## 240

241

242

243

244

245

246

| H | E | R | O | W | O | R | S | H | I | P |
|---|---|---|---|---|---|---|---|---|---|---|
|  | M |  | B |  | X |  |  | I |  | E |
| O | B | O | E |  | E | T | H | N | I | C |
|  | A |  | Y |  | N |  |  | D |  | A |
| F | R | U | I | T |  | S | C | I | O | N |
|  | G |  | N |  |  |  | E |  | R |  |
| T | O | U | G | H |  | S | N | A | I | L |
| R |  | N |  |  | O |  | S |  | G |  |
| A | D | D | I | N | G |  | O | P | A | L |
| M |  | E |  |  | R |  | R |  | M |  |
| P | A | R | T | N | E | R | S | H | I | P |

247

248

## 249

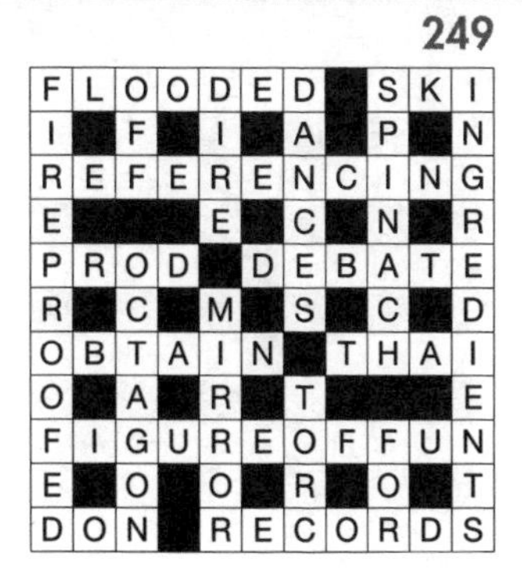

| | | | | | | | | | | |
|---|---|---|---|---|---|---|---|---|---|---|
| F | L | O | O | D | E | D | | S | K | I |
| I | | F | | I | | A | | P | | N |
| R | E | F | E | R | E | N | C | I | N | G |
| E | | | | E | | C | | N | | R |
| P | R | O | D | | D | E | B | A | T | E |
| R | | C | | M | | S | | C | | D |
| O | B | T | A | I | N | | T | H | A | I |
| O | | A | | R | | T | | | | E |
| F | I | G | U | R | E | O | F | F | U | N |
| E | | O | | O | | R | | O | | T |
| D | O | N | | R | E | C | O | R | D | S |

## 250

| | | | | | | | | | | |
|---|---|---|---|---|---|---|---|---|---|---|
| | I | G | N | O | R | A | N | C | E | |
| E | | I | | W | | L | | O | | E |
| X | E | N | O | N | | T | I | L | E | S |
| C | | | | E | | O | | L | | C |
| E | F | F | O | R | T | | T | U | B | A |
| L | | A | | S | | B | | D | | L |
| L | U | C | K | | E | U | R | E | K | A |
| E | | T | | D | | F | | | | T |
| N | O | O | N | E | | F | O | L | I | O |
| T | | R | | M | | E | | E | | R |
| | H | Y | P | O | C | R | I | T | E | |

## 251

| | | | | | | | | | | |
|---|---|---|---|---|---|---|---|---|---|---|
| L | I | A | B | I | L | I | T | I | E | S |
| | N | | R | | A | | | R | | L |
| M | E | M | O | I | R | | G | A | Z | A |
| | R | | U | | V | | | Q | | N |
| S | T | A | G | | A | C | T | I | N | G |
| | I | | H | | | | O | | E | |
| C | A | C | T | U | S | | U | R | G | E |
| O | | U | | | E | | S | | L | |
| B | I | B | S | | R | O | L | L | E | D |
| R | | I | | | U | | E | | C | |
| A | C | C | O | M | M | O | D | A | T | E |

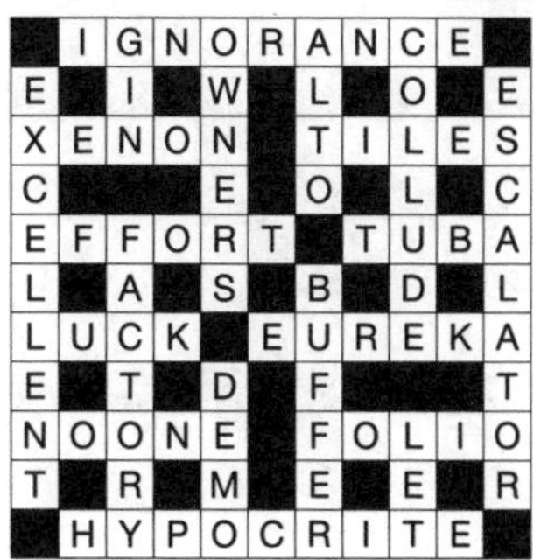

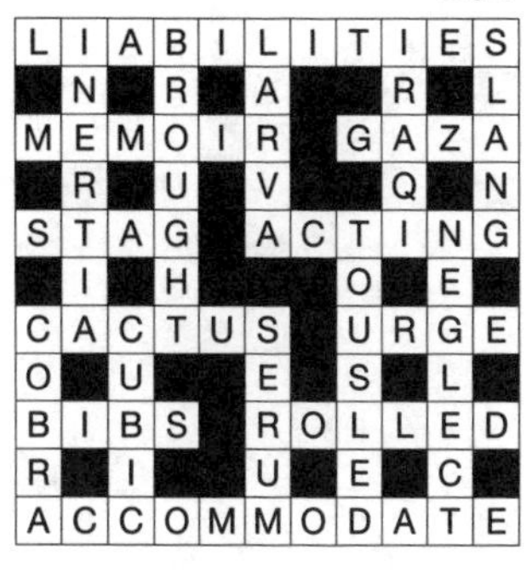

## 252

| | | | | | | | | | | |
|---|---|---|---|---|---|---|---|---|---|---|
| H | Y | D | R | O | P | H | O | B | I | A |
| A | | E | | B | | O | | A | | S |
| N | I | L | | S | Q | U | A | R | E | S |
| D | | I | | E | | R | | | | A |
| I | N | V | E | S | T | | O | F | F | S |
| C | | E | | S | | C | | U | | S |
| A | F | R | O | | B | O | N | S | A | I |
| P | | | | L | | R | | I | | N |
| P | R | O | V | I | S | O | | L | E | A |
| E | | V | | M | | N | | L | | T |
| D | E | A | D | O | R | A | L | I | V | E |

## 253

| | | | | | | | | | | |
|---|---|---|---|---|---|---|---|---|---|---|
| E | M | B | A | R | R | A | S | S | E | D |
| U | | O | | A | | B | | O | | O |
| P | A | R | | C | A | R | I | B | O | U |
| H | | R | | K | | O | | | | B |
| E | G | O | S | | D | A | N | I | E | L |
| M | | W | | E | | D | | N | | E |
| I | N | S | E | C | T | | C | H | I | C |
| S | | | | H | | B | | E | | R |
| T | A | D | P | O | L | E | | R | I | O |
| I | | U | | E | | E | | I | | S |
| C | O | O | R | D | I | N | A | T | E | S |

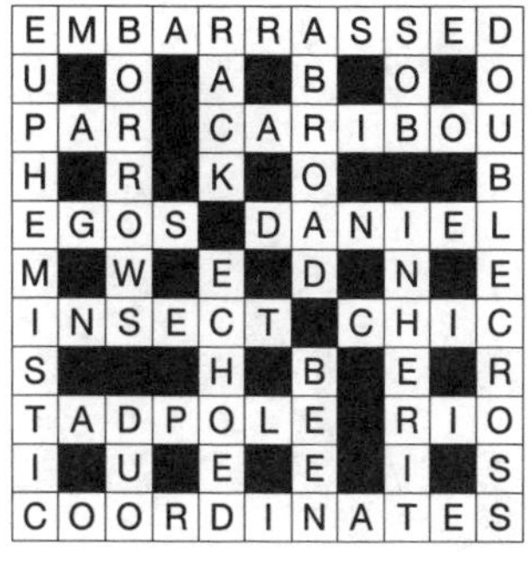

## 254

| | | | | | | | | | | |
|---|---|---|---|---|---|---|---|---|---|---|
| S | U | P | P | O | R | T | E | R | S | |
| | N | | I | | A | | V | | I | |
| S | I | N | E | W | Y | | I | S | P | Y |
| | F | | | | S | | D | | | |
| R | I | N | S | E | | M | E | A | L | Y |
| | E | | C | | | | N | | O | |
| U | S | E | R | S | | S | T | A | C | K |
| | | | I | | O | | | | K | |
| W | H | I | P | | T | A | C | T | I | C |
| | A | | T | | T | | U | | N | |
| | D | I | S | C | O | U | R | A | G | E |

## 255

| | | | | | | | | | | |
|---|---|---|---|---|---|---|---|---|---|---|
| | G | | W | | | T | R | A | D | E |
| M | O | N | A | R | C | H | | C | | A |
| | T | | R | | | R | E | I | N | S |
| S | C | O | R | E | | A | | D | | T |
| | H | | I | | A | S | P | | | |
| C | A | R | O | B | | H | I | R | E | S |
| | | | R | E | X | | C | | Q | |
| W | | F | | H | | S | T | O | U | T |
| R | O | U | T | E | | | U | | A | |
| A | | L | | S | T | E | R | I | L | E |
| P | I | L | O | T | | | E | | S | |

## 256

| | | | | | | | | | | |
|---|---|---|---|---|---|---|---|---|---|---|
| | M | A | G | N | I | T | U | D | E | |
| C | | R | | E | | U | | E | | P |
| H | A | C | K | S | | R | E | C | U | R |
| I | | | | T | | F | | O | | E |
| L | A | D | L | E | S | | E | D | I | T |
| D | | R | | D | | P | | E | | E |
| H | E | A | P | | P | A | R | D | O | N |
| O | | C | | T | | S | | | | D |
| O | T | H | E | R | | S | M | O | K | E |
| D | | M | | O | | E | | A | | D |
| | C | A | N | D | I | D | A | T | E | |

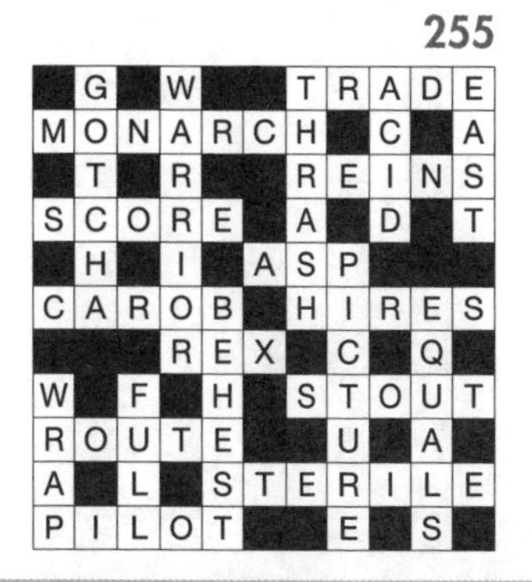

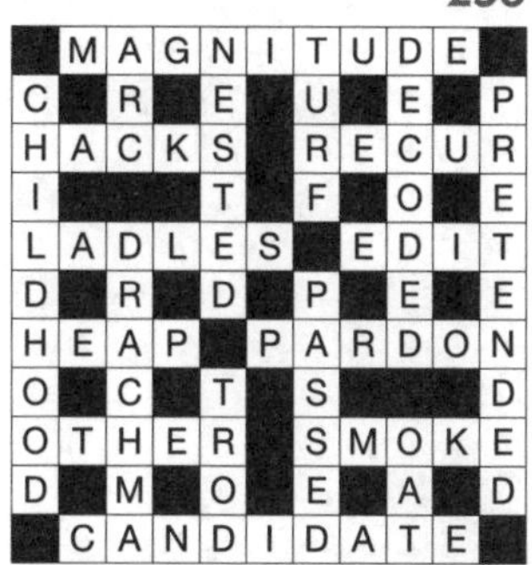

## 257

## 258

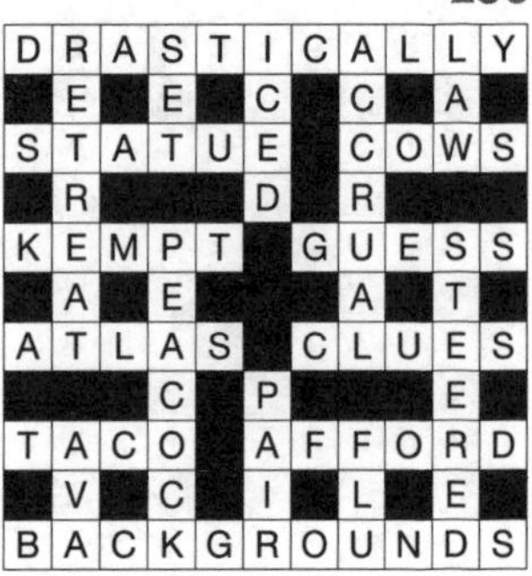

## 259

## 260

## 261

## 262

## 263

## 264

## 265

## 266

## 267

## 268

## 269

## 270

## 271

## 272

## 273

## 274

| S | T | A | T | I | C |  | D | U | F | F |
|---|---|---|---|---|---|---|---|---|---|---|
| H |  | L |  |  | O |  | R |  | I |  |
| R | E | T | U | R | N |  | U | L | N | A |
| U |  | A |  |  | T |  | N |  | A |  |
| B | U | R | S | A | R |  | K | I | N | G |
|  | N |  | T |  | A |  | E |  | C |  |
| T | H | O | U |  | D | E | N | I | E | S |
|  | E |  | M |  | I |  |  | R |  | E |
| L | A | M | B |  | C | H | O | O | S | E |
|  | R |  | L |  | T |  |  | N |  | D |
| E | D | G | E |  | S | P | R | Y | L | Y |

## 275

## 276

## 277

## 278

| P | A | R | T | I | C | I | P | A | N | T |
|---|---|---|---|---|---|---|---|---|---|---|
| R |  | A |  |  | A |  | O |  | O |  |
| O | O | D | L | E | S |  | L | E | T | S |
| O |  | I |  |  | K |  | A |  | A |  |
| F | L | O | O | D |  | C | R | I | B | S |
|  | A |  | N |  |  |  | I |  | L |  |
| B | Y | T | E | S |  | A | S | S | E | T |
|  | I |  | S |  | S |  |  | C |  | O |
| A | N | T | E |  | P | U | T | R | I | D |
|  | T |  | L |  | A |  |  | U |  | A |
| C | O | M | F | O | R | T | A | B | L | Y |

## 279

## 280

| S | U | R | M | O | U | N | T | I | N | G |
|---|---|---|---|---|---|---|---|---|---|---|
|  | N |  | E |  | D |  |  | N |  | U |
| J | A | M | M | E | D |  | O | K | R | A |
|  | W |  | E |  | E |  |  | I |  | R |
| P | A | W | N |  | R | A | I | N | E | D |
|  | R |  | T |  |  |  | M |  | N |  |
| R | E | F | O | R | M |  | P | I | T | S |
| E |  | A |  |  | O |  | O |  | I |  |
| H | A | W | K |  | V | I | S | I | T | S |
| A |  | N |  |  | I |  | E |  | L |  |
| B | U | S | I | N | E | S | S | M | E | N |

## 281

## 282

## 283

## 284

## 285

## 286

| I | N | U | T | E | R | O |  | S | P | A |
|---|---|---|---|---|---|---|---|---|---|---|
| N |  | N |  | L |  | P |  | U |  | P |
| T | R | A | N | S | I | T |  | B | O | P |
| H |  | V |  | E |  | I |  | S |  | E |
| E | L | A | N |  | P | O | S | T | A | L |
| W |  | I |  | S |  | N |  | A |  | L |
| A | L | L | O | W | S |  | A | N | N | A |
| K |  | A |  | I |  | O |  | T |  | T |
| E | B | B |  | T | E | R | M | I | N | I |
| O |  | L |  | C |  | A |  | V |  | O |
| F | O | E |  | H | O | L | B | E | I | N |

## 287

## 288

**289**

**290**

**291**

**292**

| | | | | | | | | | | |
|---|---|---|---|---|---|---|---|---|---|---|
| ■ | B | U | I | L | D | I | N | G | S | ■ |
| P | ■ | S | ■ | O | ■ | T | ■ | E | ■ | A |
| R | E | E | F | S | ■ | C | I | T | E | S |
| O | ■ | ■ | ■ | I | ■ | H | ■ | A | ■ | T |
| H | A | T | I | N | G | ■ | E | W | E | R |
| I | ■ | A | ■ | G | ■ | W | ■ | A | ■ | O |
| B | A | B | E | ■ | K | E | N | Y | A | N |
| I | ■ | L | ■ | I | ■ | I | ■ | ■ | ■ | O |
| T | R | E | N | D | ■ | G | O | L | E | M |
| S | ■ | A | ■ | O | ■ | H | ■ | E | ■ | Y |
| ■ | Q | U | A | L | I | T | I | E | S | ■ |

**293**

**294**

| | | | | | | | | | | |
|---|---|---|---|---|---|---|---|---|---|---|
| M | A | R | R | O | W | ■ | V | I | C | E |
| U | ■ | E | ■ | ■ | E | ■ | E | ■ | A | ■ |
| S | E | A | S | O | N | ■ | R | A | R | E |
| I | ■ | R | ■ | ■ | S | ■ | A | ■ | T | ■ |
| C | O | M | P | E | L | ■ | N | E | O | N |
| ■ | P | ■ | A | ■ | E | ■ | D | ■ | O | ■ |
| B | E | A | R | ■ | Y | E | A | R | N | S |
| ■ | N | ■ | S | ■ | D | ■ | ■ | I | ■ | I |
| M | I | D | I | ■ | A | R | I | S | E | N |
| ■ | N | ■ | N | ■ | L | ■ | ■ | K | ■ | K |
| A | G | O | G | ■ | E | R | A | S | E | S |

**295**

**296**

## 297

## 298

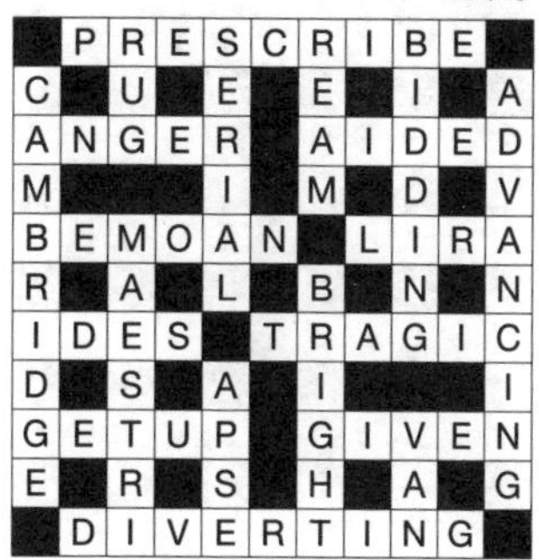

## 299

## 300

|  | U | N | W | E | L | C | O | M | E |  |
|---|---|---|---|---|---|---|---|---|---|---|
| O |  | U |  | A |  | A |  | I |  | H |
| V | E | N | U | S |  | F | E | R | R | Y |
| E |  |  |  | I |  | E |  | R |  | P |
| R | A | C | I | N | G |  | N | O | N | O |
| D |  | O |  | G |  | B |  | R |  | C |
| R | O | B | S |  | C | U | R | S | O | R |
| A |  | B |  | S |  | R |  |  |  | I |
| F | E | L | O | N |  | D | E | A | L | S |
| T |  | E |  | A |  | E |  | R |  | Y |
|  | O | R | I | G | I | N | A | T | E |  |

## 301

## 302

| A | R | S | E | N | I | C |  | P | I | E |
|---|---|---|---|---|---|---|---|---|---|---|
| L |  | U |  | O |  | A |  | H |  | N |
| L | O | P |  | P | A | R | T | I | A | L |
| O |  | E |  | E |  | P |  | L |  | I |
| C | U | R | B |  | B | E | L | O | N | G |
| A |  | M |  | M |  | T |  | S |  | H |
| T | R | A | D | E | D |  | F | O | N | T |
| I |  | R |  | T |  | G |  | P |  | E |
| O | A | K | T | R | E | E |  | H | E | N |
| N |  | E |  | I |  | N |  | E |  | E |
| S | O | T |  | C | L | E | A | R | E | D |

## 303

## 304

## 305

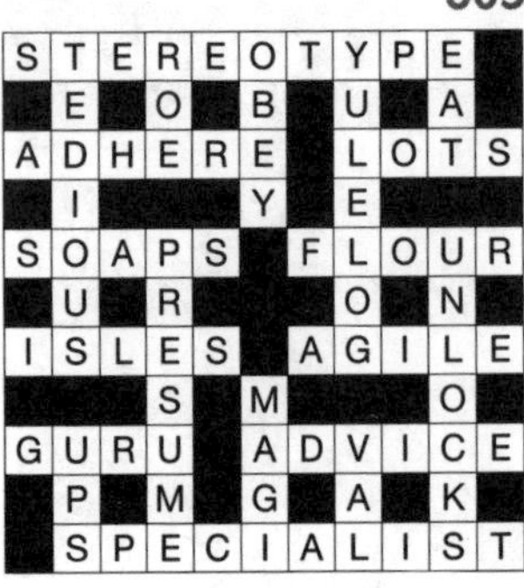

| | | | | | | | | | | |
|---|---|---|---|---|---|---|---|---|---|---|
| S | T | E | R | E | O | T | Y | P | E | |
| | E | | O | | B | | U | | A | |
| A | D | H | E | R | E | | L | O | T | S |
| | I | | | | Y | | E | | | |
| S | O | A | P | S | | F | L | O | U | R |
| | U | | R | | | | O | | N | |
| I | S | L | E | S | | A | G | I | L | E |
| | | | S | | M | | | | O | |
| G | U | R | U | | A | D | V | I | C | E |
| | P | | M | | G | | A | | K | |
| | S | P | E | C | I | A | L | I | S | T |

## 306

| | | | | | | | | | | |
|---|---|---|---|---|---|---|---|---|---|---|
| | A | D | D | R | E | S | S | E | D | |
| W | | A | | E | | E | | X | | A |
| I | D | Y | L | L | | L | A | C | K | S |
| T | | | | I | | L | | L | | S |
| H | A | C | K | E | D | | D | U | D | E |
| D | | H | | S | | P | | D | | M |
| R | I | A | L | | S | U | P | E | R | B |
| A | | T | | W | | L | | | | L |
| W | H | E | R | E | | S | N | I | D | E |
| N | | A | | A | | E | | C | | S |
| | P | U | B | L | I | S | H | E | S | |

## 307

| | | | | | | | | | | |
|---|---|---|---|---|---|---|---|---|---|---|
| B | R | I | L | L | I | A | N | T | L | Y |
| | E | | I | | D | | E | | O | |
| S | C | H | E | M | E | | G | A | G | S |
| | K | | | | A | | A | | | |
| C | O | U | G | H | | S | T | A | K | E |
| | N | | R | | | | E | | I | |
| O | S | C | A | R | | O | D | D | L | Y |
| | | | D | | C | | | | L | |
| M | E | N | U | | R | A | B | B | I | T |
| | R | | A | | U | | E | | N | |
| R | E | F | L | E | X | O | L | O | G | Y |

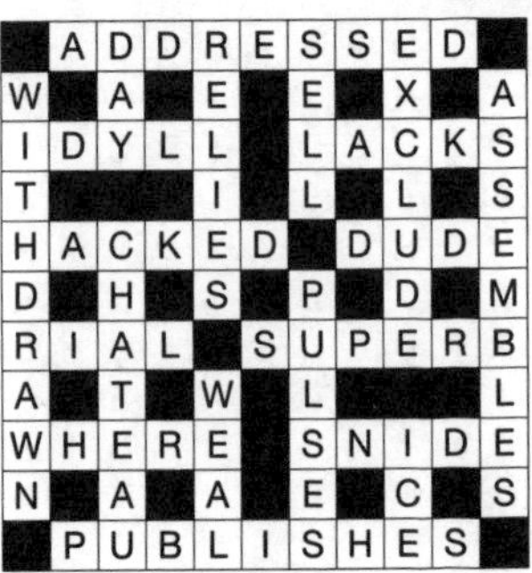

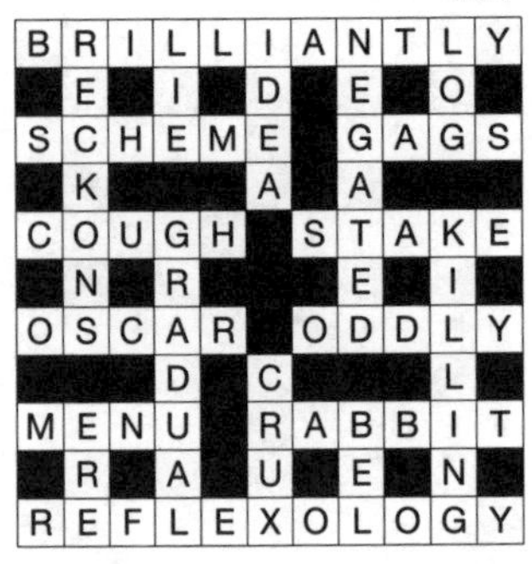

## 308

| | | | | | | | | | | |
|---|---|---|---|---|---|---|---|---|---|---|
| | H | | W | | | C | R | I | E | S |
| V | A | N | I | L | L | A | | D | | I |
| | V | | N | | | R | U | L | E | D |
| H | A | N | D | S | | B | | Y | | E |
| | N | | S | | J | O | G | | | |
| J | A | C | O | B | | N | O | O | S | E |
| | | | R | E | D | | D | | L | |
| S | | O | | C | | B | L | O | O | D |
| M | A | N | G | O | | | E | | W | |
| O | | T | | M | I | S | S | A | L | S |
| G | N | O | M | E | | | S | | Y | |

## 309

| | | | | | | | | | | |
|---|---|---|---|---|---|---|---|---|---|---|
| | P | O | R | T | R | A | Y | A | L | |
| G | | A | | U | | R | | R | | C |
| O | F | F | E | R | | M | A | R | S | H |
| T | | | | N | | Y | | I | | A |
| H | Y | P | H | E | N | | O | V | U | M |
| R | | U | | D | | G | | E | | P |
| O | W | N | S | | P | L | A | S | M | A |
| U | | J | | R | | I | | | | G |
| G | R | A | P | E | | D | O | Y | E | N |
| H | | B | | E | | E | | E | | E |
| | D | I | F | F | E | R | I | N | G | |

## 310

| | | | | | | | | | | |
|---|---|---|---|---|---|---|---|---|---|---|
| S | T | E | W | A | R | D | S | H | I | P |
| | R | | A | | E | | | Y | | I |
| W | E | A | S | E | L | | S | E | A | N |
| | M | | H | | I | | | N | | E |
| A | B | E | T | | C | H | E | A | T | S |
| | L | | U | | | | M | | E | |
| M | E | M | B | E | R | | P | A | N | T |
| O | | A | | | I | | T | | S | |
| T | O | G | A | | C | L | I | N | I | C |
| I | | I | | | C | | E | | O | |
| F | A | C | T | F | I | N | D | I | N | G |

## 311

| | | | | | | | | | | |
|---|---|---|---|---|---|---|---|---|---|---|
| C | O | M | P | R | I | S | I | N | G | |
| | R | | E | | N | | N | | U | |
| F | I | D | G | E | T | | D | A | Y | S |
| | E | | | | O | | U | | | |
| A | N | I | M | A | | A | C | N | E | D |
| | T | | A | | | | E | | Y | |
| U | S | H | E | R | | A | S | H | E | S |
| | | | S | | W | | | | W | |
| F | E | L | T | | A | F | G | H | A | N |
| | R | | R | | R | | O | | S | |
| | A | P | O | S | T | R | O | P | H | E |

## 312

| | | | | | | | | | | |
|---|---|---|---|---|---|---|---|---|---|---|
| T | Y | P | I | N | G | | U | S | E | D |
| H | | R | | E | | S | | U | | I |
| E | L | E | G | A | N | T | | B | U | S |
| O | | M | | R | | A | | S | | C |
| L | E | A | N | | E | S | K | I | M | O |
| O | | T | | S | | H | | D | | U |
| G | R | U | M | P | Y | | P | I | E | R |
| I | | R | | E | | W | | Z | | A |
| C | U | E | | A | R | I | S | I | N | G |
| A | | L | | K | | K | | N | | E |
| L | A | Y | S | | S | I | N | G | E | D |

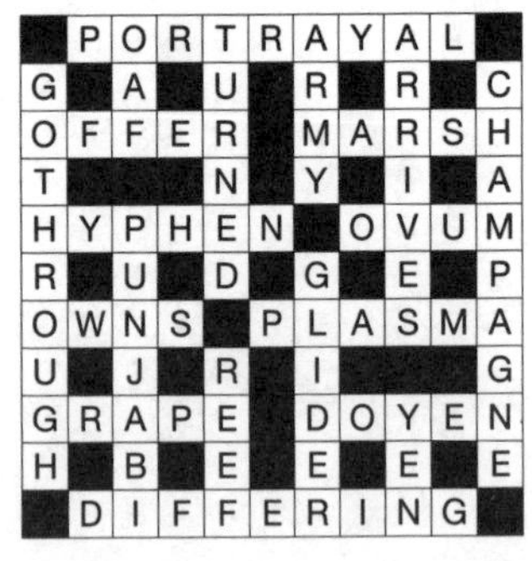

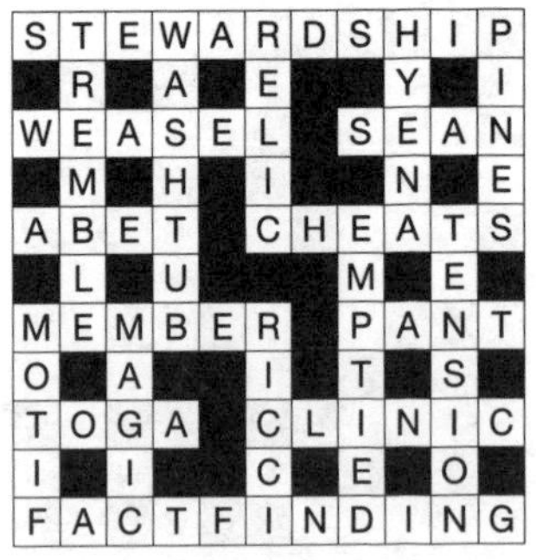

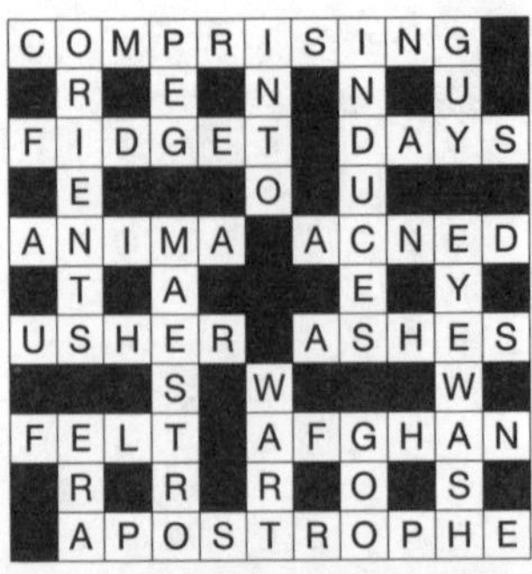

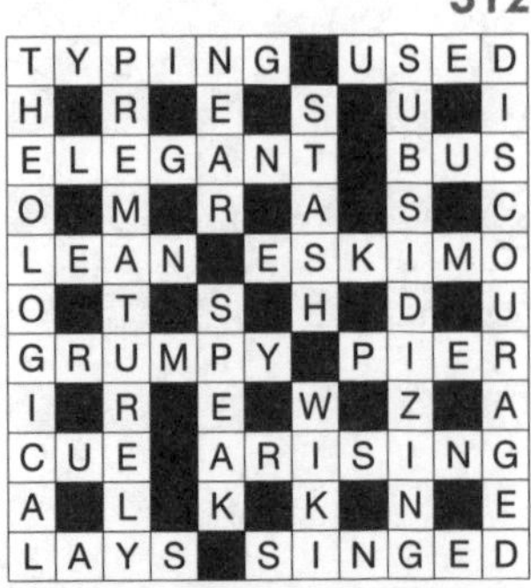

## 313

## 314

## 315

## 316

| | Y | E | S | T | E | R | D | A | Y | |
|---|---|---|---|---|---|---|---|---|---|---|
| S | | N | | R | | E | | I | | |
| Y | A | H | O | O | | A | D | L | I | B |
| N | | A | | Y | | S | | | | O |
| D | E | N | Y | | T | O | P | H | A | T |
| R | | C | | B | | N | | A | | A |
| O | P | E | N | U | P | | A | N | O | N |
| M | | | | R | | R | | D | | I |
| E | A | T | E | N | | O | A | S | E | S |
| | | W | | U | | M | | O | | T |
| | C | O | M | P | L | A | I | N | S | |

## 317

| P | R | O | L | I | F | E | R | A | T | E |
|---|---|---|---|---|---|---|---|---|---|---|
| | E | | I | | O | | | U | | X |
| C | L | E | F | | A | C | I | D | I | C |
| | E | | T | | L | | | I | | E |
| B | A | S | I | S | | S | P | O | I | L |
| | S | | N | | | | A | | N | |
| B | E | I | G | E | | K | N | I | F | E |
| A | | M | | | H | | T | | E | |
| N | I | P | P | L | E | | H | E | R | B |
| K | | E | | | L | | E | | N | |
| S | A | L | E | S | P | E | R | S | O | N |

## 318

| B | A | C | K | O | F | F | | A | R | M |
|---|---|---|---|---|---|---|---|---|---|---|
| L | | R | | D | | R | | R | | I |
| O | V | E | R | D | U | E | | C | O | S |
| O | | D | | S | | N | | H | | A |
| D | R | I | P | | S | C | R | I | M | P |
| S | | B | | H | | H | | P | | P |
| U | N | I | Q | U | E | | R | E | E | L |
| C | | L | | M | | K | | L | | Y |
| K | O | I | | B | E | N | G | A | L | I |
| E | | T | | U | | O | | G | | N |
| R | A | Y | | G | O | W | R | O | N | G |

## 319

## 320

## 321

## 322

## 323

## 324

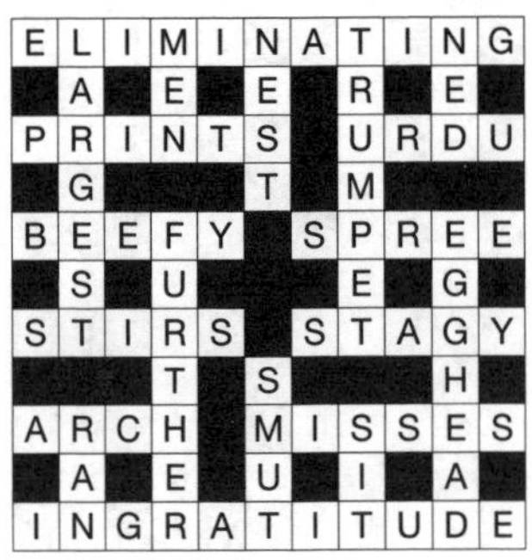

## 325

## 326

| | | | | | | | | | | |
|---|---|---|---|---|---|---|---|---|---|---|
| D | E | C | L | A | R | A | T | I | O | N |
| | Q | | U | | U | | | M | | O |
| B | U | L | L | | B | A | R | B | E | R |
| | A | | L | | Y | | | U | | M |
| S | T | E | A | K | | P | R | E | S | S |
| | O | | B | | | | H | | T | |
| P | R | A | Y | S | | T | U | N | I | S |
| A | | R | | | K | | B | | C | |
| S | A | M | P | L | E | | A | S | K | S |
| T | | E | | | G | | R | | T | |
| A | D | D | R | E | S | S | B | O | O | K |

## 327

## 328

## 329

## 330

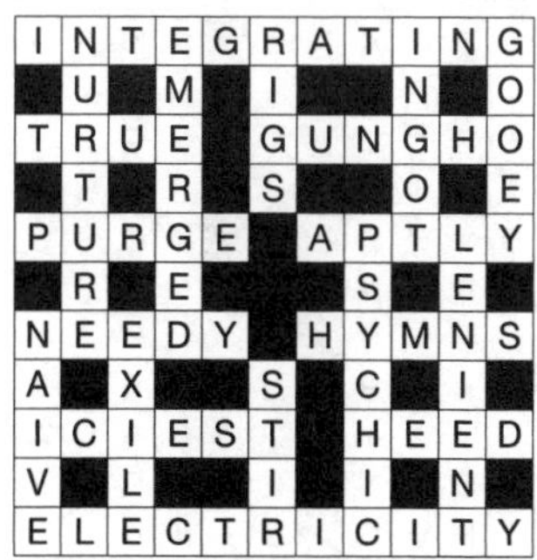

## 331

## 332

| | U | | R | | | F | A | C | T | S |
|---|---|---|---|---|---|---|---|---|---|---|
| I | N | T | E | G | E | R | | O | | I |
| | F | | S | | | I | N | P | U | T |
| H | A | B | I | T | | E | | E | | E |
| | I | | G | | A | N | T | | | |
| F | R | O | N | T | | D | O | I | N | G |
| | | | S | H | E | | O | | O | |
| E | | P | | R | | C | L | O | D | S |
| B | L | A | M | E | | | B | | O | |
| B | | L | | A | L | F | A | L | F | A |
| S | A | L | A | D | | | R | | F | |

## 333

## 334

## 335

## 336

337

338

339

340

| S | H | A | D | O | W |  | B | A | C | K |
|---|---|---|---|---|---|---|---|---|---|---|
| T |  | D |  |  | I |  | E |  | H |  |
| O | R | I | E | N | T |  | D | A | I | S |
| M |  | E |  |  | H |  | R |  | C |  |
| A | L | U | M | N | A |  | O | A | K | Y |
|  | A |  | E |  | V |  | C |  | E |  |
| A | N | N | E |  | I | R | K | I | N | G |
|  | T |  | T |  | E |  |  | N |  | U |
| S | E | M | I |  | W | A | F | F | L | E |
|  | R |  | N |  | T |  |  | E |  | S |
| S | N | U | G |  | O | P | E | R | A | S |

341

342

| E | A | R | P | I | E | R | C | I | N | G |
|---|---|---|---|---|---|---|---|---|---|---|
|  | B |  | L |  | X |  |  | D |  | R |
| T | U | T | U |  | A | P | O | L | L | O |
|  | S |  | N |  | M |  |  | E |  | W |
| D | I | N | G | Y |  | C | A | S | T | S |
|  | V |  | E |  |  |  | R |  | O |  |
| H | E | I | R | S |  | S | T | I | C | K |
| O |  | D |  |  | U |  | D |  | C |  |
| P | A | I | N | T | S |  | E | D | A | M |
| E |  | O |  |  | E |  | C |  | T |  |
| D | I | M | E | N | S | I | O | N | A | L |

343

344

| O | N | S | P | E | C |  | C | A | M | S |
|---|---|---|---|---|---|---|---|---|---|---|
| M |  | P |  |  | O |  | O |  | I |  |
| E | P | O | N | Y | M |  | N | O | N | E |
| G |  | R |  |  | P |  | T |  | I |  |
| A | T | T | I | R | E |  | E | M | M | Y |
|  | H |  | S |  | T |  | N |  | U |  |
| H | A | L | L |  | I | N | T | I | M | E |
|  | N |  | A |  | T |  |  | N |  | L |
| S | K | I | N |  | O | C | T | A | V | E |
|  | E |  | D |  | R |  |  | P |  | C |
| A | D | D | S |  | S | E | X | T | E | T |

## 345

## 346

## 347

## 348

## 349

## 350

REFINED ATS
E L E I L U
SUE WASHTUB
T X T M E R
AKIN HAIRDO
U B I Y N U
REIGNS PAST
A L D B T I
NOISIER IAN
T T G E V E
SAY ODDNESS

## 351

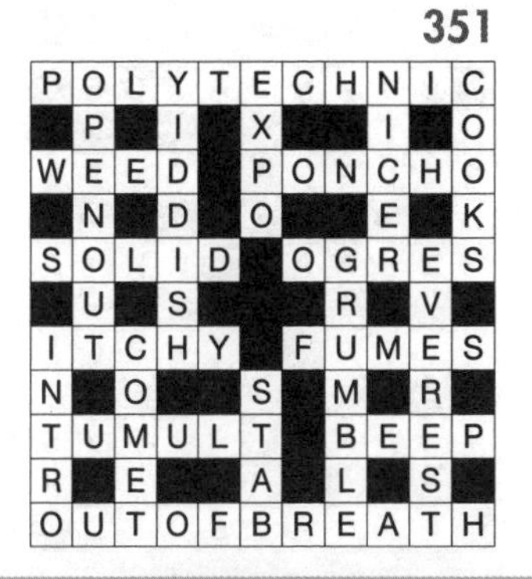


## 352

## 353

| | A | N | D | R | O | M | E | D | A | |
|---|---|---|---|---|---|---|---|---|---|---|
| S | | I | | A | | O | | I | | B |
| H | Y | P | E | R | | D | U | S | T | Y |
| A | | | | E | | E | | G | | M |
| K | E | T | T | L | E | | D | U | N | E |
| E | | O | | Y | | B | | S | | A |
| D | A | B | S | | L | I | S | T | E | N |
| O | | A | | B | | G | | | | S |
| W | I | C | C | A | | G | E | C | K | O |
| N | | C | | L | | E | | A | | F |
| | W | O | N | D | E | R | I | N | G | |

## 354

| C | O | M | E | U | N | S | T | U | C | K |
|---|---|---|---|---|---|---|---|---|---|---|
| | N | | X | | I | | | M | | E |
| S | T | E | P | I | N | | O | B | E | Y |
| | H | | L | | T | | | E | | E |
| H | E | R | O | | H | A | T | R | E | D |
| | G | | D | | | | E | | D | |
| B | O | R | E | A | L | | M | A | I | L |
| I | | A | | | A | | P | | T | |
| N | A | V | Y | | D | E | T | A | I | L |
| D | | E | | | L | | E | | O | |
| I | N | D | E | P | E | N | D | E | N | T |

## 355

| A | B | L | E | B | O | D | I | E | D | |
|---|---|---|---|---|---|---|---|---|---|---|
| | R | | G | | Y | | N | | A | |
| J | U | N | G | L | E | | V | I | B | E |
| | T | | | | Z | | A | | | |
| R | I | N | G | S | | E | D | G | E | D |
| | S | | L | | | | E | | M | |
| S | H | O | U | T | | A | D | E | P | T |
| | | | C | | G | | | | O | |
| E | C | H | O | | R | E | N | E | W | S |
| | A | | S | | A | | O | | E | |
| | P | R | E | S | B | Y | T | E | R | Y |

## 356

| | S | | S | | | D | E | V | I | L |
|---|---|---|---|---|---|---|---|---|---|---|
| R | A | V | I | O | L | I | | I | | E |
| | M | | S | | | V | E | E | R | S |
| H | O | S | T | S | | E | | S | | S |
| | S | | E | | F | R | O | | | |
| H | A | I | R | S | | T | U | R | N | S |
| | | | S | I | M | | T | | I | |
| S | | G | | T | | F | L | A | G | S |
| C | O | Y | P | U | | | I | | H | |
| A | | R | | P | E | A | N | U | T | S |
| B | L | O | W | S | | | E | | S | |

## 357

| | I | N | F | L | U | E | N | C | E | |
|---|---|---|---|---|---|---|---|---|---|---|
| U | | I | | A | | R | | R | | B |
| N | A | M | E | D | | R | O | Y | A | L |
| U | | | | I | | S | | P | | A |
| S | E | Q | U | E | L | | S | T | A | T |
| U | | U | | S | | P | | I | | A |
| A | L | A | S | | V | U | L | C | A | N |
| L | | N | | P | | R | | | | T |
| L | I | T | H | E | | V | O | W | E | L |
| Y | | U | | E | | E | | O | | Y |
| | E | M | P | L | O | Y | I | N | G | |

## 358

| | A | | A | | | D | E | I | T | Y |
|---|---|---|---|---|---|---|---|---|---|---|
| G | N | O | C | C | H | I | | R | | U |
| | N | | R | | | V | I | O | L | A |
| T | U | T | O | R | | I | | N | | N |
| | A | | B | | O | D | E | | | |
| G | L | E | A | M | | E | T | H | I | C |
| | | | T | O | G | | E | | M | |
| C | | A | | T | | W | R | A | P | S |
| R | A | B | B | I | | | N | | A | |
| A | | B | | V | A | C | A | N | C | Y |
| B | R | A | K | E | | | L | | T | |

## 359

| H | O | U | S | E | A | R | R | E | S | T |
|---|---|---|---|---|---|---|---|---|---|---|
| | W | | C | | P | | E | | W | |
| E | N | T | E | R | P | R | I | S | E | S |
| | E | | N | | | | K | | L | |
| I | R | R | E | D | U | C | I | B | L | E |
| | | O | | O | | O | | I | | |
| A | C | C | U | S | A | T | I | O | N | S |
| | L | | N | | | | O | | Y | |
| W | O | N | D | E | R | I | N | G | L | Y |
| | W | | E | | A | | I | | O | |
| I | N | T | R | O | D | U | C | I | N | G |

## 360

| | B | A | R | N | D | A | N | C | E | |
|---|---|---|---|---|---|---|---|---|---|---|
| P | | L | | O | | R | | A | | E |
| R | U | L | E | R | | C | O | M | E | S |
| O | | | | M | | S | | E | | T |
| S | U | B | W | A | Y | | A | R | I | A |
| P | | E | | L | | S | | A | | B |
| E | V | E | R | | T | I | N | S | E | L |
| C | | S | | U | | G | | | | I |
| T | O | W | N | S | | H | I | D | E | S |
| S | | A | | E | | T | | U | | H |
| | E | X | P | R | E | S | S | E | D | |

## 361

## 362

## 363

## 364

## 365

## 366

| | | | | | | | | | | |
|---|---|---|---|---|---|---|---|---|---|---|
| | A | | F | | | P | L | I | E | D |
| S | C | H | E | R | Z | O | | M | | A |
| | T | | L | | | R | E | A | D | Y |
| B | U | I | L | D | | T | | M | | S |
| | A | | O | | H | E | M | | | |
| F | L | O | W | N | | D | I | V | E | D |
| | | | S | E | W | | L | | N | |
| S | | S | | A | | S | E | V | E | N |
| L | O | W | E | R | | | A | | R | |
| O | | A | | B | A | G | G | A | G | E |
| W | I | T | T | Y | | | E | | Y | |

## 367

## 368

## 369

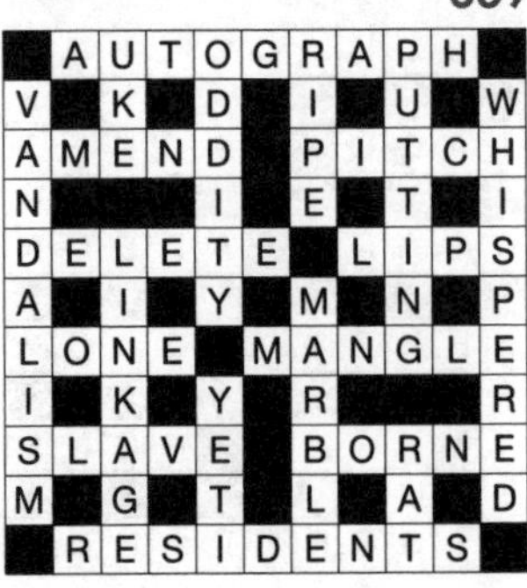

| | | | | | | | | | | |
|---|---|---|---|---|---|---|---|---|---|---|
| ■ | A | U | T | O | G | R | A | P | H | ■ |
| V | ■ | K | ■ | D | ■ | I | ■ | U | ■ | W |
| A | M | E | N | D | ■ | P | I | T | C | H |
| N | ■ | ■ | ■ | I | ■ | E | ■ | T | ■ | I |
| D | E | L | E | T | E | ■ | L | I | P | S |
| A | ■ | I | ■ | Y | ■ | M | ■ | N | ■ | P |
| L | O | N | E | ■ | M | A | N | G | L | E |
| I | ■ | K | ■ | Y | ■ | R | ■ | ■ | ■ | R |
| S | L | A | V | E | ■ | B | O | R | N | E |
| M | ■ | G | ■ | T | ■ | L | ■ | A | ■ | D |
| ■ | R | E | S | I | D | E | N | T | S | ■ |

## 370

| | | | | | | | | | | |
|---|---|---|---|---|---|---|---|---|---|---|
| ■ | P | R | I | M | A | R | I | L | Y | ■ |
| S | ■ | E | ■ | E | ■ | E | ■ | O | ■ | ■ |
| K | O | F | T | A | ■ | P | A | G | E | D |
| E | ■ | U | ■ | D | ■ | E | ■ | ■ | ■ | E |
| L | A | S | S | ■ | C | A | M | P | U | S |
| E | ■ | A | ■ | B | ■ | L | ■ | R | ■ | T |
| T | A | L | K | E | D | ■ | P | E | E | R |
| O | ■ | ■ | ■ | A | ■ | S | ■ | S | ■ | O |
| N | I | G | H | T | ■ | P | A | S | T | Y |
| ■ | ■ | E | ■ | E | ■ | A | ■ | E | ■ | S |
| ■ | A | L | O | N | G | S | I | D | E | ■ |

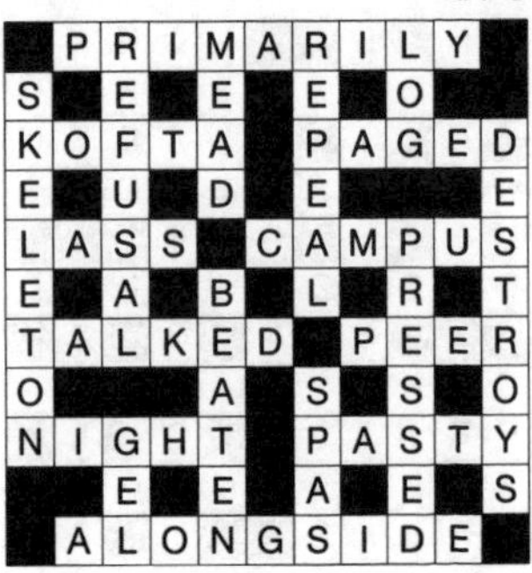

## 371

| | | | | | | | | | | |
|---|---|---|---|---|---|---|---|---|---|---|
| S | U | B | S | T | A | N | T | I | A | L |
| ■ | P | ■ | A | ■ | D | ■ | ■ | N | ■ | U |
| I | R | O | N | E | D | ■ | U | D | O | N |
| ■ | I | ■ | G | ■ | U | ■ | ■ | I | ■ | G |
| A | G | A | R | ■ | P | I | R | A | T | E |
| ■ | H | ■ | I | ■ | ■ | ■ | I | ■ | R | ■ |
| S | T | R | A | Y | S | ■ | G | R | I | M |
| M | ■ | E | ■ | ■ | L | ■ | H | ■ | U | ■ |
| A | Q | U | A | ■ | A | S | T | H | M | A |
| S | ■ | S | ■ | ■ | N | ■ | L | ■ | P | ■ |
| H | I | E | R | O | G | L | Y | P | H | S |

## 372

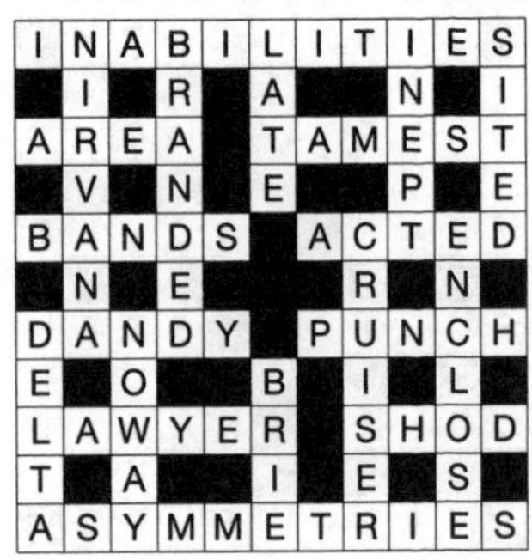

| | | | | | | | | | | |
|---|---|---|---|---|---|---|---|---|---|---|
| I | N | A | B | I | L | I | T | I | E | S |
| ■ | I | ■ | R | ■ | A | ■ | ■ | N | ■ | I |
| A | R | E | A | ■ | T | A | M | E | S | T |
| ■ | V | ■ | N | ■ | E | ■ | ■ | P | ■ | E |
| B | A | N | D | S | ■ | A | C | T | E | D |
| ■ | N | ■ | E | ■ | ■ | ■ | R | ■ | N | ■ |
| D | A | N | D | Y | ■ | P | U | N | C | H |
| E | ■ | O | ■ | ■ | B | ■ | I | ■ | L | ■ |
| L | A | W | Y | E | R | ■ | S | H | O | D |
| T | ■ | A | ■ | ■ | I | ■ | E | ■ | S | ■ |
| A | S | Y | M | M | E | T | R | I | E | S |

## 373

| | | | | | | | | | | |
|---|---|---|---|---|---|---|---|---|---|---|
| ■ | P | A | P | E | R | B | A | C | K | ■ |
| A | ■ | D | ■ | A | ■ | I | ■ | U | ■ | ■ |
| D | I | V | E | S | ■ | T | O | P | I | C |
| J | ■ | E | ■ | E | ■ | M | ■ | ■ | ■ | L |
| A | I | R | Y | ■ | S | A | L | A | M | I |
| C | ■ | S | ■ | M | ■ | P | ■ | T | ■ | P |
| E | Y | E | F | U | L | ■ | S | T | E | P |
| N | ■ | ■ | ■ | S | ■ | S | ■ | E | ■ | I |
| T | R | A | C | E | ■ | W | O | M | E | N |
| ■ | ■ | B | ■ | U | ■ | A | ■ | P | ■ | G |
| ■ | T | E | R | M | I | N | A | T | E | ■ |

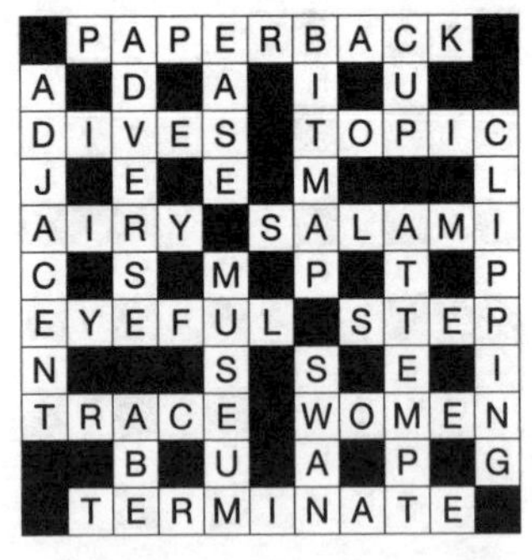

## 374

| | | | | | | | | | | |
|---|---|---|---|---|---|---|---|---|---|---|
| R | E | T | I | R | E | S | ■ | D | O | G |
| E | ■ | E | ■ | E | ■ | I | ■ | I | ■ | R |
| P | O | M | ■ | E | N | M | A | S | S | E |
| E | ■ | P | ■ | L | ■ | I | ■ | I | ■ | E |
| R | O | O | M | ■ | F | A | L | L | E | N |
| T | ■ | R | ■ | D | ■ | N | ■ | L | ■ | H |
| O | R | A | T | O | R | ■ | J | U | D | O |
| I | ■ | R | ■ | O | ■ | D | ■ | S | ■ | U |
| R | A | I | L | W | A | Y | ■ | I | F | S |
| E | ■ | L | ■ | O | ■ | E | ■ | O | ■ | E |
| S | O | Y | ■ | P | E | D | A | N | T | S |

## 375

| | | | | | | | | | | |
|---|---|---|---|---|---|---|---|---|---|---|
| A | ■ | O | ■ | B | ■ | I | ■ | G | ■ | F |
| G | E | N | D | A | R | M | E | R | I | E |
| N | ■ | C | ■ | N | ■ | P | ■ | O | ■ | A |
| O | V | E | R | A | L | L | ■ | W | I | T |
| S | ■ | ■ | ■ | N | ■ | A | ■ | U | ■ | U |
| T | I | A | R | A | ■ | U | P | P | E | R |
| I | ■ | R | ■ | S | ■ | S | ■ | ■ | ■ | E |
| C | O | G | ■ | P | A | I | N | F | U | L |
| I | ■ | U | ■ | L | ■ | B | ■ | A | ■ | E |
| S | P | E | C | I | A | L | I | Z | E | S |
| M | ■ | D | ■ | T | ■ | E | ■ | E | ■ | S |

## 376

| | | | | | | | | | | |
|---|---|---|---|---|---|---|---|---|---|---|
| ■ | P | A | S | S | W | O | R | D | S | ■ |
| F | ■ | D | ■ | I | ■ | U | ■ | E | ■ | O |
| I | M | A | G | E | ■ | C | R | E | E | P |
| S | ■ | ■ | ■ | V | ■ | H | ■ | M | ■ | P |
| H | A | C | K | E | R | ■ | L | I | M | O |
| K | ■ | O | ■ | S | ■ | B | ■ | N | ■ | N |
| N | U | M | B | ■ | T | A | N | G | L | E |
| I | ■ | P | ■ | F | ■ | S | ■ | ■ | ■ | N |
| F | E | L | L | A | ■ | S | H | O | R | T |
| E | ■ | E | ■ | I | ■ | E | ■ | W | ■ | S |
| ■ | E | X | P | R | E | S | S | E | S | ■ |

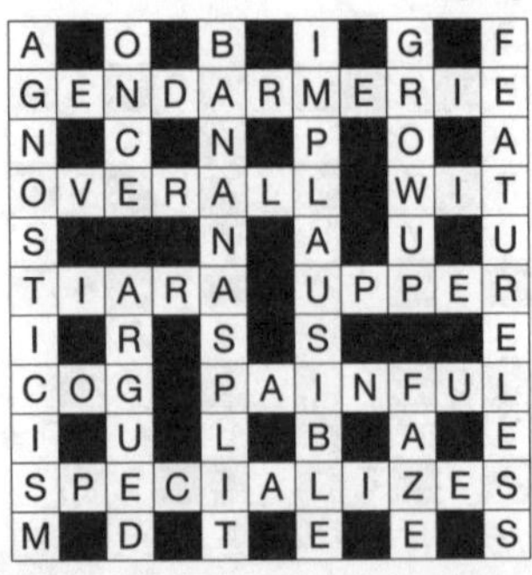

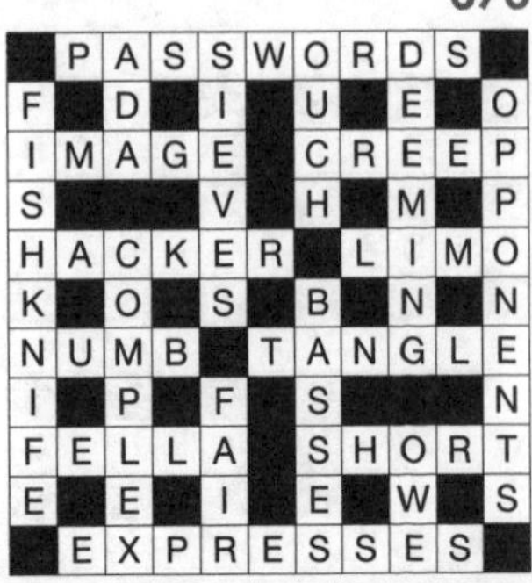

## 377

## 378

## 379

## 380

|   | O |   | M |   |   | T | A | L | E | S |
|---|---|---|---|---|---|---|---|---|---|---|
| Q | U | I | E | T | E | R |   | I |   | A |
|   | T |   | M |   |   | Y | O | K | E | S |
| G | L | O | B | E |   | I |   | E |   | H |
|   | A |   | E |   | A | N | Y |   |   |   |
| D | W | A | R | F |   | G | O | U | G | E |
|   |   |   | S | O | N |   | U |   | R |   |
| S |   | H |   | R |   | S | N | E | E | R |
| C | H | A | R | M |   |   | G |   | E |   |
| A |   | I |   | A | L | R | E | A | D | Y |
| M | U | R | A | L |   |   | R |   | Y |   |

## 381

|   | A | T | T | R | I | B | U | T | E |   |
|---|---|---|---|---|---|---|---|---|---|---|
| S |   | U |   | I |   | A |   | E |   |   |
| T | I | R | E | D |   | F | A | D | E | D |
| R |   | N |   | E |   | F |   |   |   | R |
| E | X | I | T |   | A | L | U | M | N | A |
| S |   | N |   | B |   | E |   | A |   | W |
| S | I | G | N | U | P |   | K | N | O | B |
| E |   |   |   | R |   | A |   | G |   | A |
| S | I | N | C | E |   | L | I | L | A | C |
|   |   | T |   | A |   | G |   | E |   | K |
|   | T | H | O | U | S | A | N | D | S |   |

## 382

| F | A | S | C | I | N | A | T | E | D |   |
|---|---|---|---|---|---|---|---|---|---|---|
|   | L |   | A |   | O |   | O |   | U |   |
| S | C | O | P | E | S |   | N | O | D | S |
|   | O |   |   |   | Y |   | I |   |   |   |
| S | H | I | R | T |   | A | G | E | N | T |
|   | O |   | I |   |   |   | H |   | O |   |
| B | L | A | S | T |   | S | T | A | T | E |
|   |   |   | O |   | E |   |   |   | I |   |
| W | H | A | T |   | G | O | B | A | C | K |
|   | A |   | T |   | G |   | O |   | E |   |
|   | G | O | O | D | Y | G | O | O | D | Y |

## 383

## 384

## 385

## 386

## 387

## 388

## 389

## 390

CORRECTIONS
N E A L O
SPAT MILIEU
A U E V R
SPURT SPEWS
E N L E
BRUSH BOOST
R P M T T
ASSUME TIED
V E G E R
OUTSTANDING

## 391

## 392

## 393

| R | E | Q | U | I | R | E | M | E | N | T |
|---|---|---|---|---|---|---|---|---|---|---|
|  | T |  | R |  | A |  |  | L |  | U |
| T | H | U | G |  | M | U | F | F | I | N |
|  | I |  | E |  | S |  |  | I |  | E |
| S | C | A | N | T |  | A | C | N | E | D |
|  | A |  | C |  |  |  | A |  | L |  |
| P | L | A | Y | S |  | S | T | E | E | P |
| U |  | N |  |  | H |  | C |  | G |  |
| N | E | G | A | T | E |  | H | E | I | R |
| T |  | E |  |  | R |  | U |  | A |  |
| S | E | L | F | R | E | S | P | E | C | T |

## 394

|  | S |  | S |  |  | T | A | N | K | S |
|---|---|---|---|---|---|---|---|---|---|---|
| M | I | S | H | E | A | R |  | O |  | U |
|  | E |  | R |  |  | A | L | O | U | D |
| G | R | A | I | L |  | I |  | K |  | S |
|  | R |  | V |  | I | N | K |  |  |  |
| W | A | F | E | R |  | S | N | O | W | Y |
|  |  |  | L | E | G |  | O |  | R |  |
| S |  | S |  | M |  | A | B | B | E | Y |
| W | H | O | L | E |  |  | B |  | C |  |
| A |  | L |  | D | I | S | L | I | K | E |
| G | O | D | L | Y |  |  | Y |  | S |  |

## 395

|  | S | T | A | I | R | C | A | S | E |  |
|---|---|---|---|---|---|---|---|---|---|---|
| R |  | O |  | M |  | O |  | M |  | A |
| E | X | T | R | A |  | W | H | I | L | E |
| L |  |  |  | G |  | L |  | L |  | S |
| E | D | G | I | E | R |  | L | I | L | T |
| V |  | L |  | S |  | C |  | N |  | H |
| A | R | A | B |  | B | O | G | G | L | E |
| N |  | C |  | C |  | M |  |  |  | T |
| C | H | I | M | E |  | B | L | I | N | I |
| E |  | E |  | N |  | A |  | M |  | C |
|  | P | R | O | T | O | T | Y | P | E |  |

## 396

| C | A | L | I | P | H |  | P | U | C | E |
|---|---|---|---|---|---|---|---|---|---|---|
| O |  | I |  |  | I |  | O |  | R |  |
| L | O | V | I | N | G |  | R | E | A | P |
| I |  | E |  |  | H |  | T |  | C |  |
| C | E | R | E | A | L |  | I | N | K | S |
|  | V |  | A |  | I |  | C |  | U |  |
| L | O | N | G |  | G | R | O | U | P | S |
|  | L |  | E |  | H |  |  | R |  | W |
| O | V | E | R |  | T | O | G | G | L | E |
|  | E |  | L |  | E |  |  | E |  | D |
| E | D | D | Y |  | D | R | E | D | G | E |

## 397

| L | U | M | I | N | E | S | C | E | N | T |
|---|---|---|---|---|---|---|---|---|---|---|
|  | N |  | N |  | A |  |  | L |  | U |
| G | U | L | F |  | R | A | N | D | O | M |
|  | S |  | E |  | N |  |  | E |  | M |
| J | U | I | C | E |  | F | U | R | R | Y |
|  | A |  | T |  |  |  | N |  | E |  |
| F | L | A | S | H |  | S | K | U | L | L |
| I |  | T |  |  | W |  | E |  | E |  |
| E | N | O | U | G | H |  | M | O | A | N |
| L |  | M |  |  | E |  | P |  | R |  |
| D | E | S | I | G | N | A | T | I | N | G |

## 398

|  | E | M | O | T | I | O | N | A | L |  |
|---|---|---|---|---|---|---|---|---|---|---|
| T |  | E |  | I |  | O |  | P |  | P |
| E | X | A | L | T |  | P | A | P | E | R |
| R |  |  |  | L |  | S |  | A |  | E |
| R | U | P | E | E | S |  | P | R | O | S |
| O |  | E |  | S |  | S |  | E |  | E |
| R | O | A | R |  | A | M | P | L | E | R |
| I |  | S |  | L |  | I |  |  |  | V |
| S | T | A | R | E |  | L | A | R | G | E |
| T |  | N |  | A |  | E |  | U |  | S |
|  | S | T | U | P | I | D | I | T | Y |  |

## 399

| A | D | V | E | R | S | I | T | I | E | S |
|---|---|---|---|---|---|---|---|---|---|---|
|  | E |  | X |  | U |  |  | N |  | E |
| C | R | O | P |  | M | U | D | D | L | E |
|  | A |  | O |  | P |  |  | I |  | D |
| A | N | G | S | T |  | A | V | E | R | S |
|  | G |  | E |  |  |  | O |  | H |  |
| S | E | N | S | E |  | C | L | O | U | D |
| Q |  | E |  |  | T |  | C |  | B |  |
| U | N | W | I | S | E |  | A | D | A | M |
| I |  | L |  |  | N |  | N |  | R |  |
| B | E | Y | O | N | D | D | O | U | B | T |

## 400

| U | N | I | O | N | S |  | K | N | E | E |
|---|---|---|---|---|---|---|---|---|---|---|
| N |  | L |  | A |  | F |  | O |  | M |
| A | L | L | O | V | E | R |  | R | U | B |
| M |  | U |  | E |  | E |  | T |  | A |
| B | U | S | H |  | F | A | T | H | E | R |
| I |  | T |  | S |  | K |  | D |  | R |
| G | U | R | K | H | A |  | H | A | H | A |
| U |  | A |  | O |  | O |  | K |  | S |
| O | P | T |  | P | E | R | I | O | D | S |
| U |  | E |  | S |  | E |  | T |  | E |
| S | A | S | S |  | A | S | S | A | Y | S |

## 401

| O | R | I | E | N | T | A | T | I | N | G |
|---|---|---|---|---|---|---|---|---|---|---|
| | E | | N | | U | | | N | | R |
| P | A | N | G | | G | H | E | T | T | O |
| | C | | I | | S | | | E | | U |
| S | T | U | N | T | | S | C | R | A | P |
| | O | | E | | | | O | | T | |
| C | R | U | S | T | | C | L | I | F | F |
| A | | N | | | V | | L | | I | |
| U | P | S | I | D | E | | A | U | R | A |
| S | | E | | | R | | G | | S | |
| E | N | T | O | M | B | M | E | N | T | S |

## 402

| A | B | R | A | C | A | D | A | B | R | A |
|---|---|---|---|---|---|---|---|---|---|---|
| D | | E | | O | | R | | A | | C |
| V | I | C | | A | S | I | A | T | I | C |
| E | | Y | | T | | V | | | | E |
| N | O | C | K | | V | E | S | S | E | L |
| T | | L | | G | | R | | H | | E |
| U | N | E | V | E | N | | T | O | U | R |
| R | | | | M | | H | | W | | A |
| O | U | T | S | I | D | E | | B | E | T |
| U | | O | | N | | E | | I | | E |
| S | P | E | C | I | A | L | I | Z | E | D |

## 403

| P | R | O | T | U | B | E | R | A | N | T |
|---|---|---|---|---|---|---|---|---|---|---|
| L | | C | | | E | | I | | O | |
| A | R | C | A | D | E | | B | O | M | B |
| N | | U | | | S | | C | | A | |
| T | E | R | M | S | | M | A | I | D | S |
| | X | | I | | | | G | | I | |
| W | O | R | S | E | | M | E | R | C | Y |
| | T | | T | | S | | | O | | E |
| V | I | S | A | | T | R | A | U | M | A |
| | C | | K | | O | | | T | | R |
| S | A | L | E | S | P | E | R | S | O | N |

## 404

| S | C | E | N | I | C | | P | A | I | D |
|---|---|---|---|---|---|---|---|---|---|---|
| E | | A | | | E | | R | | N | |
| L | E | T | H | A | L | | E | N | V | Y |
| L | | U | | | E | | M | | O | |
| S | U | P | E | R | B | | I | C | K | Y |
| | N | | N | | R | | U | | E | |
| T | I | N | S | | A | L | M | O | S | T |
| | C | | U | | T | | | V | | E |
| S | O | U | R | | I | G | U | A | N | A |
| | R | | E | | O | | | T | | M |
| O | N | U | S | | N | O | V | E | L | S |

## 405

| W | A | L | K | O | N | | P | O | L | E |
|---|---|---|---|---|---|---|---|---|---|---|
| A | | A | | | E | | H | | O | |
| G | A | B | B | L | E | | O | R | B | S |
| E | | E | | | D | | E | | S | |
| R | E | L | I | E | F | | N | O | T | E |
| | M | | N | | U | | I | | E | |
| A | P | E | D | | L | U | X | U | R | Y |
| | T | | E | | N | | | N | | A |
| J | I | N | X | | E | D | I | T | O | R |
| | E | | E | | S | | | I | | D |
| B | R | A | D | | S | M | E | L | L | S |

## 406

| | E | L | O | Q | U | E | N | C | E | |
|---|---|---|---|---|---|---|---|---|---|---|
| I | | E | | U | | R | | O | | D |
| N | U | D | G | E | | G | E | N | I | E |
| T | | | | B | | O | | F | | V |
| R | I | P | P | E | D | | M | E | S | A |
| O | | R | | C | | A | | S | | S |
| D | O | O | M | | O | F | F | S | E | T |
| U | | T | | T | | G | | | | A |
| C | H | E | E | R | | H | E | I | S | T |
| E | | C | | I | | A | | V | | E |
| | A | T | T | O | R | N | E | Y | S | |

## 407

| S | C | A | F | F | O | L | D | I | N | G |
|---|---|---|---|---|---|---|---|---|---|---|
| | O | | U | | T | | | N | | R |
| D | U | L | C | E | T | | P | U | M | A |
| | G | | H | | E | | | I | | N |
| T | H | U | S | | R | E | S | T | E | D |
| | U | | I | | | | E | | R | |
| S | P | R | A | W | L | | R | O | O | T |
| A | | O | | | O | | P | | S | |
| V | A | S | T | | C | R | E | D | I | T |
| E | | T | | | A | | N | | O | |
| S | T | I | M | U | L | A | T | I | N | G |

## 408

| T | A | C | T | I | C | | R | O | B | E |
|---|---|---|---|---|---|---|---|---|---|---|
| O | | O | | | O | | U | | O | |
| K | I | L | L | E | R | | N | I | T | S |
| E | | O | | | P | | O | | H | |
| N | U | N | C | I | O | | V | I | E | W |
| | N | | O | | R | | E | | R | |
| T | E | R | M | | A | T | R | I | S | K |
| | Q | | P | | T | | | D | | N |
| Z | U | L | U | | I | M | P | O | S | E |
| | A | | T | | O | | | L | | E |
| F | L | O | E | | N | O | I | S | E | S |

## 409

## 410

## 411

## 412

| | | | | | | | | | | |
|---|---|---|---|---|---|---|---|---|---|---|
| C | O | P | O | U | T | | B | O | W | L |
| H | | O | | | O | | O | | E | |
| A | S | L | E | E | P | | O | I | L | S |
| F | | A | | | P | | L | | C | |
| F | A | R | M | E | R | | E | R | O | S |
| | B | | E | | I | | A | | M | |
| R | I | F | T | | O | U | N | C | E | S |
| | L | | H | | R | | | R | | E |
| D | I | D | O | | I | N | J | U | R | E |
| | T | | D | | T | | | E | | M |
| D | Y | E | S | | Y | I | E | L | D | S |

## 413

## 414

| | | | | | | | | | | |
|---|---|---|---|---|---|---|---|---|---|---|
| I | N | T | E | R | R | O | G | A | T | E |
| | A | | N | | A | | | U | | V |
| S | U | N | G | | G | I | G | G | L | E |
| | G | | L | | E | | | U | | N |
| C | H | A | I | N | | C | A | R | E | S |
| | T | | S | | | | I | | L | |
| M | Y | T | H | S | | F | R | A | U | D |
| O | | W | | | C | | M | | D | |
| D | R | I | V | E | L | | A | R | I | D |
| E | | S | | | A | | I | | N | |
| M | E | T | H | O | D | O | L | O | G | Y |

## 415

## 416

## 417

## 418

## 419

## 420

## 421

## 422

| U | N | S | E | P | A | R | A | T | E | D |
|---|---|---|---|---|---|---|---|---|---|---|
| N |  | U |  |  | N |  | L |  | Y |  |
| Z | Y | G | O | T | E |  | T | H | E | Y |
| I |  | A |  |  | W |  | E |  | B |  |
| P | A | R | T | S |  | C | R | O | A | T |
|  | S |  | W |  |  |  | E |  | L |  |
| P | O | S | I | T |  | A | D | U | L | T |
|  | C |  | S |  | A |  |  | N |  | H |
| M | I | T | T |  | P | A | N | I | N | I |
|  | A |  | E |  | E |  |  | T |  | R |
| I | L | L | D | I | S | P | O | S | E | D |

## 423

## 424

## 425

## 426

## 427

## 428

## 429

## 430

| | | | | | | | | | | |
|---|---|---|---|---|---|---|---|---|---|---|
| | G | | G | | | C | A | R | E | D |
| D | E | C | L | A | R | E | | O | | A |
| | L | | A | | | N | O | S | E | S |
| H | A | I | R | Y | | S | | E | | H |
| | T | | I | | B | U | S | | | |
| D | O | I | N | G | | S | P | I | N | E |
| | | | G | A | B | | R | | A | |
| G | | L | | R | | L | I | E | I | N |
| L | L | A | M | A | | | N | | V | |
| I | | U | | G | O | G | G | L | E | S |
| B | A | D | G | E | | | S | | R | |

## 431

## 432

433

434

435

436

437

438

| | | | | | | | | | | |
|---|---|---|---|---|---|---|---|---|---|---|
| | P | R | E | G | N | A | N | C | Y | |
| I | | O | | A | | R | | R | | P |
| N | E | W | E | R | | T | O | U | C | H |
| N | | | | B | | Y | | S | | E |
| E | A | S | I | L | Y | | T | H | E | N |
| R | | T | | E | | B | | E | | O |
| T | E | A | S | | G | Y | P | S | U | M |
| U | | T | | M | | E | | | | E |
| B | R | I | N | E | | B | E | G | A | N |
| E | | O | | M | | Y | | E | | A |
| | I | N | T | E | R | E | S | T | S | |

439

440

## 441

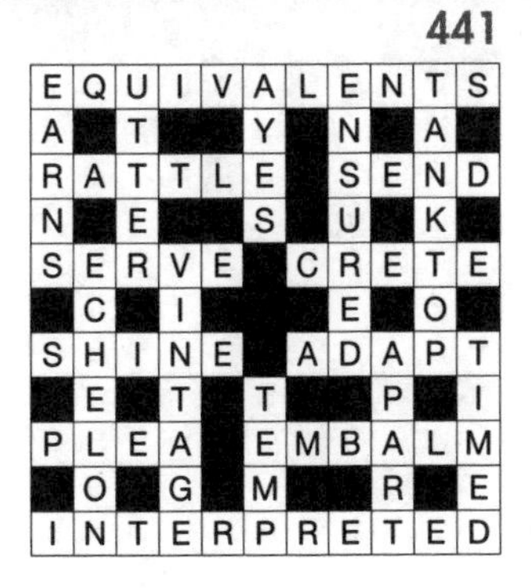

| | | | | | | | | | | |
|---|---|---|---|---|---|---|---|---|---|---|
| E | Q | U | I | V | A | L | E | N | T | S |
| A | | T | | | Y | | N | | A | |
| R | A | T | T | L | E | | S | E | N | D |
| N | | E | | | S | | U | | K | |
| S | E | R | V | E | | C | R | E | T | E |
| | C | | I | | | | E | | O | |
| S | H | I | N | E | | A | D | A | P | T |
| | E | | T | | T | | | P | | I |
| P | L | E | A | | E | M | B | A | L | M |
| | O | | G | | M | | | R | | E |
| I | N | T | E | R | P | R | E | T | E | D |

## 442

| | | | | | | | | | | |
|---|---|---|---|---|---|---|---|---|---|---|
| | I | N | S | U | R | A | N | C | E | |
| A | | I | | N | | I | | A | | H |
| M | E | T | E | R | | D | O | L | L | Y |
| P | | | | E | | S | | L | | P |
| L | I | S | T | E | D | | M | O | J | O |
| I | | O | | L | | G | | U | | C |
| T | A | P | E | | B | U | R | S | A | R |
| U | | R | | S | | E | | | | I |
| D | R | A | N | K | | S | M | A | R | T |
| E | | N | | I | | T | | V | | E |
| | P | O | S | S | E | S | S | E | S | |

## 443

| | | | | | | | | | | |
|---|---|---|---|---|---|---|---|---|---|---|
| A | P | P | A | L | L | I | N | G | L | Y |
| | L | | U | | U | | A | | O | |
| B | A | S | K | E | T | | S | A | T | E |
| | N | | | | E | | C | | | |
| S | T | O | P | S | | B | E | E | R | S |
| | E | | R | | | | N | | E | |
| A | D | H | O | C | | S | T | U | C | K |
| | | | V | | B | | | | R | |
| S | H | O | O | | O | U | T | P | U | T |
| | E | | K | | O | | I | | I | |
| E | X | T | E | R | M | I | N | A | T | E |

## 444

| | | | | | | | | | | |
|---|---|---|---|---|---|---|---|---|---|---|
| O | R | I | G | I | N | A | T | I | N | G |
| C | | N | | | O | | E | | O | |
| T | O | D | D | L | E | | R | O | V | E |
| E | | E | | | S | | R | | E | |
| T | A | X | I | S | | W | I | L | L | S |
| | S | | M | | | | F | | T | |
| W | I | S | P | S | | M | Y | E | Y | E |
| | N | | A | | M | | | V | | X |
| M | I | S | S | | A | L | P | A | C | A |
| | N | | S | | Y | | | D | | C |
| D | E | V | E | L | O | P | M | E | N | T |

## 445

| | | | | | | | | | | |
|---|---|---|---|---|---|---|---|---|---|---|
| P | R | O | G | R | A | M | M | E | R | S |
| | A | | R | | U | | | X | | P |
| M | I | R | O | | N | I | P | P | L | E |
| | N | | S | | T | | | E | | N |
| A | B | U | S | E | | I | D | L | E | D |
| | O | | L | | | | R | | A | |
| S | W | A | Y | S | | G | Y | P | S | Y |
| E | | P | | | Z | | D | | T | |
| T | I | P | T | O | E | | O | W | E | D |
| T | | L | | | R | | C | | R | |
| O | V | E | R | L | O | O | K | I | N | G |

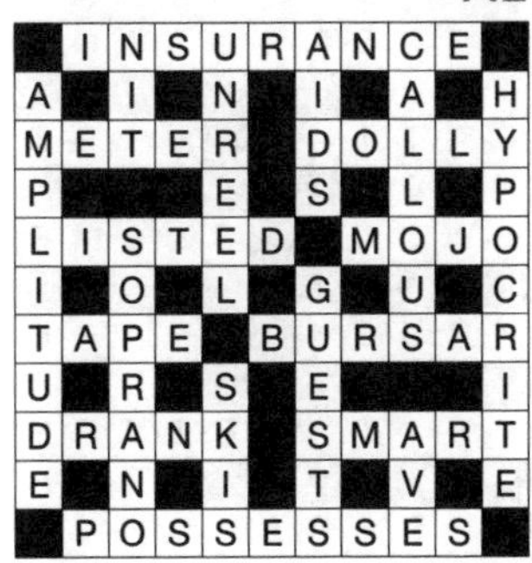

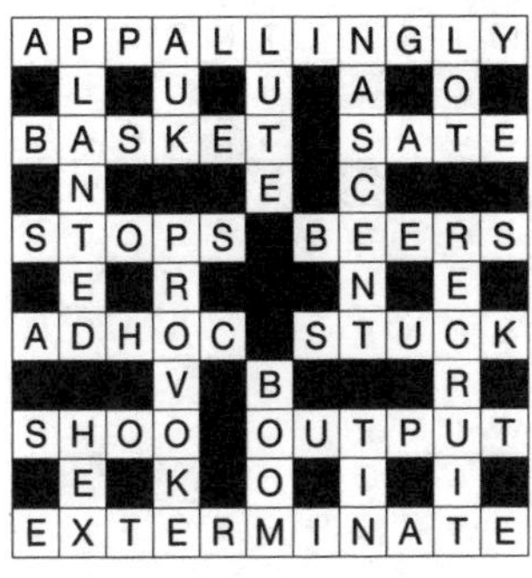

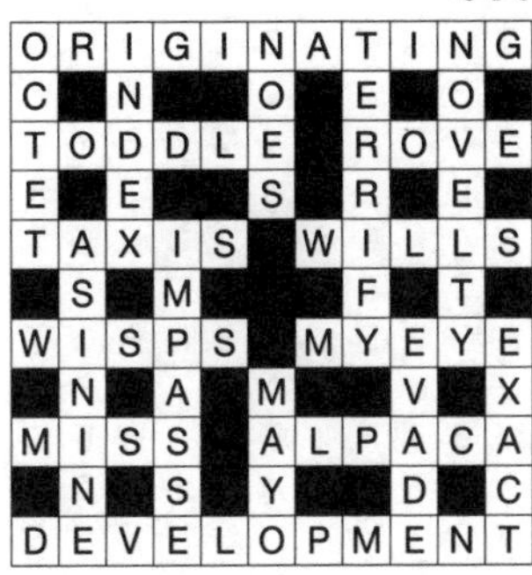

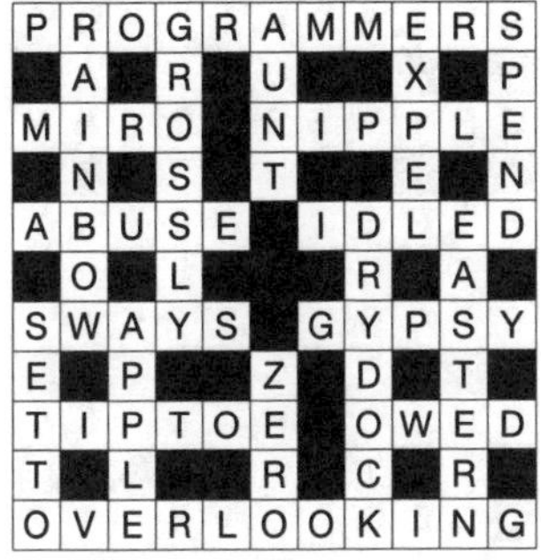

## 446

| | | | | | | | | | | |
|---|---|---|---|---|---|---|---|---|---|---|
| | I | N | N | O | C | E | N | C | E | |
| S | | I | | L | | T | | U | | A |
| E | M | B | E | D | | C | R | E | E | D |
| N | | | | E | | H | | B | | N |
| S | T | R | E | S | S | | J | A | V | A |
| I | | E | | T | | S | | L | | U |
| T | I | N | Y | | S | T | Y | L | E | S |
| I | | E | | B | | A | | | | E |
| V | O | W | E | L | | M | A | M | M | A |
| E | | E | | U | | P | | A | | M |
| | A | D | D | R | E | S | S | E | E | |

## 447

| | | | | | | | | | | |
|---|---|---|---|---|---|---|---|---|---|---|
| | B | R | I | N | G | D | O | W | N | |
| A | | U | | U | | O | | A | | |
| P | R | I | N | T | | C | A | R | O | B |
| P | | N | | S | | T | | | | U |
| A | X | I | S | | D | O | D | G | E | R |
| L | | N | | S | | R | | R | | N |
| L | O | G | G | E | D | | S | A | I | D |
| E | | | | T | | Z | | B | | O |
| D | I | G | I | T | | E | L | B | O | W |
| | | A | | E | | T | | E | | N |
| | A | S | R | E | G | A | R | D | S | |

## 448

| | | | | | | | | | | |
|---|---|---|---|---|---|---|---|---|---|---|
| | M | | F | | | S | I | Z | E | D |
| D | I | S | A | B | L | E | | E | | R |
| | K | | N | | | I | N | A | N | E |
| F | A | I | T | H | | Z | | L | | W |
| | D | | A | | B | E | V | | | |
| J | O | I | S | T | | D | A | I | S | Y |
| | | | Y | E | P | | R | | T | |
| H | | P | | M | | S | Y | N | O | D |
| E | Q | U | I | P | | | I | | O | |
| M | | R | | T | E | E | N | A | G | E |
| P | A | R | K | S | | | G | | E | |

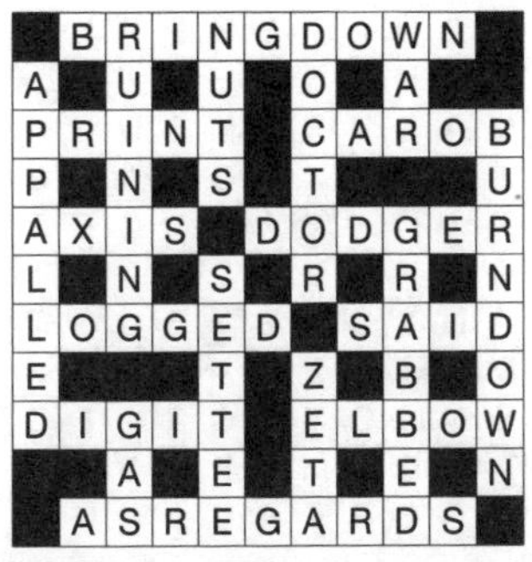

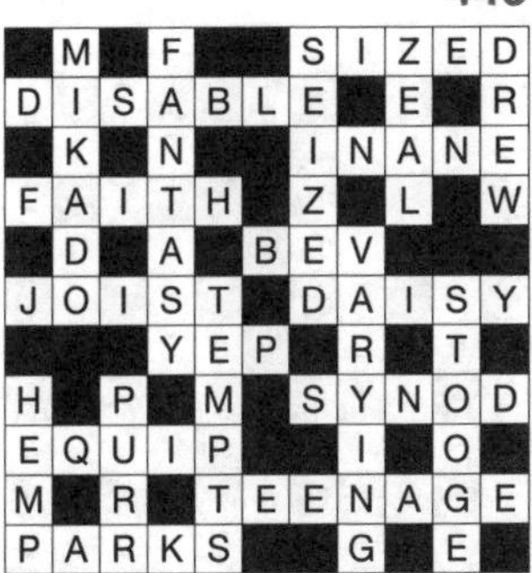

## 449

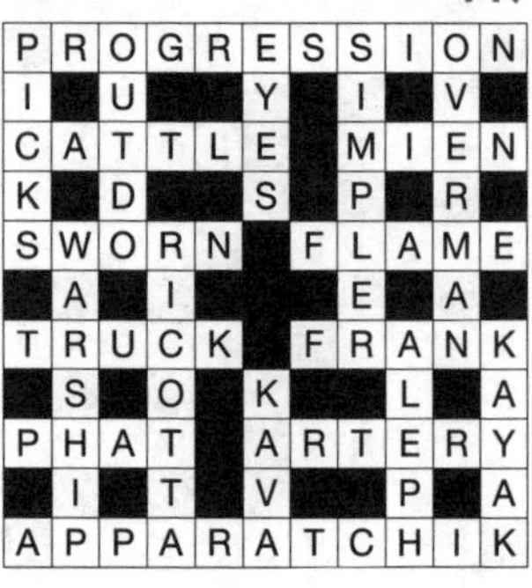

| | | | | | | | | | | |
|---|---|---|---|---|---|---|---|---|---|---|
| P | R | O | G | R | E | S | S | I | O | N |
| I | | U | | | Y | | I | | V | |
| C | A | T | T | L | E | | M | I | E | N |
| K | | D | | | S | | P | | R | |
| S | W | O | R | N | | F | L | A | M | E |
| | A | | I | | | | E | | A | |
| T | R | U | C | K | | F | R | A | N | K |
| | S | | O | | K | | | L | | A |
| P | H | A | T | | A | R | T | E | R | Y |
| | I | | T | | V | | | P | | A |
| A | P | P | A | R | A | T | C | H | I | K |

## 450

| | | | | | | | | | | |
|---|---|---|---|---|---|---|---|---|---|---|
| V | O | L | U | N | T | A | R | I | L | Y |
| | M | | T | | U | | E | | O | |
| R | I | V | E | R | S | | S | O | B | S |
| | T | | | | K | | U | | | |
| S | T | A | R | E | | S | M | O | C | K |
| | E | | E | | | | E | | L | |
| E | D | I | F | Y | | A | D | D | E | D |
| | | | U | | B | | | | A | |
| O | W | L | S | | O | T | H | E | R | S |
| | O | | A | | O | | U | | U | |
| F | O | R | L | O | R | N | H | O | P | E |

## 451

| | | | | | | | | | | |
|---|---|---|---|---|---|---|---|---|---|---|
| T | R | A | M | P | O | L | I | N | E | S |
| | E | | A | | V | | | O | | W |
| O | P | E | N | | E | M | B | R | Y | O |
| | L | | A | | N | | | T | | R |
| H | A | N | G | S | | A | C | H | E | D |
| | C | | E | | | | O | | X | |
| H | E | R | D | S | | E | N | A | C | T |
| U | | O | | | W | | T | | E | |
| M | E | A | N | I | E | | A | W | E | D |
| A | | S | | | A | | I | | D | |
| N | O | T | H | I | N | G | N | E | S | S |

## 452

| | | | | | | | | | | |
|---|---|---|---|---|---|---|---|---|---|---|
| M | I | S | A | N | T | H | R | O | P | Y |
| O | | T | | | A | | E | | L | |
| D | O | U | B | T | S | | G | O | A | L |
| E | | M | | | S | | U | | Y | |
| L | A | P | S | E | | F | L | E | E | T |
| | R | | H | | | | A | | R | |
| B | A | N | A | L | | C | R | A | S | H |
| | B | | M | | J | | | B | | O |
| W | I | M | P | | E | N | T | O | M | B |
| | A | | O | | E | | | U | | B |
| I | N | C | O | R | R | E | C | T | L | Y |

## 453

| | | | | | | | | | | |
|---|---|---|---|---|---|---|---|---|---|---|
| S | M | A | L | L | C | H | A | N | G | E |
| | U | | E | | O | | | A | | X |
| U | N | F | O | L | D | | M | I | N | I |
| | D | | P | | E | | | V | | S |
| G | A | G | A | | D | I | R | E | C | T |
| | N | | R | | | | A | | I | |
| M | E | A | D | O | W | | T | O | T | S |
| I | | L | | | H | | T | | I | |
| M | O | A | T | | A | B | L | A | Z | E |
| I | | R | | | L | | E | | E | |
| C | O | M | P | R | E | S | S | I | N | G |

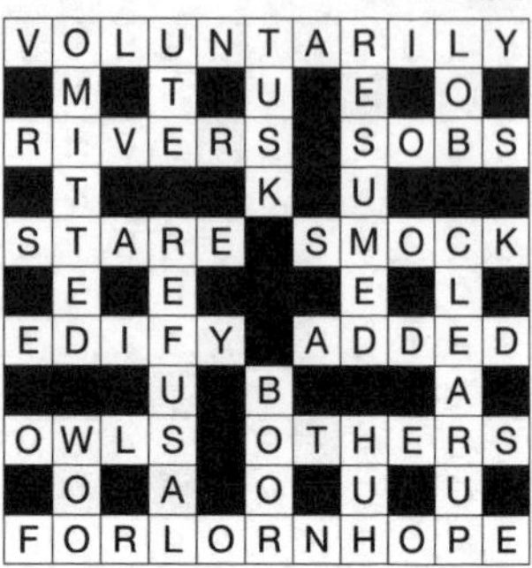

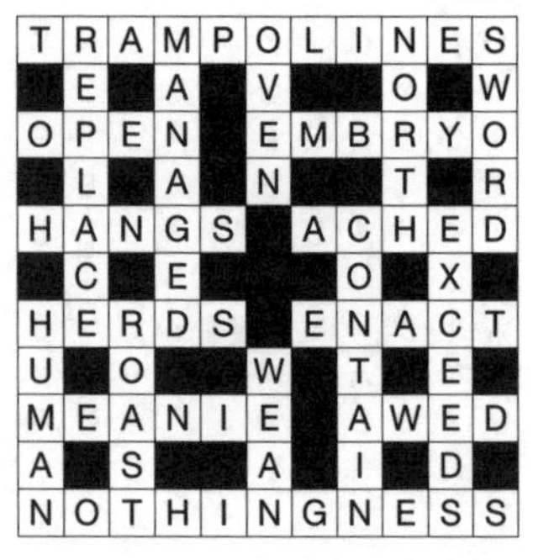

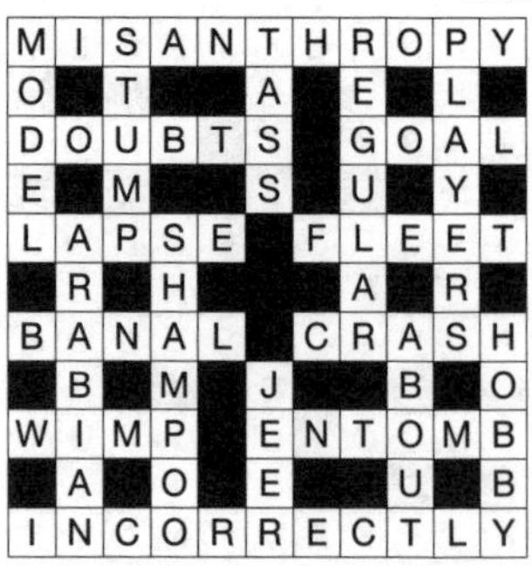

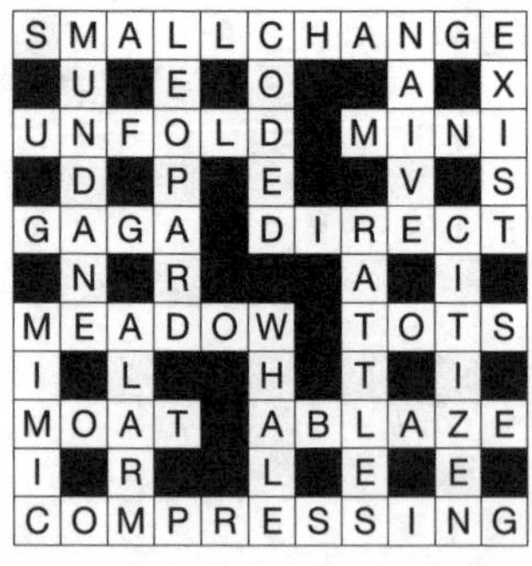

## 454

| | | | | | | | | | | |
|---|---|---|---|---|---|---|---|---|---|---|
| O | V | E | R | P | R | I | C | E | D | |
| | E | | U | | U | | L | | I | |
| C | R | I | M | E | S | | O | X | E | N |
| | D | | | | H | | S | | | |
| F | I | R | S | T | | W | E | E | N | Y |
| | C | | C | | | | S | | E | |
| S | T | O | O | D | | S | T | E | A | L |
| | | | R | | C | | | | R | |
| S | H | I | P | | H | A | L | T | E | D |
| | I | | I | | A | | E | | S | |
| | C | O | O | R | D | I | N | A | T | E |

## 455

| | | | | | | | | | | |
|---|---|---|---|---|---|---|---|---|---|---|
| A | L | L | E | G | A | T | I | O | N | S |
| | E | | V | | I | | | R | | A |
| S | I | L | O | | D | E | T | A | I | L |
| | S | | L | | E | | | T | | T |
| C | U | R | V | E | | E | L | E | G | Y |
| | R | | E | | | | I | | O | |
| B | E | A | S | T | | S | T | A | R | K |
| E | | B | | | Y | | E | | I | |
| S | P | A | R | S | E | | R | O | L | L |
| E | | C | | | A | | A | | L | |
| T | A | K | E | T | H | E | L | E | A | D |

## 456

| | | | | | | | | | | |
|---|---|---|---|---|---|---|---|---|---|---|
| | S | U | F | F | E | R | E | R | S | |
| O | | N | | E | | E | | I | | |
| V | A | L | V | E | | M | E | D | E | A |
| E | | U | | L | | O | | | | L |
| R | I | C | H | | A | V | O | C | E | T |
| C | | K | | E | | E | | A | | I |
| A | N | Y | O | N | E | | B | U | S | T |
| M | | | | Z | | A | | T | | U |
| E | N | J | O | Y | | C | R | I | E | D |
| | | O | | M | | E | | O | | E |
| | R | E | R | E | A | D | I | N | G | |

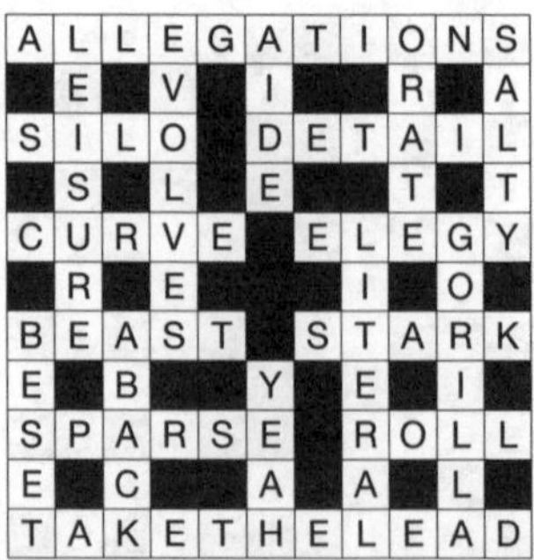

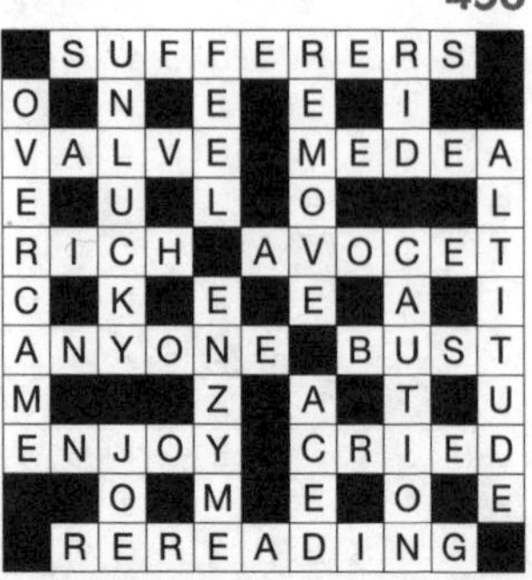

## 457

## 458

## 459

## 460

## 461

## 462

| | | | | | | | | | | |
|---|---|---|---|---|---|---|---|---|---|---|
| D | I | S | C | O | V | E | R | I | N | G |
| U | | U | | | E | | E | | O | |
| T | E | M | P | L | E | | V | A | T | S |
| C | | U | | | R | | E | | I | |
| H | A | P | P | Y | | S | N | A | C | K |
| | I | | I | | | | G | | E | |
| C | R | A | Z | Y | | T | E | N | D | S |
| | M | | Z | | V | | | E | | I |
| M | A | Y | A | | E | D | G | I | E | R |
| | I | | Z | | R | | | G | | E |
| E | L | I | Z | A | B | E | T | H | A | N |

## 463

## 464

## 465

## 466

## 467

## 468

## 469

|   | D |   | C |   |   | F | I | L | E | D |
|---|---|---|---|---|---|---|---|---|---|---|
| P | A | R | A | S | O | L |   | E |   | U |
|   | C |   | P |   |   | O | N | E | N | D |
| L | A | T | I | N |   | R |   | K |   | S |
|   | P |   | T |   | Y | E | P |   |   |   |
| W | O | M | A | N |   | T | R | A | I | L |
|   |   |   | L | I | D |   | E |   | N |   |
| S |   | C |   | M |   | S | P | A | S | M |
| C | L | I | M | B |   |   | A |   | E |   |
| U |   | A |   | L | I | B | R | A | R | Y |
| D | R | O | V | E |   |   | E |   | T |   |

## 470

| P | A | T | R | I | A | R | C | H | A | L |
|---|---|---|---|---|---|---|---|---|---|---|
|   | B |   | E |   | R |   |   | A |   | A |
| S | O | U | P |   | M | U | S | L | I | N |
|   | L |   | E |   | Y |   |   | V |   | D |
| V | I | C | A | R |   | O | P | E | N | S |
|   | S |   | T |   |   |   | E |   | U |   |
| C | H | E | S | T |   | P | L | U | M | E |
| U |   | L |   |   | S |   | I |   | E |   |
| T | A | U | G | H | T |   | C | U | R | D |
| I |   | D |   |   | A |   | A |   | I |   |
| E | L | E | C | T | R | O | N | I | C | S |

## 471

## 472

**474**

**475**

**476**

| | | | | | | | | | | |
|---|---|---|---|---|---|---|---|---|---|---|
| C | U | S | T | O | M | | D | O | G | E |
| H | | I | | | A | | E | | O | |
| A | R | G | A | L | I | | S | O | U | L |
| R | | M | | | N | | I | | N | |
| T | E | A | P | O | T | | R | O | D | E |
| | X | | S | | A | | E | | E | |
| S | P | R | Y | | I | N | S | U | R | E |
| | L | | C | | N | | | N | | N |
| G | O | S | H | | I | N | V | I | T | E |
| | D | | E | | N | | | T | | M |
| W | E | N | D | | G | R | E | E | D | Y |

**478**

| | | | | | | | | | | |
|---|---|---|---|---|---|---|---|---|---|---|
| B | I | S | H | O | P | | F | A | C | E |
| I | | A | | | R | | A | | A | |
| T | A | T | T | O | O | | L | A | B | S |
| E | | I | | | G | | L | | B | |
| R | E | N | D | E | R | | F | L | A | B |
| | P | | Y | | A | | O | | G | |
| S | I | G | N | | M | E | R | G | E | D |
| | T | | A | | M | | | A | | I |
| T | O | N | S | | I | S | O | M | E | R |
| | M | | T | | N | | | E | | T |
| B | E | V | Y | | G | L | O | S | S | Y |

**479**

| | | | | | | | | | | |
|---|---|---|---|---|---|---|---|---|---|---|
| S | E | A | R | C | H | | V | A | S | T |
| T | | M | | | A | | E | | H | |
| A | P | P | E | A | R | | H | A | I | L |
| M | | L | | | D | | I | | P | |
| P | R | E | A | C | H | | C | A | P | S |
| | E | | P | | I | | L | | E | |
| P | A | C | T | | T | R | E | N | D | S |
| | D | | N | | T | | | O | | U |
| L | I | F | E | | I | N | S | T | E | P |
| | L | | S | | N | | | E | | E |
| G | Y | P | S | | G | L | I | D | E | R |

**480**

## 481

## 482

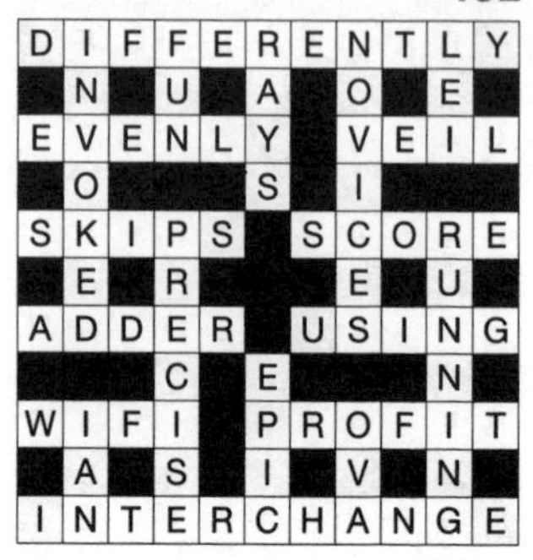

## 483

## 484

| M | A | S | A | L | A | ■ | B | O | S | S |
|---|---|---|---|---|---|---|---|---|---|---|
| A | ■ | P | ■ | ■ | C | ■ | R | ■ | W | ■ |
| T | R | A | G | I | C | ■ | O | P | A | L |
| C | ■ | W | ■ | ■ | O | ■ | A | ■ | L | ■ |
| H | O | N | S | H | U | ■ | D | O | L | T |
| ■ | W | ■ | H | ■ | N | ■ | E | ■ | O | ■ |
| A | N | N | A | ■ | T | H | R | O | W | S |
| ■ | G | ■ | L | ■ | A | ■ | ■ | O | ■ | O |
| J | O | W | L | ■ | N | O | R | M | A | L |
| ■ | A | ■ | O | ■ | T | ■ | ■ | P | ■ | I |
| B | L | O | W | ■ | S | I | G | H | E | D |

## 485

## 486

| S | T | U | D | I | O | C | O | U | C | H |
|---|---|---|---|---|---|---|---|---|---|---|
| ■ | O | ■ | O | ■ | W | ■ | B | ■ | A | ■ |
| B | U | T | T | O | N | ■ | L | O | D | E |
| ■ | R | ■ | ■ | ■ | S | ■ | I | ■ | ■ | ■ |
| W | I | C | C | A | ■ | A | G | A | P | E |
| ■ | S | ■ | A | ■ | ■ | ■ | E | ■ | L | ■ |
| S | T | A | R | S | ■ | I | D | E | A | L |
| ■ | ■ | ■ | I | ■ | B | ■ | ■ | ■ | N | ■ |
| S | N | O | B | ■ | L | O | O | K | E | D |
| ■ | A | ■ | O | ■ | A | ■ | I | ■ | T | ■ |
| T | H | O | U | G | H | T | L | E | S | S |

## 487

## 488

## 489

## 490

## 491

## 492

## 493

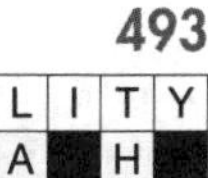

## 494

OBSTRUCTION
R E P A A
REVERT LETS
A O E
STAFF ANGEL
H R T N
USHER ASSET
T T M
GAFF EXOTIC
W U C W E
HEALTHINESS

## 495

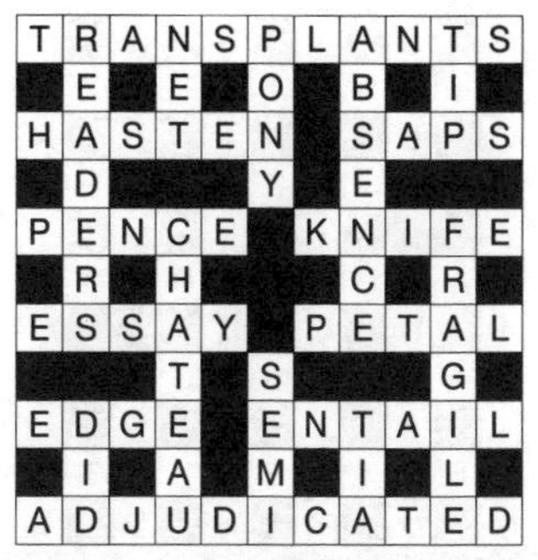


## 496

## 497

## 498

## 499

## 500

## 501

## 502

AMBIENT SHE
N U V O C X
ADS ELEGIAC
L I N S N E
OUNCES STEP
G E D B I T
OUST NUCLEI
U S E N L O
SAMURAI ANN
L E I O T A
YEN CONCEAL

## 503

## 504

## 505

## 506

## 507

## 508

| A | | W | | O | | R | | W | | T |
|---|---|---|---|---|---|---|---|---|---|---|
| P | R | O | P | R | I | E | T | A | R | Y |
| P | | K | | I | | C | | S | | P |
| E | V | E | R | E | S | T | | T | O | E |
| A | | | | N | | A | | E | | W |
| R | E | S | E | T | | N | A | D | I | R |
| A | | T | | A | | G | | | | I |
| N | O | R | | T | R | U | M | P | E | T |
| C | | I | | I | | L | | R | | I |
| E | X | P | L | O | R | A | T | I | O | N |
| S | | S | | N | | R | | M | | G |

## 509

## 510

| B | E | L | I | E | F | | S | H | A | M |
|---|---|---|---|---|---|---|---|---|---|---|
| I | | L | | | U | | U | | S | |
| L | E | A | D | E | R | | S | A | S | S |
| L | | M | | | T | | A | | A | |
| S | C | A | M | P | I | | N | O | U | N |
| | U | | I | | V | | N | | L | |
| A | N | O | N | | E | X | A | L | T | S |
| | N | | U | | N | | | O | | E |
| L | I | F | T | | E | S | T | A | T | E |
| | N | | E | | S | | | N | | D |
| E | G | O | S | | S | P | A | S | M | S |

## 511

## 512

**513**

**514**

**515**

**516**

**517**

**518**

**519**

**520**

## 521

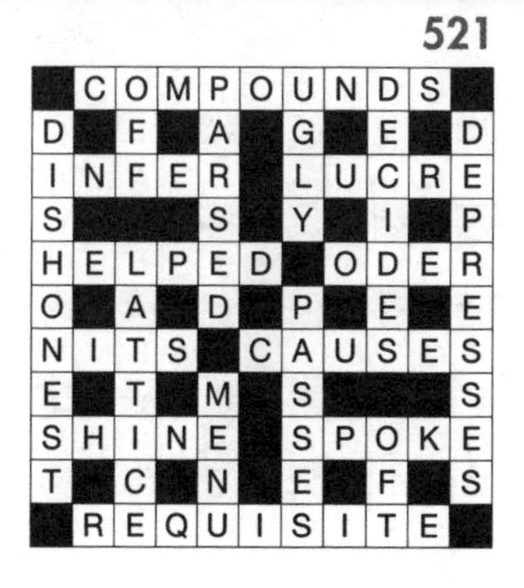

| | | | | | | | | | | |
|---|---|---|---|---|---|---|---|---|---|---|
| | C | O | M | P | O | U | N | D | S | |
| D | | F | | A | | G | | E | | D |
| I | N | F | E | R | | L | U | C | R | E |
| S | | | | S | | Y | | I | | P |
| H | E | L | P | E | D | | O | D | E | R |
| O | | A | | D | | P | | E | | E |
| N | I | T | S | | C | A | U | S | E | S |
| E | | T | | M | | S | | | | S |
| S | H | I | N | E | | S | P | O | K | E |
| T | | C | | N | | E | | F | | S |
| | R | E | Q | U | I | S | I | T | E | |

## 522

| | | | | | | | | | | |
|---|---|---|---|---|---|---|---|---|---|---|
| | C | U | R | I | O | S | I | T | Y | |
| H | | N | | O | | A | | A | | |
| A | S | H | E | N | | F | A | U | L | T |
| R | | E | | S | | E | | | | R |
| D | E | A | D | | P | L | A | S | M | A |
| S | | R | | H | | Y | | C | | P |
| H | A | D | E | A | N | | P | R | E | P |
| I | | | | W | | E | | E | | I |
| P | U | K | K | A | | V | I | E | W | S |
| | | O | | I | | I | | N | | T |
| | L | I | M | I | T | L | E | S | S | |

## 523

| | | | | | | | | | | |
|---|---|---|---|---|---|---|---|---|---|---|
| E | N | V | I | R | O | N | M | E | N | T |
| | O | | M | | K | | | B | | U |
| L | I | S | P | | R | O | B | B | E | D |
| | S | | A | | A | | | E | | O |
| D | I | G | I | N | | U | D | D | E | R |
| | E | | R | | | | U | | M | |
| F | R | E | S | H | | A | T | T | I | C |
| A | | E | | | U | | I | | N | |
| L | A | R | G | E | R | | F | E | E | S |
| S | | I | | | D | | U | | N | |
| E | V | E | N | T | U | A | L | I | T | Y |

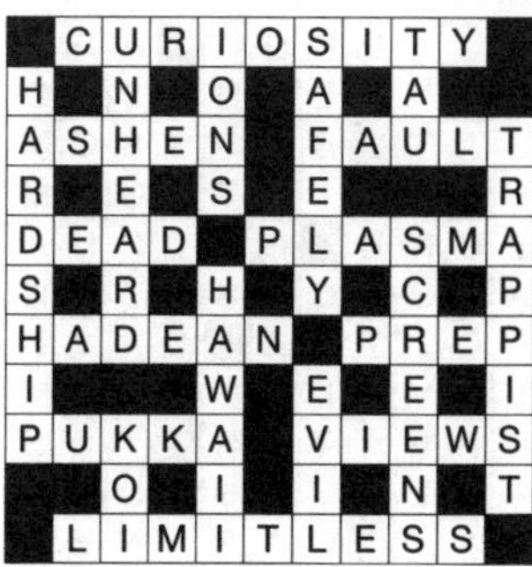

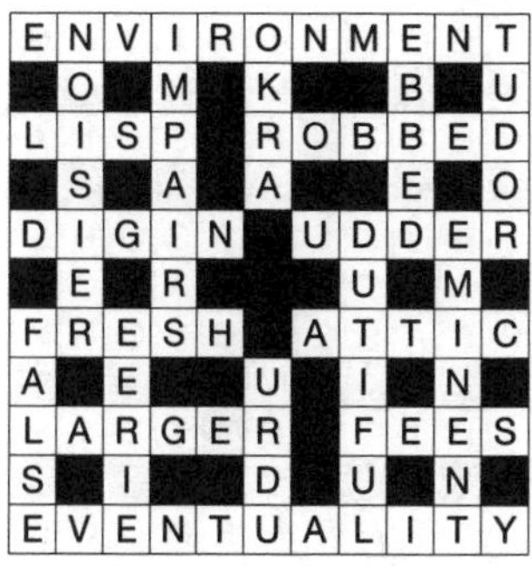

## 524

| | | | | | | | | | | |
|---|---|---|---|---|---|---|---|---|---|---|
| Q | U | E | B | E | C | | S | U | C | K |
| U | | X | | | O | | C | | R | |
| A | M | A | Z | O | N | | A | L | O | E |
| I | | L | | | T | | T | | S | |
| L | E | T | T | E | R | | T | O | S | S |
| | M | | A | | A | | E | | E | |
| T | O | R | C | | C | E | R | I | S | E |
| | T | | K | | T | | | D | | L |
| M | I | N | I | | I | N | D | I | G | O |
| | O | | N | | O | | | O | | P |
| S | N | A | G | | N | E | S | T | L | E |

## 525

| | | | | | | | | | | |
|---|---|---|---|---|---|---|---|---|---|---|
| A | B | R | A | C | A | D | A | B | R | A |
| C | | O | | O | | U | | A | | D |
| C | O | T | | S | Y | M | P | T | O | M |
| U | | A | | M | | B | | | | I |
| M | A | T | R | I | X | | I | C | O | N |
| U | | E | | C | | C | | O | | I |
| L | A | D | Y | | T | H | E | M | E | S |
| A | | | | T | | E | | P | | T |
| T | E | E | N | I | E | R | | O | D | E |
| E | | O | | E | | U | | S | | R |
| D | I | S | T | R | I | B | U | T | E | S |

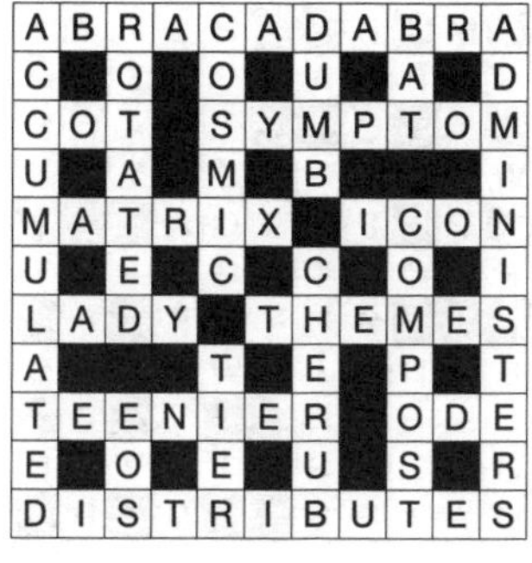

## 526

| | | | | | | | | | | |
|---|---|---|---|---|---|---|---|---|---|---|
| S | P | E | A | K | E | V | I | L | O | F |
| P | | X | | I | | I | | Y | | I |
| R | E | P | | S | P | A | N | N | E | R |
| E | | A | | S | | B | | | | I |
| A | U | N | T | | A | L | B | I | O | N |
| D | | D | | C | | E | | N | | G |
| S | I | S | T | E | R | | U | S | E | S |
| H | | | | A | | Y | | I | | Q |
| E | N | M | A | S | S | E | | G | N | U |
| E | | I | | E | | T | | H | | A |
| T | R | A | N | S | M | I | T | T | E | D |

## 527

| | | | | | | | | | | |
|---|---|---|---|---|---|---|---|---|---|---|
| P | R | E | F | E | R | R | I | N | G | |
| | E | | L | | U | | N | | O | |
| A | M | O | U | N | T | | V | O | T | E |
| | I | | | | H | | E | | | |
| S | N | I | D | E | | A | N | I | O | N |
| | D | | R | | | | T | | P | |
| A | S | I | A | N | | A | S | S | E | S |
| | | | S | | C | | | | N | |
| S | O | R | T | | Z | O | M | B | I | E |
| | A | | I | | A | | A | | N | |
| | R | E | C | O | R | D | I | N | G | S |

## 528

| | | | | | | | | | | |
|---|---|---|---|---|---|---|---|---|---|---|
| G | O | U | P | I | N | S | M | O | K | E |
| | C | | I | | O | | | N | | B |
| B | A | R | R | E | D | | O | T | T | O |
| | R | | A | | E | | | A | | N |
| K | I | L | N | | S | U | P | P | L | Y |
| | N | | H | | | | A | | A | |
| G | A | L | A | X | Y | | C | U | T | S |
| A | | I | | | U | | K | | V | |
| M | O | B | S | | C | R | I | S | I | S |
| E | | R | | | C | | N | | A | |
| R | E | A | R | R | A | N | G | I | N | G |

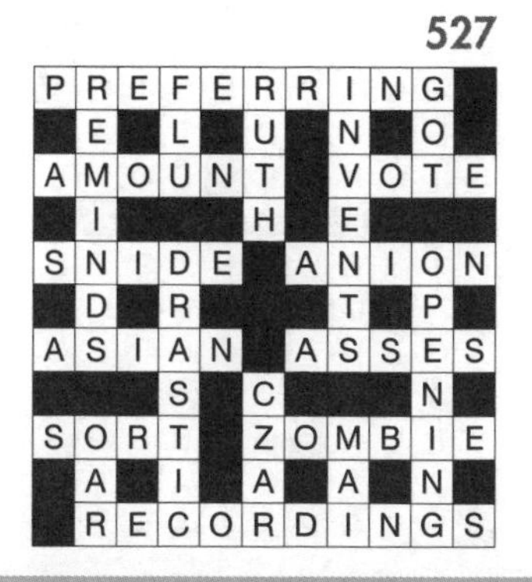

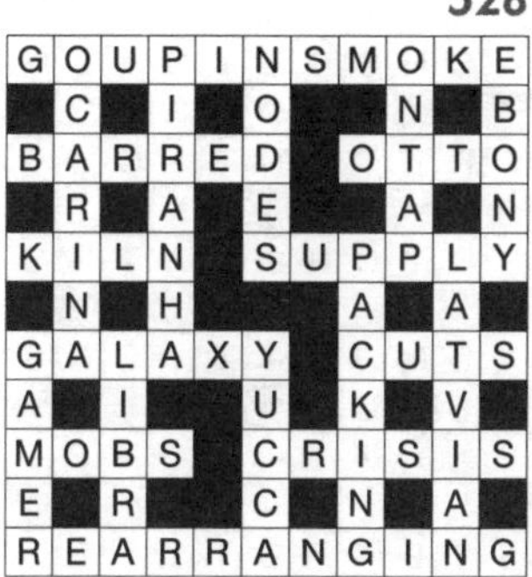

## 529

## 530

## 531

## 532

## 533

## 534

| | | | | | | | | | | |
|---|---|---|---|---|---|---|---|---|---|---|
| ■ | M | ■ | P | ■ | ■ | H | E | F | T | Y |
| S | O | P | R | A | N | O | ■ | E | ■ | O |
| ■ | T | ■ | O | ■ | ■ | T | R | A | C | K |
| W | H | I | C | H | ■ | D | ■ | T | ■ | E |
| ■ | E | ■ | E | ■ | M | O | A | ■ | ■ | ■ |
| F | R | O | S | T | ■ | G | R | A | N | T |
| ■ | ■ | ■ | S | H | Y | ■ | R | ■ | E | ■ |
| B | ■ | D | ■ | I | ■ | W | I | L | E | S |
| L | I | E | I | N | ■ | ■ | V | ■ | D | ■ |
| O | ■ | L | ■ | G | R | I | E | V | E | D |
| C | L | I | P | S | ■ | ■ | D | ■ | D | ■ |

## 535

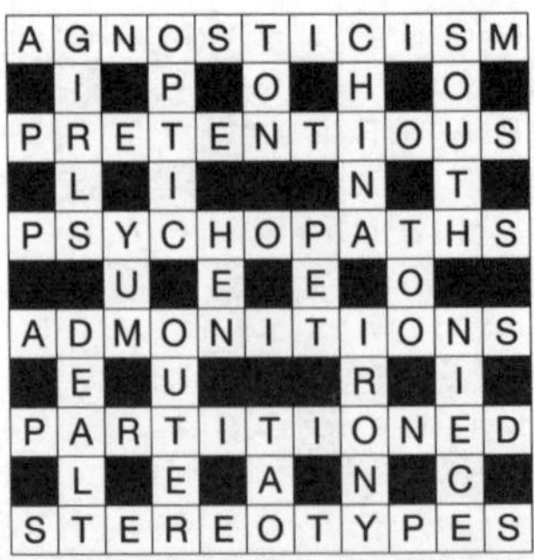

## 536

## 537

## 538

## 539

## 540

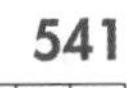

## 542

| | | | | | | | | | | |
|---|---|---|---|---|---|---|---|---|---|---|
| T | Y | P | I | C | A | L | | S | I | C |
| H | | I | | O | | I | | E | | U |
| R | E | C | R | U | I | T | M | E | N | T |
| E | | | | P | | T | | K | | T |
| A | C | E | S | | G | E | M | I | N | I |
| T | | N | | N | | R | | N | | N |
| E | X | T | R | A | S | | A | G | O | G |
| N | | I | | R | | B | | | | E |
| I | N | T | E | R | R | U | P | T | E | D |
| N | | L | | O | | R | | E | | G |
| G | E | E | | W | A | R | F | A | R | E |

## 543

## 544

## 545

## 546

## 547

## 548

## 549

## 550

PHENOMENON
A U O A E
TRUTHS IRON
M S L
OFFAL WIVES
U M N V
ALLEY AGLOW
R S L
TAXI TWELVE
H C A V E
AVANTGARDE

## 551

## 552

## 553

| F | I | R | E | W | A | L | K | I | N | G |
|---|---|---|---|---|---|---|---|---|---|---|
|  | N |  | V |  | R |  | I |  | I |  |
| A | D | V | E | N | T |  | D | U | B | S |
|  | O |  |  |  | S |  | D |  |  |  |
| D | U | M | P | S |  | V | I | X | E | N |
|  | B |  | R |  |  |  | N |  | L |  |
| S | T | O | O | D |  | O | G | L | E | S |
|  |  |  | M |  | F |  |  |  | G |  |
| A | M | M | O |  | O | R | D | E | A | L |
|  | I |  | T |  | C |  | A |  | N |  |
| E | X | P | E | R | I | M | E | N | T | S |

## 554

| R | E | C | O | N | D | I | T | I | O | N |
|---|---|---|---|---|---|---|---|---|---|---|
| E |  | I |  |  | O |  | E |  | B |  |
| L | U | R | K | E | D |  | E | L | S | E |
| I |  | C |  |  | O |  | T |  | C |  |
| C | R | A | F | T |  | D | E | B | U | G |
|  | E |  | I |  |  |  | R |  | R |  |
| A | P | T | L | Y |  | I | S | L | E | T |
|  | L |  | M |  | C |  |  | I |  | A |
| M | I | D | I |  | H | O | B | N | O | B |
|  | C |  | N |  | E |  |  | K |  | B |
| D | A | N | G | E | R | O | U | S | L | Y |

## 555

| S | E | M | I | N | A | R |  | P | E | C |
|---|---|---|---|---|---|---|---|---|---|---|
| E |  | A |  | U |  | A |  | A |  | O |
| R | E | G | U | L | A | R |  | R | U | M |
| I |  | N |  | L |  | I |  | T |  | P |
| O | M | I | T |  | U | N | L | I | K | E |
| U |  | F |  | H |  | G |  | C |  | T |
| S | L | I | P | O | N |  | W | I | K | I |
| N |  | C |  | T |  | S |  | P |  | T |
| E | W | E |  | T | I | M | P | A | N | I |
| S |  | N |  | U |  | U |  | T |  | O |
| S | O | T |  | B | E | T | W | E | E | N |

## 556

| U | N | C | O | N | S | C | I | O | U | S |
|---|---|---|---|---|---|---|---|---|---|---|
| N |  | E |  |  | A |  | N |  | N |  |
| T | A | L | E | N | T |  | F | L | I | P |
| I |  | E |  |  | E |  | R |  | F |  |
| L | O | B | B | Y |  | D | O | N | O | R |
|  | V |  | R |  |  |  | N |  | R |  |
| Z | E | R | O | S |  | S | T | E | M | S |
|  | R |  | T |  | D |  |  | V |  | H |
| B | L | A | H |  | A | F | R | I | C | A |
|  | A |  | E |  | M |  |  | T |  | R |
| A | P | P | R | O | P | R | I | A | T | E |

## 557

|  | P | R | O | T | O | T | Y | P | E |  |
|---|---|---|---|---|---|---|---|---|---|---|
| O |  | E |  | O |  | U |  | U |  | R |
| F | E | D | U | P |  | B | A | R | G | E |
| F |  |  |  | I |  | S |  | S |  | C |
| E | F | F | E | C | T |  | Y | U | C | K |
| N |  | U |  | S |  | C |  | I |  | O |
| S | A | S | H |  | M | I | T | T | E | N |
| I |  | I |  | M |  | T |  |  |  | I |
| V | A | L | V | E |  | R | O | W | A | N |
| E |  | L |  | G |  | I |  | A |  | G |
|  | F | I | N | A | N | C | I | N | G |  |

## 558

|  | F |  | A |  |  | L | I | V | E | D |
|---|---|---|---|---|---|---|---|---|---|---|
| M | A | E | S | T | R | I |  | I |  | O |
|  | C |  | S |  |  | Z | O | N | E | S |
| S | T | R | I | P |  | A |  | E |  | E |
|  | O |  | G |  | A | R | M |  |  |  |
| B | R | I | N | G |  | D | A | I | L | Y |
|  |  |  | S | A | G |  | S |  | E |  |
| O |  | S |  | L |  | A | T | L | A | S |
| D | I | T | T | O |  |  | E |  | V |  |
| E |  | Y |  | S | T | A | R | V | E | D |
| S | I | X | T | H |  |  | S |  | S |  |

## 559

| C | O | S | T | I | N | G |  | S | A | C |
|---|---|---|---|---|---|---|---|---|---|---|
| E |  | U |  | N |  | E |  | P |  | O |
| L | A | P |  | C | O | N | F | O | R | M |
| E |  | E |  | H |  | I |  | I |  | M |
| B | A | R | K |  | N | U | C | L | E | I |
| R |  | V |  | L |  | S |  | S |  | S |
| A | N | I | M | A | L |  | O | P | U | S |
| T |  | S |  | D |  | F |  | O |  | I |
| I | N | I | T | I | A | L |  | R | I | O |
| N |  | N |  | D |  | A |  | T |  | N |
| G | A | G |  | A | R | T | I | S | T | S |

## 560

|  | I | N | T | E | R | R | U | P | T |  |
|---|---|---|---|---|---|---|---|---|---|---|
| H |  | E |  | X |  | I |  | U |  | X |
| I | N | D | I | E |  | B | U | S | H | Y |
| T |  |  |  | M |  | S |  | H |  | L |
| O | C | C | U | P | Y |  | K | I | L | O |
| R |  | O |  | T |  | M |  | N |  | P |
| M | A | U | L |  | L | E | N | G | T | H |
| I |  | L |  | H |  | R |  |  |  | O |
| S | L | O | P | E |  | G | R | E | E | N |
| S |  | M |  | A |  | E |  | Y |  | E |
|  | A | B | O | L | I | S | H | E | S |  |

## 561

## 562

## 563

## 564

| C | A | S | T | L | E | | W | A | V | E |
|---|---|---|---|---|---|---|---|---|---|---|
| L | | T | | | N | | H | | E | |
| I | T | A | L | I | C | | E | R | R | S |
| M | | I | | | O | | T | | A | |
| B | U | R | E | A | U | | H | I | N | T |
| | S | | F | | N | | E | | D | |
| C | U | F | F | | T | H | R | E | A | T |
| | A | | O | | E | | | L | | H |
| S | L | U | R | | R | E | G | I | M | E |
| | L | | T | | E | | | T | | F |
| G | Y | M | S | | D | E | C | E | N | T |

## 565

| | I | N | A | D | V | A | N | C | E | |
|---|---|---|---|---|---|---|---|---|---|---|
| A | | A | | I | | I | | U | | M |
| U | R | G | E | S | | M | I | S | T | Y |
| T | | | | M | | S | | T | | T |
| O | C | U | L | A | R | | B | O | T | H |
| G | | N | | Y | | T | | M | | O |
| R | U | D | E | | D | I | E | S | E | L |
| A | | E | | H | | N | | | | O |
| P | A | R | S | E | | S | U | I | N | G |
| H | | G | | C | | E | | R | | Y |
| | L | O | O | K | A | L | I | K | E | |

## 566

| R | A | C | E | M | E | E | T | I | N | G |
|---|---|---|---|---|---|---|---|---|---|---|
| O | | L | | | L | | R | | E | |
| U | T | O | P | I | A | | A | Q | U | A |
| G | | W | | | N | | C | | T | |
| H | A | N | D | Y | | S | K | I | R | T |
| | R | | R | | | | E | | A | |
| E | T | H | O | S | | A | D | D | L | E |
| | D | | P | | U | | | W | | N |
| H | E | R | O | | S | W | E | E | P | S |
| | C | | F | | E | | | E | | U |
| C | O | M | F | O | R | T | A | B | L | E |

## 567

## 568

## 569

## 570

## 571

## 572

## 573

## 574

## 575

## 576

## 577

| P | I | C | N | I | C |  | P | O | S | T |
|---|---|---|---|---|---|---|---|---|---|---|
| U |  | O |  |  | L |  | R |  | U |  |
| L | O | U | N | G | E |  | O | F | F | S |
| L |  | N |  |  | A |  | V |  | F |  |
| S | E | T | T | E | R |  | I | R | I | S |
|  | C |  | H |  | H |  | S |  | C |  |
| T | H | A | W |  | E | V | O | K | E | D |
|  | O |  | A |  | A |  |  | E |  | A |
| L | I | A | R |  | D | I | N | N | E | R |
|  | N |  | T |  | E |  |  | D |  | E |
| E | G | G | S |  | D | E | V | O | I | D |

## 578

## 579

## 580

## 581

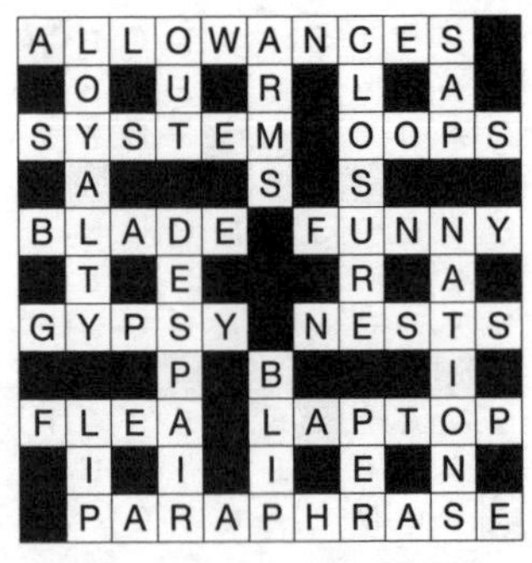

## 582

| M | I | S | T | A | K | E | N | L | Y |  |
|---|---|---|---|---|---|---|---|---|---|---|
|  | S |  | I |  | I |  | E |  | A |  |
| C | O | U | N | T | S |  | G | A | P | E |
|  | L |  |  |  | S |  | A |  |  |  |
| M | A | L | E | S |  | S | T | A | K | E |
|  | T |  | U |  |  |  | E |  | I |  |
| F | E | A | R | S |  | E | D | I | C | T |
|  |  |  | A |  | A |  |  |  | K |  |
| E | B | B | S |  | C | O | M | M | I | T |
|  | O |  | I |  | I |  | E |  | N |  |
|  | B | Y | A | N | D | L | A | R | G | E |

## 583

## 584

## 585

## 586

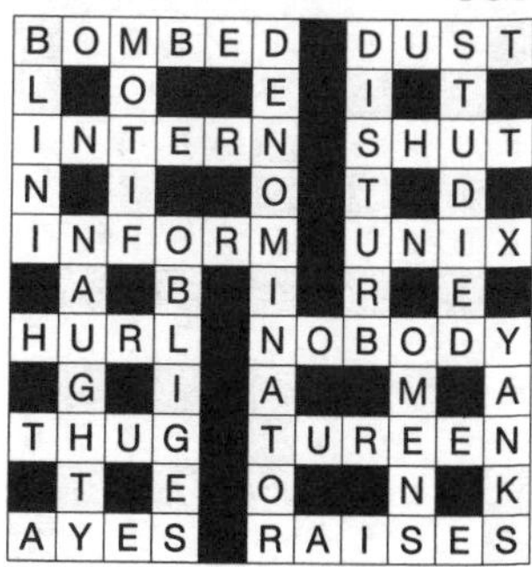


## 587

## 588

CHARGE GUSH
A B N R I
RELIEF OWLS
O E O W L
BORDER NAIL
V A C U E
WARM EMPIRE
T P M L A
SINE EDGIER
O S N U N
CNUT THEMES

## 590

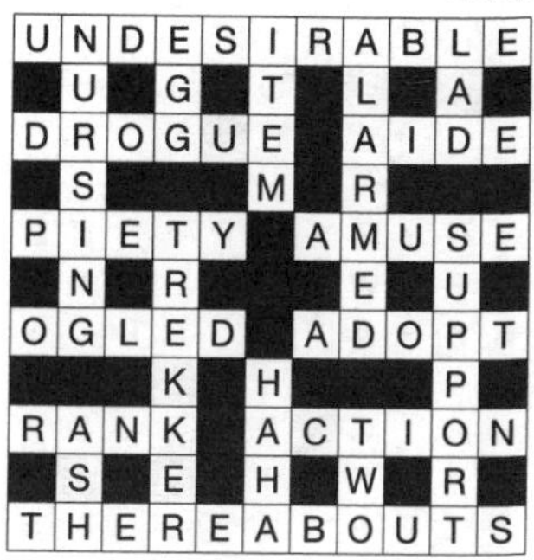


## 591

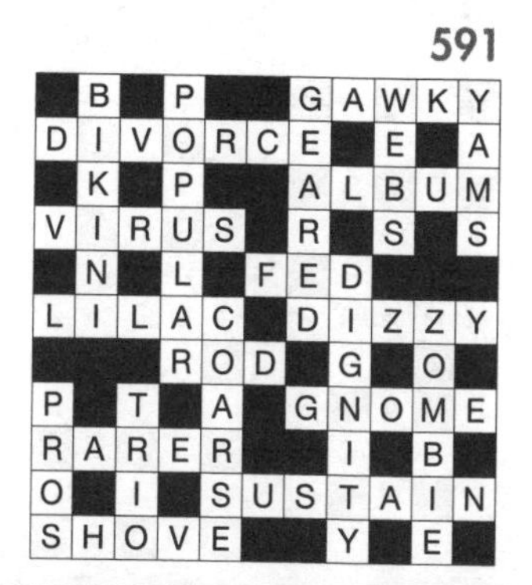


## 592

## 593

## 594

## 595

| | | | | | | | | | | |
|---|---|---|---|---|---|---|---|---|---|---|
| C | O | S | M | I | C | ■ | C | A | F | E |
| A | ■ | U | ■ | ■ | A | ■ | O | ■ | R | ■ |
| D | I | S | A | R | M | ■ | N | O | E | L |
| E | ■ | H | ■ | ■ | P | ■ | F | ■ | T | ■ |
| T | R | I | V | I | A | ■ | I | F | F | Y |
| ■ | E | ■ | A | ■ | I | ■ | R | ■ | U | ■ |
| A | V | E | R | ■ | G | A | M | B | L | E |
| ■ | O | ■ | I | ■ | N | ■ | ■ | U | ■ | A |
| G | L | U | E | ■ | I | R | K | I | N | G |
| ■ | V | ■ | T | ■ | N | ■ | ■ | L | ■ | L |
| L | E | V | Y | ■ | G | E | N | T | L | E |

## 596

| | | | | | | | | | | |
|---|---|---|---|---|---|---|---|---|---|---|
| T | E | C | H | N | I | C | A | L | L | Y |
| W | ■ | E | ■ | ■ | B | ■ | N | ■ | A | ■ |
| A | L | L | E | G | E | ■ | D | A | Y | S |
| N | ■ | L | ■ | ■ | X | ■ | R | ■ | I | ■ |
| G | L | O | V | E | ■ | J | O | I | N | S |
| ■ | A | ■ | E | ■ | ■ | ■ | I | ■ | T | ■ |
| S | M | A | R | M | ■ | A | D | H | O | C |
| ■ | P | ■ | B | ■ | P | ■ | ■ | O | ■ | O |
| H | O | B | O | ■ | H | A | I | R | D | O |
| ■ | O | ■ | S | ■ | I | ■ | ■ | S | ■ | P |
| I | N | T | E | L | L | I | G | E | N | T |

## 597

## 598

| | | | | | | | | | | |
|---|---|---|---|---|---|---|---|---|---|---|
| G | A | D | G | E | T | ■ | V | E | R | B |
| E | ■ | I | ■ | A | ■ | P | ■ | X | ■ | A |
| N | O | S | T | R | I | L | ■ | C | A | Y |
| E | ■ | T | ■ | S | ■ | I | ■ | L | ■ | O |
| R | A | R | E | ■ | B | E | H | A | L | F |
| A | ■ | I | ■ | F | ■ | D | ■ | M | ■ | B |
| L | A | B | E | L | S | ■ | P | A | T | E |
| I | ■ | U | ■ | A | ■ | W | ■ | T | ■ | N |
| Z | I | T | ■ | W | E | A | R | I | N | G |
| E | ■ | E | ■ | S | ■ | D | ■ | O | ■ | A |
| S | O | D | A | ■ | K | E | N | N | E | L |

## 599

| | | | | | | | | | | |
|---|---|---|---|---|---|---|---|---|---|---|
| M | O | C | K | U | P | ■ | C | O | D | A |
| A | ■ | O | ■ | ■ | R | ■ | O | ■ | A | ■ |
| G | E | L | A | T | O | ■ | U | R | N | S |
| I | ■ | I | ■ | ■ | P | ■ | G | ■ | C | ■ |
| C | U | C | K | O | O | ■ | H | A | I | L |
| ■ | P | ■ | I | ■ | S | ■ | U | ■ | N | ■ |
| | G | E | D | ■ | I | M | P | U | G | N |
| | | ■ | N | ■ | T | ■ | ■ | N | ■ | E |
| | | | | ■ | I | C | I | C | L | E |
| | | | | ■ | O | ■ | ■ | L | ■ | D |
| | | | | | | I | C | E | L | Y |

## 600